RECITATIONS

OLD AND NEW

FOR BOYS AND GIRLS

And if one is bad now and then,
And makes a great rackety noise,
They only look over their specs
And say, "Ah, these boys will be [illegible]

Life is only so short at the best;
Let the children be happy to-d[illegible]
Then they look for a while at the [illegible]
And the hills that are far, far a[illegible]

Quite often, as twilight comes o[illegible]
Grandmothers sing hymns ve[illegible]
To themselves, as they rock by the [illegible]
About heaven, and when they [illegible]

And then a boy, stopping to think[illegible]
Will find a hot tear in his eye[illegible]
To know what must come at the [illegible]
For grandmothers all have to [illegible]

I wish they could stay here and p[illegible]
For a boy needs their prayers [illegible]
Some boys more than others, I s[illegible]
Such fellers as me need a [illegible]

THE BAREFOOT BOY

Blessings on thee, little man,
Barefoot boy, with cheek of [illegible]
With thy turned-up pantaloons,
And thy merry whistled tunes;
With thy red lip, redder still
Kissed by strawberries on the hill;
With the sunshine on thy fa[illegible]
Through thy torn brim's jaunty [illegible]
From my heart I give thee jo[illegible]
I was once a barefoot boy!

RECITATIONS
OLD AND NEW
FOR BOYS AND GIRLS

BY

GRACE GAIGE

INTRODUCTION BY

CHRISTOPHER MORLEY

Granger Poetry Library

GRANGER BOOK CO., INC.
Great Neck, NY

First Published 1924
Reprinted 1979

INTERNATIONAL STANDARD BOOK NUMBER
0-89609-112-0

LIBRARY OF CONGRESS CATALOG NUMBER
78-73486

PRINTED IN THE UNITED STATES OF AMERICA

IN APPRECIATION OF MANY YEARS OF HAPPY SERVICE, I GRATEFULLY DEDICATE THIS BOOK TO

MR. JESSE I. STRAUS
MR. PERCY S. STRAUS
MR. HERBERT N. STRAUS

FOREWORD

"The air of the New World," says Joseph Conrad in *Nostromo,* "seems favorable to the art of declamation." And I suppose it is perhaps true that the delights of public utterance have been more enjoyed in this hemisphere than in any of the others. Yet the declamatory instinct is so primary and universal that I don't believe we can identify it with any particular climate or race. Reciting "pieces" is one of the most exciting pleasures known to mankind: a youth spent without having been called upon to deliver "Marco Bozzaris" or "Casabianca" is a youth partly wasted. Public recitation has been the first step forward in the career of many an orator.

It would be agreeable to pursue this theme through all its knots and windings. Surely one reason for the strong appeal reciting has for the human spirit is that it grants the privilege of dramatic release without the penalty of thinking. We all are darkly aware that the most difficult problem in life is to find the expressive words for the strong feelings that beset us. But when we "recite" the words are provided. All we have to do, so the authorities on forensic art assure us, is "Bring the breath from the bottom of the lungs, throw it against the roof of the mouth, and form the voice with the lips." I quote this from the late Governor John P. Altgeld's "How to Be an Orator." He continues: "The aim is to get a perfect combustion of the breath into tone. The test of pure tone is to hold a lighted candle to the mouth while running the scale."

So if you see anyone holding a candle to his mouth while running the scale, you can be warned in time that he is going to make an oration. Neither Altgeld nor any other chrysostom ever believes it necessary to give the budding declaimer any suggestions for learning to *think.* It is with the pneumatic details that they concern themselves.

But the sad thing (to stick a little more closely to our topic) is that so many of us never do any more reciting after school days are passed. There should be universal ritual declamations for all the crises of adult life. How happily one could unlock the private energies of his bosom, whiff away all those repressed emotions, polish his self-esteem, by bursting on occasion into public harangue or verse. Only wise fellows like Vachel Lindsay get this pleasure. There should be appropriate Declamations written for the joyous and difficult turning points of our careers. A ritual magnificat for Having Caught a Train, a dirge for Losing a Job, and so on. This is not merely a humorous suggestion. It is violently necessary to the human spirit to flourish and posture a bit now and then, to come forward with expanded lung and threatening eye. We are all aware of the pleasure of imaginary harangues delivered to imaginary audiences. How agreeable is the art of public speech when conducted in secret solitude! How much more agreeable it must be in actuality, once the dismays of embarrassment are overcome. The only difficulty is to find a friendly and patient audience.

Miss Gaige's collection, however, will have no difficulty in finding a friendly audience. With sagacious wisdom she has adhered in many of her choosings to material that is simple and familiar. There is a particular kind of poetry that is most sharply congenial to the capacities of audiences. It should be, in the famous phrase, "simple, sensuous, impassioned." Audiences, whether young or old, don't want to be improved. They want to be amused or thrilled or frightened. Like the speaker himself, they don't want to be compelled to think too arduously. The old favorite "pieces" that do service over and over again in collections of this sort do so for good reason. They do so because there is some honest and fundamental humanity in their melodies, a mellow and comforting homeliness that is reassuring to the heart. In the dangerous experiment of living the poets have done more than any others to console us. We owe it to them, as well as to ourselves, to come forward now and then and roll their words grandly and violently and as publicly as possible. In every schoolroom, in every private home, there is the chance that some child who is called on to "show off" may thus learn the peculiar and enchanting problems of art.

What, in the eye of eternity, is all art, all religion, all philosophy, but humanity's gallant attempt to show off?

CHRISTOPHER MORLEY

ACKNOWLEDGMENTS

For permission to use copyrighted material included in this volume, the compiler is indebted to the following authors and publishers, whose courtesy is hereby gratefully acknowledged:

Barse and Hopkins, the poems by Robert W. Service and Walt Mason.

Bobbs Merrill Company, the poems by James Whitcomb Riley, copyright, 1890, by Bobbs Merrill Company. Used by special permission of the publisher.

The Century Company, the poems from *The St. Nicholas Book of Verse*, by Pauline Frances Camp, John Kendrick Bangs, Alice Maude Ewell, Margaret Eytinge, Mary Mapes Dodge, Laura E. Richards, Albert Bigelow Paine, Tudor Jenks, and Malcolm Douglas.

Dodd Mead and Company, the poems by Angela Morgan, by Austin Dobson, and by S. Naidu.

George H. Doran Company, the poems by Joyce Kilmer, by Burton Braley, and by Christopher Morley.

Doubleday, Page and Company, the poems by Rudyard Kipling and Edwin Markham.

Duffield and Company, the poem by Mildred Whitney Stillman.

E. P. Dutton and Company, the poems by James Foley and Phillips Brookes.

Forbes and Company, the poem by Ben King.

Harcourt, Brace and Company, the poems by Margaret Widdener and Louis Untermeyer.

Houghton Mifflin and Company. The selections from the poems of Henry W. Longfellow, James Russell Lowell, Oliver Wendell Holmes, Ralph Waldo Emerson, John Burroughs, J. G. Saxe, E. C. Stedman, E. S. P. Ward, Bayard Taylor, J. T. Trowbridge, and John Greenleaf Whittier are used by permission of, and by special arrangement with, Houghton Mifflin and Company, the authorized publishers of their works.

George W. Jacobs and Company, the poems by Rupert Sargent Holland.

J. B. Lippincott Company, the poems by T. Buchanan Reed and George H. Boker.

Little, Brown and Company, the poems by Laura E. Richards, by C. G. Rossetti, and by Susan Coolidge.

Penn Publishing Company, "What Time Is It?" "Little by Little," "Kate," and "Blowing Bubbles," from *One Hundred Choice Selec-*

tions, by permission of the Penn Publishing Company, Philadelphia.

G. P. Putnam's Sons, the poems by Robert Gordon Anderson, by Norman Gale, by E. Streeter Brooks, by T. L. Beddoes, and by William Roscoe.

Reilly and Lee Company. The poems by Edgar A. Guest are used by permission of, and special arrangement with, the Reilly and Lee Company, the authorized publishers and proprietor of the copyright thereof.

Charles Scribner's Sons, the poems by Eugene Field, by Robert Louis Stevenson, by H. C. Bunner, and J. G. Holland.

Frederick A. Stokes Company, "The New Duckling," by Alfred Noyes. Reprinted by permission from *Collected Poems*, volume 3, by Alfred Noyes. Copyright, 1920, by Frederick A. Stokes.

The editor is deeply grateful to the following poets, editors, magazines, and individual holders of copyright for permission graciously given her to use the following poems:

Dr. Frank Crane, for permission to use "My Country," by Frank Crane.

Curtis Publishing Company, for permission to use "With the Tide," by Edith Wharton.

Rupert Sargent Holland, for permission to use "When I Grow Up," "Flourishing Flowers," "Jack in the Pulpit," "The Top Dragon," and "P's and Q's," by Rupert Sargent Holland.

Burgess Johnson, for permission to use "My Sore Thumb," by Burgess Johnson.

Rudyard Kipling, for permission to use "If" and "Playing Robinson Crusoe," by Rudyard Kipling.

Douglas Malloch, for permission to use "The Man Behind the Gun," by Douglas Malloch.

Mrs. Edwin Markham, for permission to use "The Man With the Hoe," "Rules for the Road," "The League of Love in Action," by Edwin Markham.

Ella Malone Watson, for permission to use the poem, "Opportunity," by Judge Walter Malone.

Carolyn Wells, for permission to use "An Over-Worked Elocutionist" and "A Thanksgiving," by Carolyn Wells.

Edith Wharton, for permission to use "With the Tide," by Edith Wharton.

CONTENTS

LITTLE ONES

BIRDS AND ANIMALS

FLOWERS AND SEASONS

HUMOR

PATRIOTISM

MOTHERS' DAY

FOR THE LITTLE ONES

[illegible] scattered now and fled,
Some are married, some are de[illegible]
And when I ask, with throbs of [illegible]
[illegible]h! when shall they all [illegible]
[illegible]s in the days long since gone [illegible]
The ancient timepiece makes [illegible]
"Forever—never!
Never—for[illegible]

[illegible]
Never here, forever there[illegible]
Where all parting, pain, and [illegible]
And death, and time shall [illegible]
Forever there, but never he[illegible]
The horologe of Eternity
Sayeth this incessantly,[illegible]
"Forever—never!
Never—for[illegible]

[illegible]

[illegible] ISLE.—THE LADY OF [illegible]

THE western waves of [illegible]
Roll'd o'er the glen their [illegible]
Each purple peak, each [illegible]
W[illegible]
But not a setting beam could [illegible]
Within the dark ravines below[illegible]
Where twined the path in shadow [illegible]
Round many a rocky pyramid[illegible]

* * * * * * *

Boon nature scatter'd, free and [illegible]
Each plant or flower, the mountain's [illegible]
Here eglantine embalm'd the air[illegible]
Hawthorn and hazel mingled there[illegible]
The primrose pale and violet flower[illegible]
Found in each cliff a narrow bower[illegible]

HIS NEW BROTHER

YES, I've got a little brother,
Never asked for him from mother,
But he's here;
But I s'pose they went and bought him,
For last week the doctor brought him;
Ain't it queer?

When I heard the news from Molly,
Why, I thought at first 'twas jolly;
'Cause you see
I just 'magined I could get him,
And our dear mamma would let him
Play with me.

But when once I had lookéd at him,
I cried out: "Oh, dear! Is that him?
Just that mite?"
They said, "Yes, you may kiss him!"
Well, I'm sure I'd never miss him.
He's a fright!

He's so small, it's just amazing,
And you'd think that he was blazing,
He's so red;
And his nose is like a berry,
And he's bald as Uncle Jerry
On his head.

He's no kind of good whatever,
And he cries as if he'd never,
Never stop;
Won't sit up—you can't arrange him,
Oh, why doesn't father change him
At the shop?

Now, we've got to dress and feed him,
And we really didn't need him,
Little frog!
And I cannot think why father
Should have bought him when I'd rather
Have a dog!

ANONYMOUS

LITTLE MIDGET

MY papa sometimes scolds and says,
I'm always in a fidget;
But mamma says, I keep quite still
For such a little midget.

My teacher said to-day, she thought
That it was very smart
For such a little thing as I
To learn a speech "by heart."

ANONYMOUS

SOMETHING NEW

THERE'S something new at our home—I'm s'prised you didn't know it;
It makes papa feel awful proud, although he hates to show it.
The thing is not so very big, but money couldn't buy it;
If any fellow thinks it could, I'd like to see him try it.

It's half-a-dozen things at once—a dove, a love, a flower;
Mamma calls it a hundred names, and new ones every hour;
It is a little music box, with tunes for every minute;
You haven't got one at your house, and so you are not in it.

It puckers up its wee, wee mouth, as if it meant to whistle;
A gold mine weighed against it then were lighter than a
thistle;
Papa said so the other night—I thought it sounded splendid,
And said it to myself until I fell asleep, and ended.

Of course you've guessed it by this time—our gift that came
from heaven;
Mamma declares the darling thing was by the angels given.
But then some folks are very slow, and some are stupid;
maybe
I ought to say, right straight and plain, come home and see
our baby.

MARGARET E. SANGSTER

HER NAME

IN search from "A" to "Z" they passed,
And "Marguerita" chose at last;
But thought it sounded far more sweet
To call the baby "Marguerite."
When grandma saw the little pet,
She called her "darling Margaret."
Next Uncle Jack and Cousin Aggie
Sent cup and spoon to "little Maggie."
And grandpapa the right must beg
To call the lassie "bonnie Meg";
(From "Marguerita" down to "Meg")
And now she's simply "little Peg."

ANONYMOUS

THE STEAM MAN

WHEN Gran'mama puts on the kettle,
And fills it and stirs up the fire,
And reads while the water is heating,
And I'm in my rocking chair by her,

I rock and I look and I listen,
  Till right in the kettle I hear
The littlest, funniest singing,
  And know that the Steam Man is near.

And then I say, "Gran'ma, he's coming!"
  And Gran'ma she looks and says, "Oh,
Sure enough, so he is! and directly
  He'll do some gymnastics, I know!"
And while I keep rocking and watching,
  The lid goes to jumping about;
For the little Steam Man in the kettle
  Is trying his best to get out.

And once, when she put on the stewpan,
  And left off the cover, he came;
And I said, "Oh, come, Gran'ma, we'll see him,
  The Steam Man, and ask him his name."
But—wasn't it funny?—we couldn't,
  Though I sat there for ever so long,
While the little Steam Man in the little stewpan
  Was dancing and singing his song.

ALBERT BIGELOW PAINE

POT AND KETTLE

"OHO!" said the pot to the kettle;
  "You're dirty and ugly and black!
Sure no one would think you were metal,
  Except when you're given a crack."

"Not so! not so!" kettle said to the pot.
  " 'Tis your own dirty image you see;
For I am so clean—without blemish or blot—
  That your blackness is mirrored in me."

UNKNOWN

ANIMAL CRACKERS *

ANIMAI crackers, and cocoa to drink,
That is the finest of suppers, I think;
When I'm grown up and can have what I please
I think I shall always insist upon these.

What do *you* choose when you're offered a treat?
When Mother says, "What would you like best
to eat?"
Is it waffles and syrup, or cinnamon toast?
It's cocoa and animal crackers that *I* love most!

The kitchen's the cosiest place that I know:
The kettle is singing, the stove is aglow,
And there in the twilight, how jolly to see
The cocoa and animals waiting for me.

Daddy and Mother dine later in state,
With Mary to cook for them, Susan to wait;
But they don't have nearly as much fun as I
Who eat in the kitchen with Nurse standing by;
And Daddy once said, he would like to be me
Having cocoa and animals once more for tea!

CHRISTOPHER MORLEY

THE RUNAWAY BOY

WUNST I sassed my Pa, an' he
Won't stand that, an' punished
me,—
Nen when he was gone that day,
I slipped out an' runned away.

I tooked all my copper cents,
An' clumbed over our back fence
In the jim'son weeds 'at growed
Ever'where all down the road.

* From "Songs for a Little House," by Christopher Morley, copyright, 1917, George H. Doran Company, Publishers.

Nen I got out there, an' nen
I runned some—an' runned again
When I met a man 'at led
A big cow 'at shooked her head.

I went down a long, long lane
Where was little pigs a-play'n';
An' a grea'-big pig went "Booh!"
An' jumped up, an' skeered me too.

Nen I scampered past, an' they
Was somebody hollered "Hey!"
An' I ist looked ever'where,
An' they was nobody there.

I *want* to, but I'm 'fraid to try
To go back. . . . An' by-an'-by
Somepin' hurts my throat inside—
An' I want my Ma—an' cried.

Nen a grea'-big girl come though
Where's a gate, an' telled me who
Am I? an' ef I tell where
My home's at she'll show me there.

But I couldn't ist but tell
What's my *name*; an' she says well,
An' she tooked me up an' says
She know where I live, she guess.

Nen she telled me hug wite close
Round her neck!—an' off she goes
Skippin' up the street! An' nen
Purty soon I'm home again.

An' my Ma, when she kissed me,
Kissed the *big girl* too, an' *she*
Kissed me—ef I p'omise *shore*
I won't run away no more!

James Whitcomb Riley

THE BOY THAT LAUGHS

I KNOW a funny little boy,
  The happiest ever born;
His face is like a beam of joy,
  Although his clothes are torn.

I saw him tumble on his nose,
  And waited for a groan;
But how he laughed! Do you suppose
  He struck his funny bone?

No matter how the day may go;
  You cannot make him cry;
He's worth a dozen boys I know,
  Who pout, and mope, and sigh.

George Cooper

AT AUNTY'S HOUSE

ONE time, when we'z at Aunty's house—
  'Way in the country!—where
They's ist but woods—an' pigs, an' cows—
  An' all's outdoors an' air!—
An' orchurd swing; an' churry trees—
An' *churries* in 'em!—Yes, an' these-
Here red-head birds steals all they please,
  An' tetch 'em ef you dare!—
W'y, wunst, one time, when we wuz there,
  We et out on the porch!

Wite where the cellar-door wuz shut
  The table wuz, an' I
Let Aunty set by me an' cut
  My vittuls up—an' pie.
'Tuz awful funny!—I could see
The red-heads in the churry tree;

An' beehives, where you got to be
  So keerful, goin' by;—
An' "comp'ny" there an' all!—an' we—
  We et out on the porch!

An' I ist et *p'surves* an' things
  'At Ma don't 'low me to—
An' *chickun-gizzurds*—(don't like *wings*
  Like *parunts* does! do *you?*)
An' all the time, the wind blowed there,
An' I could feel it in my hair,
An' ist smell clover *ever'*where!—
  An' a' old red-head flew
Purt' nigh wite over my high chair,
  When we et on the porch!

JAMES WHITCOMB RILEY

A LARGE ROOM

MY teacher told me the other day that I owned one of the largest rooms she ever saw. She said it was called the Room for Improvement.

MRS. E. J. H. GOODFELLOW

TWO LITTLE GIRLS I KNOW

I KNOW a little girl
    (You? Oh, no!)
Who, when she's asked to go to bed,
    Does just so:
She brings a dozen wrinkles out,
    And takes the dimples in;

She puckers up her pretty lips
And then she does begin:
"Oh, dear me! I don't see why
All the others sit up late,
And why can't I?"

Another little girl I know,
With curly pate,
Who says, "When I'm a great big girl,
I'll sit up late.
But mamma says 'twill make me grow
To be an early bird."
So she and dolly trot away
Without another word.
Oh, the sunny smile and the eye so blue,
And—why, yes, now I think of it,
She looks like you!

ANONYMOUS

MY SPEECH

FOLKS think I'm such a tiny tot
That I can't make a speech,
For some one said to Mamma
I am too young to teach.

But I can tell a story
I'm sure you never heard;
And if you'll only listen,
I'll tell you every word.

One morning very early
I heard a whisper low,
It came from near my bedside,
This little voice, you know.

"Oh dear, I'm very wretched,
Is any one more tried?
For just behold my trouble,
I'm broken in my side.

"I'm torn and bruised and scratched
And grown so very thin,
It is indeed a really sad
Condition I am in."

And then another voice replied
"I'm sorry you are sad,
But misery loves company
And I am just as bad.

"I've worked all day from morn till eve,
Right side by side with you;
I've suffered woes, until, until—
My sole's worn through and through."

"Then let us creep together, close,
Our waning life to spend;
For this is just a solemn fact,
We are too bad to mend."

Just then I opened wide my eyes
To hear such awful news,
And by my bed I only saw
My little worn out shoes.

MRS. E. J. H. GOODFELLOW

DON'T

I MIGHT have just the mostest fun
If 'twasn't for a word,
I think the very worstest one
'At ever I have heard.
I wish 'at it 'd go away,

But I'm afraid it won't.
I s'pose 'at it'll always stay—
That awful word of "don't."

It's "don't you make a bit of noise,"
And "don't go out of door,"
And "don't you spread your stock of toys
About the parlor floor;"
And "don't you dare play in the dust,"
And "don't you tease the cat,"
And "don't you get your clothing mussed,"
And "don't" do this and that.

It seems to me I've never found
A thing I'd like to do
But what there's some one close around
'At's got a "don't" or two.
And Sunday—'at's the day 'at "don't"
Is worse of all the seven.
Oh, goodness! but I hope there won't
Be any "don'ts" in Heaven!

NIXON WATERMAN

THE REASON

WHEN Rachel and Jessie are both at play
Everything runs in the smoothest way;
Each dear little face is sunny and sweet,—
Watching them play is a pleasant treat.

For they never quarrel or disagree,
Nor snatch the playthings, nor come to me
With tiresome complaints that make me sorry,
As do their cousins Kate and Florrie.

I was thinking what the reason could be—
Although they're the sweetest girls I see;
So I called them up to make the case plain,
And asked them the puzzle to explain.

And Jessie looked red and shook her shy head,
While our wise little Rachel quickly said,
Smilingly droll, "I think it must be
'Cause I let Jessie, and Jessie lets me!"

M. Eloise Jones

WHEN I AM BIG

WHEN I am big I mean to buy
A dozen platters of pumpkin pie,
A barrel of nuts, to have 'em handy,
And fifty pounds of sugar-candy.

When I am big, I mean to wear
A long-tailed coat, and crop my hair;
I'll buy a paper, and read the news,
And sit up late whenever I choose.

Unknown

SCHOOL GREETING

I GREET you now, my schoolmates dear,
With best of wishes and loving cheer;
With peace and love within my heart,
I bid you share my joy to part.

Our holidays have come at last,—
I hope they will not go too fast,
But that each day will bring you joy
And happiness without alloy.

Now that our study time is past,
We'll run, and play, and grow so fast,
That when our school begins once more
We'll study better than before.

When playing mid the summer flowers,
We'll not forget our schoolday hours;
I hope to meet you, one and all,
When school commences in the fall.

G. Scott

MRS. JUNE'S PROSPECTUS

To parents and friends: Mrs. June,
Of the firm of Summer & Sun,
Announces the opening of her school,
Established in the year one.

An unlimited number received;
There is nothing at all to pay;
All that is asked is a merry heart,
And time enough to be gay.

The Junior class will bring,
In lieu of all supplies,
Eight little fingers and two little thumbs
For the making of pretty sand pies.

The Senior class, a mouth
For strawberries and cream,
A nose apiece for a rose apiece,
And a tendency to dream.

The lectures are thus arranged:
Professor Cherry Tree
Will lecture to the climbing class,
Terms of instruction—free.

Professor De Forest Spring
Will take the class on Drink;
And the class on Titillation
Sage Mr. Bobolink.

Young Mr. Ox Eye Daisy
  Will demonstrate each day
On Botany, on native plants,
  And the properties of hay.

Miss Nature, the class in Fun
  (A charming class to teach);
And the Swinging Class and the Bird Nest Class
  Miss Hickory and Miss Beech.

And the Sleepy Class at night,
  And the Dinner Class at noon,
And the Fat and Laugh and Roses Class,
  They fall to Mrs. June.

And she hopes her little friends
  Will be punctual as the sun;
For the term, alas! is very short,
  And she wants them every one.

SUSAN COOLIDGE

A BOY'S DREAM

OH, what fun to live forever
  In a country running o'er
With fig-paste, jujube, and taffy,
  Caramels a countless store.

Where fresh gumdrops would keep falling
  Just like snowflakes from the sky;
While the lemon, mint, and cream sticks,
  Well—just everywhere should lie!

Where those candied fruits so lovely,
  That they'll never let us eat;
Cakes of coconut and raisins,
  Oh, so luscious and so sweet;

With whole lots of figs and citron,
  Should lie scattered all around;
While nuts, dates, and sugar-almonds,
  Cover every inch of ground!

"What a country for the youngsters,"
  Said grandmama with a smile,
"Like the little grunting piggies,
  They'd be stuffing all the while.

"Over all those heaps of goodies
  Such a jubilee they'd make;
Every day a glorious feasting,
  Every night a stomach ache!"

Ruth Argyle

LINES TO KATE

THERE'S something in the name of Kate,
  Which many will condemn;
But listen now while I relate
  The trials of some of them.

There's advo-Kate, a charming miss;
  Could you her hand obtain,
She'll lead you in the path of bliss,
  Nor plead your cause in vain.

There's deli-Kate, a modest dame,
  And worthy of your love;
She's nice and beautiful in frame,
  As gentle as a dove.

Communi-Kate's intelligent,
  As we may well suppose;
Her fruitful mind is ever bent
  On telling what she knows.

There's intri-Kate; she's so obscure
'Tis hard to find her out,
For she is often very sure
To put your wits to rout.

Prevari-Kate's a stubborn mind,
She's sure to have her way;
The cavilling, contrary jade
Objects to all you say.

There's alter-Kate, a perfect pest,
Much given to dispute;
Her prattling tongue can never rest;
You cannot her refute.

There's dislo-Kate, quite in a fret,
Who fails to gain her point;
Her case is quite unfortunate,
And sorely out of joint.

Equivo-Kate no one will woo,
The thing would be absurd;
She is faithless and untrue,
You cannot take her word.

There's vindi-Kate; she's good and true,
And strives with all her might
Her duty faithfully to do,
And battles for the right.

There's rusti-Kate, a country lass,
Quite fond of rural scenes;
She likes to ramble through the grass,
And through the evergreens.

Of all the maidens you can find,
There's none like edu-Kate;
Because she elevates the mind,
And aims for something great.

UNKNOWN

LITTLE BY LITTLE

ONE step and then another, and the longest walk is
 ended;
One stitch and then another, and the widest rent is mended;
One brick upon another, and the highest wall is made;
One flake upon another, and the deepest snow is laid.

Then do not frown nor murmur at the work you have to do,
Or say that such a mighty task you never can get through;
But just endeavor, day by day, another point to gain,
And soon the mountain that you feared will prove to be a
 plain.

UNKNOWN

THE WAY TO DO IT

I'LL tell you how I speak a piece:
 First, I make my bow;
Then I bring my words out clear
 And plain as I know how.

Next, I throw my hands up—so!
 Then I lift my eyes:
That's to let my hearers know
 Something doth surprise.

Next, I grin and show my teeth,
 Nearly every one,
Shake my shoulders, hold my sides:
 That's the sign of fun.

Next, I start, and knit my brows,
 Hold my head erect:
Something's wrong, you see, and I
 Decidedly object.

Then I wabble at my knees,
 Clutch at shadows near,

Tremble well from top to toe:
That's the sign of fear.

Now I start, and with a leap,
Seize an airy dagger.
"Wretch!" I cry: That's tragedy,
Every soul to stagger.

Then I let my voice grow faint,
Gasp, and hold my breath,
Tumble down and plunge about:
That's a villain's death.

Quickly then I come to life,
Perfectly restored;
With a bow my speech is done.
Now you'll please applaud.

Mary Mapes Dodge

SUPPOSE

Suppose, my little lady,
Your doll should break her head,
Could you make it whole by crying
Till your eyes and nose are red?
And wouldn't it be pleasanter
To treat it as a joke,
And say you're glad 'twas dolly's
And not your head that broke?

Suppose you're dressed for walking,
And the rain comes pouring down,
Will it clear off any sooner
Because you scold and frown?
And wouldn't it be nicer
For you to smile than pout,
And so make sunshine in the house
When there is none without?

Suppose your task, my little man,
  Is very hard to get,
Will it make it any easier
  For you to sit and fret?
And wouldn't it be nicer
  Than waiting like a dunce,
To go to work in earnest
  And learn the thing at once?

UNKNOWN

THE COURAGEOUS BOY

SOME of the boys in our school,
  Whose elbows I can't reach,
Are ten times more ashamed than I
  To rise and make a speech.

I guess they are afraid some girl
  Who is about their age,
May laugh and criticize their looks
  When they come on the stage.

UNKNOWN

A TERNARIE OF LITTLES

A LITTLE saint best fits a little shrine,
  A little prop best fits a little vine;
As my small cruse best fits my little wine.

A little seed best fits a little soil,
A little trade best fits a little toil;
As my small jar best fits my little oil.

A little bin best fits a little bread,
A little garland fits a little head;
As my small stuff best fits my little shed.

A little hearth best fits my little fire,
A little chapel fits a little choir;
As my small bell best fits my little spire.

A little stream best fits a little boat,
A little lead best fits a little float;
As my small pipe best fits my little note.

ROBERT HERRICK

ESCAPE AT BEDTIME

THE lights from the parlor and kitchen shone out
Through the blinds and the windows and bars;
And high overhead and all moving about,
There were thousands of millions of stars.

There ne'er were such thousands of leaves on a tree,
Nor of people in church or the Park,
As the crowds of the stars that looked down upon me,
And that glittered and winked in the dark.

The Dog, and the Plow, and the Hunter, and all,
And the star of the sailor, and Mars,
These shone in the sky, and the pail by the wall
Would be half full of water and stars.

They saw me at last, and they chased me with cries,
And they soon had me packed into bed;
But the glory kept shining, and bright in my eyes,
And the stars going round in my head.

ROBERT LOUIS STEVENSON

HEARTS, LIKE DOORS

HEARTS, like doors, will ope with ease
  To very, very little keys,
And don't forget that two of these
Are "I thank you" and "If you please."

UNKNOWN

CHILD'S TALK IN APRIL

I WISH you were a pleasant wren,
  And I your small accepted mate;
How we'd look down on toilsome men!
  We'd rise and go to bed at eight,
  Or it may not be quite so late.

Then you should see the nest I'd build,
  The wondrous nest for you and me;
The outside rough, perhaps, but filled
  With wool and down; ah, you should see
  The cosy nest that it would be.

We'd have our change of hope and fear,
  Some quarrels, reconcilements sweet;
I'd perch by you to chirp and cheer,
  Or hop about on active feet,
  And fetch you dainty bits to eat.

We'd be so happy by the day,
  So safe and happy through the night,
We both should feel, and I should say,
  It's all one season of delight,
  And we'll make merry whilst we may.

Perhaps some day there'd be an egg
  When spring had blossomed from the snow:
I'd stand triumphant on one leg;

Like chanticleer I'd almost crow
To let our little neighbors know.

Next you should sit, and I would sing
Through lengthening days of sunny spring;
Till, if you wearied of the task,
I'd sit; and you should spread your wing
From bough to bough; I'd sit and bask.

Fancy the breaking of the shell,
The chirp, the chickens wet and bare,
The untried proud paternal swell;
And you with housewife-matron air
Enacting choicer bills of fare.

Fancy the embryo coats of down,
The gradual feathers soft and sleek;
Till clothed and strong from tail to crown,
With virgin warblings in their beak,
They too go forth to soar and seek.

So would it last an April through
And early summer fresh with dew,
Then should we part and live as twain:
Love time would bring me back to you
And build our happy nest again.

Christina Georgina Rossetti

TRY AGAIN

'TIS a lesson you should heed,
Try again;
If at first you don't succeed,
Try again;
Then your courage should appear,
For if you will *persevere,*
You will conquer, never fear,
Try again.

Once or twice, though you should fail,
Try again;
If you would at last prevail,
Try again;
If we strive, 'tis no disgrace
Though we do not win the race;
What should we do in that case?
Try again.

If you find your task is hard,
Try again;
Time will bring you your reward,
Try again;
All that other folk can do,
Why, with patience, may not you?
Only keep this rule in view,
Try again.

William Edward Hickson

SEEIN' THINGS

I AIN'T afeard uv snakes, or toads, or bugs, or worms, or mice,
An' things 'at girls are skeered uv I think are awful nice!
I'm pretty brave, I guess; an' yet I hate to go to bed,
For, when I'm tucked up warm an' snug an' when my prayers are said,
Mother tells me "Happy dreams!" and takes away the light,
An' leaves me lyin' all alone an' seein' things at night!

Sometimes they're in the corner, sometimes they're by the door,
Sometimes they're all a-standin' in the middle uv the floor;
Sometimes they are a-sittin' down, sometimes they're walkin' round
So softly an' so creepylike they never make a sound!

Sometimes they are as black as ink, an' other times they're
white—
But the color ain't no difference when you see things at
night!

Once, when I licked a feller 'at had just moved on our street,
An' father sent me up to bed without a bite to eat,
I woke up in the dark an' saw things standin' in a row,
A-lookin' at me cross-eyed an' p'intin' at me—so!
Oh, my! I wuz so skeered that time I never slep' a mite—
It's almost alluz when I'm bad I see things at night!

Lucky thing I ain't a girl, or I'd be skeered to death!
Bein' I'm a boy, I duck my head an' hold my breath;
An' I am, oh! *so* sorry I'm a naughty boy, an' then
I promise to be better an' I say my prayers again!
Gran'ma tells me that's the only way to make it right
When a feller has been wicked an' sees things at night!

An' so, when other naughty boys would coax me into sin,
I try to skwush the Tempter's voice 'at urges me within;
An' when they's pie for supper, or cakes 'at's big an' nice,
I want to—but I do not pass my plate f'r them things twice!
No, ruther let Starvation wipe me slowly out o' sight
Than I should keep a-livin' on an' seein' things at night!

EUGENE FIELD

THE LAND OF STORY-BOOKS

AT evening when the lamp is lit,
Around the fire my parents sit;
They sit at home and talk and sing,
And do not play at anything.

Now, with my little gun, I crawl
All in the dark along the wall,
And follow round the forest track
Away behind the sofa back.

There, in the night, where none can spy,
All in my hunter's camp I lie,
And play at books that I have read
Till it is time to go to bed.

These are the hills, these are the woods,
These are my starry solitudes;
And there the river by whose brink
The roaring lions come to drink.

I see the others far away
As if in firelit camp they lay,
And I, like to an Indian scout,
Around their party prowled about,

So, when my nurse comes in for me,
Home I return across the sea,
And go to bed with backward looks
At my dear land of Story-books.

Robert Louis Stevenson

LAMENT OF A LITTLE GIRL

MY brother Will, he used to be
  The nicest kind of girl,
He wore a little dress like me,
  And had his hair in curl.
We played with dolls and tea sets then,
  And every kind of toy;
But all those good old times are gone,
  Will turned into a boy.

Mamma made him little suits,
  With pockets in his pants,
And cut off all his yellow curls
  And sent them to my aunts;

And Will, he was so pleased, I believe
  He almost jumped for joy,
And I must own I didn't like
  Will turned into a boy.

And now he plays with horrid tops
  I don't know how to spin,
And marbles that I try to shoot,
  But never hit nor win,
And leapfrog—I can't give a "back"
  Like Charlie, Frank, or Roy;
Oh, no one knows how bad I feel
  Since Will has turned a boy.

UNKNOWN

THE NEW BABY

MUZZER'S bought a baby—
  'Ittle bits of zing;
Zink I mos' could put him
  Froo my rubber ring.

Ain't he awful ugly?
  Ain't he awful pink?
Just come dowd from heaven!
  Dat's a fib, I zink.

Doctor told annuzer
  Great big awful lie;
Nose ain't out of joyent—
  Dat ain't why I cry.

Zink I ought to love him?
  No, I won't—so zere!
Nassy, crying baby—
  Ain't got any hair.

Send me off wiz Biddy
  Every single day:
"Be a good boy, Charley—
  Run away and play."

Dot all my nice kisses—
  Dot my place in bed:
Mean to take my drumstick
  And hit him on ze head.

UNKNOWN

MARY AND THE SWALLOW

(A dialogue for two little girls)

M. The lilacs are in blossom, the cherry flowers are white;
I hear a sound above me, a twitter of delight:
It is my friend the swallow, as sure as I'm alive!
I'm very glad to see you! Pray, when did you arrive?
S. I'm very glad to get here: I only came to-day;
I was this very morning a hundred miles away.
M. It was a weary journey: how tired you must be!
S. Oh, no! I'm used to traveling, and it agrees with me.
M. You left us last September, and pray where did you go?
S. I went South for the winter, I always do, you know.
M. The South! How do you like it?
S. I like its sunny skies;
And round the orange-blossoms I caught the nicest flies.
But when the spring had opened, I wanted to come back.
M. You're still the same old swallow! Your wings are just as black.
S. I always wear dark colors: I'm ever on the wing;
A sober suit for traveling I think the proper thing.
M. Your little last year's nestlings, do tell me how they grow.

Mary is on the stage, but the girl impersonating the swallow should be out of sight of the audience. An imitative twittering may be heard before the dialogue commences.

S. My nestlings are great swallows, and mated long ago.
M. And shall you build this summer among the flowers
and leaves?
S. No. I have taken lodgings beneath the stable eaves.
You'll hear each night and morning my twitter in the
sky.
M. That sound is always welcome. And now good-by!
S. Good-by.

Marian Douglas

WORDS ON WELCOME

(An opening address for school or Sunday-school entertainment)

KIND friends and dear parents, we welcome you here
To our nice pleasant schoolroom, and teacher so dear;
We wish but to show how much we have learned,
And how to our lessons our hearts have been turned.

But hope you'll remember we all are quite young,
And when we have spoken, recited and sung,
You will pardon our blunders, which, as all are aware,
May even extend to the President's chair.

Our life is a schooltime, and till that shall end,
With our Father in heaven for teacher and friend,
Oh, let us perform well each task that is given,
Till our time of probation is ended in heaven.

Unknown

THE FIRST PAIR OF BREECHES

(For a bright little boy of five years)

I'VE got a pair of breeches now,
And I'll have to be a man;
I know I can if just I try,
My mamma says I can!

I'm going to school now very soon,
And learn my A, B, C;
My mamma says I'm too young yet,
But I am 'way past three.

And I've got pockets in my pants,
To put my pencil in;
For mamma says that I must write
In school when I begin.

I'll soon be tall as papa—now
I'll grow as fast as I can,
And don't you think that very soon
I'll be a full-grown man?

UNKNOWN

GRANDPAPA'S SPECTACLES

GRANDPAPA'S spectacles cannot be found;
He has searched all the rooms, high and low, 'round and 'round;
Now he calls to the young ones, and what does he say?
"Ten cents for the child who will find them to-day."

Then Henry and Nelly and Edward all ran,
And a most thorough hunt for the glasses began,
And dear little Nell, in her generous way,
Said: "I'll look for them, grandpa, without any pay."

All through the big Bible she searches with care
That lies on the table by grandpapa's chair;
They feel in his pockets, they peep in his hat,
They pull out the sofa, they shake out the mat.
Then down on all fours, like two good-natured bears,
Go Harry and Ned under tables and chairs,
Till, quite out of breath, Ned is heard to declare,
He believes that those glasses are *not anywhere.*

But Nelly, who, leaning on grandpapa's knee,
Was thinking most earnestly where they *could* be,
Looked suddenly up in the kind, faded eyes,
And her own shining brown ones grew big with surprise.

She slapped both her hands—all her dimples came out—
She turned to the boys with a bright, roguish shout:
"You may leave off your looking, both Harry and Ned,
For there are the glasses on grandpapa's head!"

UNKNOWN

VALEDICTORY

IT now, kind friends, devolves on me
To speak our Val-e-dic-to-ry;
You've seen our exhibition through,
We've tried to please each one of you—
And if we've failed in any part,
Lay it to *head* and not to *heart;*

We thank you for your presence here,
With kindly smiles our work to cheer,
Our youthful zeal you do inspire
To set our mark a little higher—
But there's much more than words can tell,—
So thanking you we'll say—*farewell.*

UNKNOWN

AN OPENING ADDRESS

(Speak in a half-embarrassed and conversational tone)

I AM a very little boy (or girl), and I suppose that is why the teacher puts me first to-day. But I am big enough to tell you that we are very glad to see you.

I hope you will like this school very much. We will sing our best songs, and say our prettiest verses, and be just as good as we can all the time you stay, for we want you to come again.

(Straighten up with dignity and speak loud and strong)

And now I'll say my speech. This is it:

Kind friends, we welcome you to-day
With songs of merry glee;
Your loving smiles we strive to win,
Each face we love to see.

Sweet welcomes then to one and all,
And may your smiles approve;
And may we never miss the light
Of faces that we love.

UNKNOWN

WHEN MAMMA WAS A LITTLE GIRL

(For a girl of seven or eight years with a saucy air)

WHEN mamma was a little girl
(Or so they say to me)
She never used to romp and run,
Nor shout and scream with noisy fun,
Nor climb an apple tree.
She always kept her hair in curl,—
When mamma was a little girl.

When mamma was a little girl
(It seems to her, you see)
She never used to tumble down,
Nor break her doll, nor tear her gown,
Nor drink her papa's tea.
She learned to knit, "plain," "seam," and "purl,"—
When mamma was a little girl.

But grandma says—it must be true—
"How fast the seasons o'er us whirl!
Your mamma, dear, was just like you,
When she was grandma's little girl."

UNKNOWN

WHAT DOES LITTLE BIRDIE SAY?

WHAT does little birdie say
In her nest at peep of day?
Let me fly, says little birdie,
Mother, let me fly away.
Birdie, rest a little longer,
Till the little limbs are stronger,
So she rests a little longer,
Then she flies away.

What does little baby say,
In her bed at peep of day?
Baby says, like little birdie,
Let me rise and fly away.
Baby, sleep a little longer,
Till the little limbs are stronger,
If she sleeps a little longer,
Baby too shall fly away.

ALFRED TENNYSON

P'S AND Q'S

IT takes a lot of letters to make up the alphabet,
And two or three of them are very easy to forget;
There's K—a funny letter—and X and Y and Z—
There's hardly any use at all for any of those three!
The vowels are busy ones, A, E, I, O, U—

They've twice the work that all the other letters have to do;
I don't know why it is that grown-up people always choose
To tell us children to be sure and mind our P'S and Q's.

They're funny-looking letters, particularly Q,
It never goes around except in company with U;
P is much more important, it starts off pie and play,
It's not hard to remember if you think of it that way;
But lots of words begin with F and H and S and T,
They're just as worth remembering as any, seems to me;
Yet when we've strangers in the house, my parents always
say,
"Be sure you don't forget to mind your P'S and Q's to-
day!"

RUPERT SARGENT HOLLAND

TWINKLE, TWINKLE, LITTLE STAR

TWINKLE, twinkle, little star,
How I wonder what you are!
Up above the world so high
Like a diamond in the sky.

When the blazing sun is gone,
When he nothing shines upon,
Then you show your little light,
Twinkle, twinkle, all the night.

Then the traveler in the dark
Thanks you for your tiny spark!
He could not see which way to go,
If you did not twinkle so.

In the dark blue sky you keep,
And often through my curtains peep,
For you never shut your eye
Till the sun is in the sky.

As your bright and tiny spark
Lights the traveler in the dark,
Though I know not what you are,
Twinkle, twinkle, little star.

JANE TAYLOR

WHEN I'M A MAN

I THINK it would be fine, don't you?
To sit in a big, high seat
And drive the rumbling water cart
Up and down the street?
If I were that great big man I'd let
The little boys get good and wet—
And I'd find room up there—beside
For them to sit by me—and ride!
When I grow up—well, if I can—
I'll be a water cart-driving man!

UNKNOWN

BABY

WHERE did you come from, baby dear?
"Out of the everywhere into here."

Where did you get those eyes so blue?
"Out of the sky as I came through."

What makes the light in them sparkle and spin?
"Some of the starry spikes left in."

Where did you get that little tear?
"I found it waiting when I got here."

What makes your forehead so smooth and high?
"A soft hand stroked it as I went by."

What makes your cheek like a warm white rose?
"I saw something better than any one knows."

Whence that three-cornered smile of bliss?
"Three angels gave me at once a kiss."

Where did you get this pearly ear?
"God spoke, and it came out to hear."

Where did you get those arms and hands?
"Love made itself into bonds and bands."

Feet, whence did you come, you darling things?
"From the same box as the cherubs' wings."

How did they all just come to be you?
"God thought about me, and so I grew."

But how did you come to us, you dear?
"God thought about you, and so I am here."

George MacDonald

MR. NOBODY

I KNOW a funny little man,
As quiet as a mouse,
Who does the mischief that is done
In everybody's house!
There's no one ever sees his face,
And yet we all agree
That every plate we break was cracked
By Mr. Nobody.

'Tis he who always tears our books,
  Who leaves the door ajar,
He pulls the buttons from our shirts,
  And scatters pins afar;
That squeaking door will always squeak
  For, prithee, don't you see,
We leave the oiling to be done
  By Mr. Nobody.

He puts damp wood upon the fire,
  That kettles cannot boil;
His are the feet that bring in mud,
  And all the carpets soil.
The papers always are mislaid,
  Who had them last but he?
There's no one tosses them about
  But Mr. Nobody.

The finger marks upon the door
  By none of us are made;
We never leave the blinds unclosed,
  To let the curtains fade.
The ink we never spill, the boots
  That lying round you see
Are not our boots; they all belong
  To Mr. Nobody.

UNKNOWN

WHEN I GROW UP

WHEN I grow up, I mean to go
Where all the biggest rivers flow,
And take a ship and sail around
The Seven Seas until I've found
Robinson Crusoe's famous isle,
And there I'll land and stay a while,
And see how it would feel to be
Lord of an island in the sea.

When I grow up, I mean to rove
Through orange and palmetto grove,
To drive a sledge across the snow
Where great explorers like to go,
To hunt for treasures hid of old
By buccaneers and pirates bold,
And see if somewhere there may be
A mountain no one's climbed but me.

When I grow up, I mean to do
The things I've always wanted to;
I don't see why grown people stay
At home, when they could be away.

RUPERT SARGENT HOLLAND

THE LOST DOLL

I ONCE had a sweet little doll, dears,
  The prettiest doll in the world;
Her cheeks were so red and so white, dears,
  And her hair was so charmingly curled.
But I lost my poor little doll, dears,
  As I played in the heath one day;
And I cried for her more than a week, dears;
  But I never could find where she lay.

I found my poor little doll, dears,
  As I played in the heath one day;
Folks say she is terribly changed, dears,
  For her paint is all washed away,
And her arms trodden off by the cows, dears,
  And her hair not the least bit curled:
Yet for old sakes' sake she is still, dears,
  The prettiest doll in the world.

CHARLES KINGSLEY

ONE, TWO, THREE *

IT was an old, old, old, old lady,
And a boy that was half-past three,
And the way that they played together
Was beautiful to see.

She couldn't go romping and jumping,
And the boy no more could he,
For he was a thin little fellow,
With a thin little twisted knee.

They sat in the yellow sunlight,
Out under the maple tree,
And the game that they played I'll tell you,
Just as it was told to me.

It was Hide-and-Go-Seek they were playing
Though you'd never have known it to be—
With an old, old, old, old lady,
And a boy with a twisted knee.

The boy would bend his face down
On his little sound right knee,
And he guessed where she was hiding
In guesses, One, Two, Three.

"You are in a china closet!"
He would laugh and cry with glee—
It wasn't the china closet,
But he still had Two and Three.

"You are up in papa's big bedroom,
In the chest with the queer old key,"
And she said: "You are warm and warmer;
But you are not quite right," said she.

"It can't be the little cupboard
Where mamma's things used to be—
So it must be in the clothes-press, gran'ma,"
And he found her with his Three.

* From *Poems of H. C. Bunner;* copyright by Charles Scribner's Sons.

Then she covered her face with her fingers,
That were wrinkled and white and wee,
And she guessed where the boy was hiding,
With a One and a Two and a Three.

And they never had stirred from their places
Right under the maple tree—
This old, old, old, old lady
And the boy with the lame little knee—
This dear, dear, dear, dear old lady,
And the boy who was half-past three.

HENRY CUYLER BUNNER

GOOD NIGHT AND GOOD MORNING

A FAIR little girl sat under a tree,
Sewing as long as her eyes could see:
Then smoothed her work, and folded it right,
And said, "Dear work, good night! Good night!"

Such a number of rooks came over her head,
Crying, "Caw! caw!" on their way to bed:
She said, as she watched their curious flight,
"Little black things, good night! Good night!"

The horses neighed, and the oxen lowed,
The sheep's "Bleat! bleat!" came over the road:
All seeming to say, with a quiet delight,
"Good little girl, good night! Good night!"

She did not say to the sun, "Good night!"
Though she saw him there like a ball of light;
For she knew he had God's time to keep
All over the world and never could sleep.

The tall pink foxglove bowed his head—
The violet curtsied and went to bed;
And good little Lucy tied up her hair,
And said on her knees her favorite prayer.

And while on her pillow she softly lay,
She knew nothing more till again it was day:
And all things said to the beautiful sun,
"Good morning! Good morning! Our work is begun!"

LORD HOUGHTON

THE ELF AND THE DORMOUSE

UNDER a toadstool
Crept a wee Elf,
Out of the rain
To shelter himself.

Under the toadstool,
Sound asleep,
Sat a big Dormouse
All in a heap.

Trembled the wee Elf,
Frightened, and yet
Fearing to fly away
Lest he get wet.

To the next shelter—
Maybe a mile!
Sudden the wee Elf
Smiled a wee smile.

Tugged till the toadstool
Toppled in two.
Holding it over him,
Gayly he flew.

Soon he was safe home,
  Dry as could be.
Soon woke the Dormouse—
  "Good gracious me!

"Where is my toadstool?"
  Loud he lamented.
And that's how umbrellas
  First were invented.

OLIVER HERFORD

I LOVE LITTLE PUSSY

I LOVE little Pussy.
  Her coat is so warm,
And if I don't hurt her,
  She'll do me no harm.
So I'll not pull her tail,
  Or drive her away,
But Pussy and I
  Very gently will play.
She will sit by my side,
  And I'll give her her food,
And she'll like me because
  I am gentle and good.

I'll pat little Pussy,
  And then she will purr,
And thus show her thanks
  For my kindness to her;
I'll not pinch her ears,
  Nor tread on her paw,
Lest I should provoke her
  To use her sharp claw;
I never will vex her,
  Nor make her displeased,
For Pussy can't bear
  To be worried or teased.

JANE TAYLOR

WONDERFUL WORLD

GREAT, wide, beautiful, wonderful World,
With the wonderful water round you curled,
And the wonderful grass upon your breast—
World, you are beautifully drest.

The wonderful air is over me,
And the wonderful wind is shaking the tree,
It walks on the water, and whirls the mills,
And talks to itself on the tops of the hills.

You friendly Earth! how far do you go,
With the wheat fields that nod and the rivers that flow,
With cities, and gardens, and cliffs, and isles,
And people upon you for thousands of miles?

Ah, you are so great, and I am so small,
I tremble to think of you, World, at all;
And yet, when I said my prayers to-day,
A whisper inside me seemed to say,
"You are more than the Earth, though you are such a dot:
You can love and think, and the Earth cannot!"

William Brighty Rands

WATER JEWELS

A MILLION little diamonds
Twinkled on the trees;
And all the little maidens said,
"A jewel, if you please!"

But when they held their hands outstretched
To catch the diamond gay,
A million little sunbeams came,
And stole them all away.

Mary F. Butts

THE DIFFERENCE

EIGHT fingers,
  Ten toes,
Two eyes,
  And one nose.
Baby said
  When she smelt the rose,
"Oh! what a pity
  I've only one nose!"

Ten teeth
  In even rows,
Three dimples,
  And one nose.
Baby said
  When she smelt the snuff,
"Deary me!
  One nose is enough."

LAURA E. RICHARDS

CHOOSING A NAME

I HAVE got a new-born sister;
  I was nigh the first that kissed her.
When the nursing woman brought her
To papa, his infant daughter,
How papa's dear eyes did glisten!—
She will shortly be to christen;
And papa has made the offer,
I shall have the naming of her.
Now I wonder what would please her,
Charlotte, Julia, or Louisa?
Ann and Mary, they're too common;
Joan's too formal for a woman;
Jane's a prettier name beside;
But we had a Jane that died.

They would say, if 'twas Rebecca,
That she was a little Quaker.
Edith's pretty, but that looks
Better in old English books;
Ellen's left off long ago;
Blanche is out of fashion now.
None that I have named as yet
Are so good as Margaret.
Emily is neat and fine,
What do you think of Caroline?
How I'm puzzled and perplexed
What to choose or think of next!
I am in a little fever
Lest the name that I shall give her
Should disgrace her or defame her;
I will leave papa to name her.

CHARLES AND MARY LAMB

GYMNASTIC CLOCK

THE little clock is friends with me,
It talks as plain as plain can be,
And says, each morning as it rises,
"Now, don't forget your exercises!
Both hands above your head, you know!
Then lower them very slowly, so;
Ho, don't get tired and stop, that way!
I exercise like this, all day!"

Right in its face then, I say, "Pooh!
I wouldn't boast of it, like you,
But I can swing my arms 'round, too!"
And so the clock then looks at me,
And I look back, and I and he
Each single morning, when we rise,
Just exercise and exercise!

M. C. DAVIES

HOW THE LITTLE KITE LEARNED TO FLY

"I NEVER can do it," the little kite said,
As he looked at the others high over his head;
"I know I should fall if I tried to fly."
"Try," said the big kite; "only try!
Or I fear you never will learn at all."
But the little kite said, "I'm afraid I'll fall."

The big kite nodded: "Ah, well, good-by;
I'm off"; and he rose toward the tranquil sky.
Then the little kite's paper stirred at the sight,
And trembling he shook himself free for flight.
First whirling and frightened, then braver grown,
Up, up he rose through the air alone,
Till the big kite looking down could see
The little one rising steadily.

Then how the little kite thrilled with pride,
As he sailed with the big kite side by side!
While far below he could see the ground,
And the boys like small spots moving round.
They rested high in the quiet air,
And only the birds and clouds were there.
"Oh, how happy I am!" the little kite cried;
"And all because I was brave, and tried."

KATHARINE PYLE

LITTLE THINGS

LITTLE drops of water,
Little grains of sand,
Make the mighty ocean
And the pleasant land.

Thus the little minutes,
Humble though they be,
Make the mighty ages
Of eternity.

Thus our little errors
  Lead the soul away
From the path of virtue,
  Far in sin to stray.

Little deeds of kindness,
  Little words of love,
Make our earth an Eden,
  Like the heaven above.

Little seeds of mercy,
  Sown by youthful hands,
Grow to bless the nations
  Far in heathen lands.

EBENEZER COBHAM BREWER

SEVEN TIMES ONE

THERE'S no dew left on the daisies and clover,
  There's no rain left in heaven:
I've said my "seven times" over and over,
  Seven times one are seven.

I am old, so old, I can write a letter;
  My birthday lessons are done;
The lambs play always, they know no better;
  They are only one times one.

O moon! in the night I have seen you sailing
  And shining so round and low;
You were bright! ah, bright! but your light is failing—
  You are nothing now but a bow.

You moon, have you done something wrong in heaven
  That God has hidden your face?
I hope if you have you will soon be forgiven,
  And shine again in your place.

O velvet bee, you're a dusty fellow,
You've powdered your legs with gold!
O brave marsh marybuds, rich and yellow,
Give me your money to hold!

O columbine, open your folded wrapper,
Where two twin turtle-doves dwell!
O cuckoopint, toll me the purple clapper
That hangs in your clear, green bell!

And show me your nest with the young ones in it;
I will not steal them away;
I am old! you may trust me, linnet, linnet—
I am seven times one to-day.

Jean Ingelow

HOW DOTH THE LITTLE BUSY BEE

HOW doth the little busy bee
Improve each shining hour,
And gather honey all the day
From every opening flower!

How skillfully she builds her cell!
How neat she spreads the wax!
And labors hard to store it well
With the sweet food she makes.

In works of labor or of skill,
I would be busy too;
For Satan finds some mischief still
For idle hands to do.

In books, or work, or healthful play,
Let my first years be past,
That I may give for every day
Some good account at last.

Isaac Watts

BIRDS AND ANIMALS

THE BLUEBIRD

LISTEN a moment, I pray you; what was that sound
that I heard?
Wind in the budding branches, the ripple of brooks, or a
bird?
Hear it again, above us! and see a flutter of wings!
The bluebird knows it is April, and soars toward the sun
and sings.

Never the song of the robin could make my heart so glad;
When I hear the bluebird singing in spring, I forget to
be sad.
Hear it! a ripple of music! sunshine changed into song!
It sets me thinking of summer when the days and their
dreams are long.

Winged lute that we called a bluebird, you blend in a
silver strain
The sound of the laughing water, the patter of spring's
sweet rain.
The voice of the winds, the sunshine, and fragrance of
blossoming things,
Ah! you are an April poem, that God has dowered with
wings!

EBEN EUGENE REXFORD

THE BROWN THRUSH

THERE'S a merry brown thrush sitting up in a tree—
"He's singing to me; he's singing to me!"
And what does he say, little girl, little boy?
"'Oh, the world's running over with joy!

Don't you hear? Don't you see?
Hush! Look! In my tree,
I'm as happy as happy can be!' "

And the brown thrush keeps singing—"A nest do you see
And five eggs, hid by me in the juniper tree?
Don't meddle! don't touch! little girl, little boy,
Or the world will lose some of its joy.
Now I'm glad! Now I'm free!
And I always shall be,
If you never bring sorrow to me."

So the merry brown thrush sings away in the tree,
To you and to me, to you and to me;
And he sings all the day, little girl, little boy,
"Oh, the world's running over with joy;
But long it won't be,
Don't you know? Don't you see?
Unless we're as good as can be!"

LUCY LARCOM

AT THE DOG SHOW *

(To an Irish Wolf Hound)

LONG and gray and gaunt he lies,
A Lincoln among dogs; his eyes,
Deep and clear of sight, appraise
The meaningless and shuffling ways
Of human folk that stop to stare.
One witless woman seeing there
How tired, how contemptuous
He is of all the smell and fuss
Asks him, "Poor fellow, are you sick?"

Yea, sick, and weary to the quick
Of heat and noise from dawn to dark.
He will not even stoop to bark

* From "Songs for a Little House," by Christopher Morley, copyright, 1917, George H. Doran Company, Publishers.

His protest, like the lesser bred.
Would he might know, one gazer read
The wistful longing in his face,
The thirst for wind and open space
And stretch of limbs to him begrudged.
There came a little, dapper, fat,
And bustling man, with cane and spat
And pearl-gray vest and derby hat—
Such were the judger and the judged!

CHRISTOPHER MORLEY

THREE THINGS TO REMEMBER

A ROBIN REDBREAST in a cage
Puts all Heaven in a rage.

A skylark wounded on the wing
Doth make a cherub cease to sing.

He who shall hurt the little wren
Shall never be beloved by men.

WILLIAM BLAKE

THE MOUNTAIN AND THE SQUIRREL

THE mountain and the squirrel
Had a quarrel,
And the former called the latter "Little prig;"
Bun replied,
"You are doubtless very big;
But all sorts of things and weather
Must be taken in together
To make up a year,
And a sphere.
And I think it no disgrace
To occupy my place.
If I'm not so large as you,

You are not so small as I,
And not half so spry:
I'll not deny you make
A very pretty squirrel track.
Talents differ; all is well and wisely put;
If I cannot carry forests on my back,
Neither can you crack a nut."

Ralph Waldo Emerson

MY DOVES

My little doves have left a nest
  Upon an Indian tree,
Whose leaves fantastic take their rest
  Or motion from the sea;
For, ever there the sea winds go
With sunlit paces to and fro.

The tropic flowers looked up to it,
  The tropic stars looked down,
And there my little doves did sit
  With feathers softly brown,
And glittering eyes that showed their right
To general Nature's deep delight.

My little doves were ta'en away
  From that glad nest of theirs,
Across an ocean rolling gray,
  And tempest-clouded airs.
My little doves who lately knew
The sky and wave by warmth and blue.

And now, within the city prison
  In mist and chillness pent,
With sudden upward look they listen
  For sounds of past content,
For lapse of water, smell of breeze,
Or nut fruit falling from the trees.

Elizabeth Barrett Browning

TO THE CUCKOO

O BLITHE newcomer! I have heard,
  I hear thee and rejoice.
O Cuckoo! shall I call thee Bird,
  Or but a wandering Voice?

While I am lying on the grass
  Thy twofold shout I hear;
From hill to hill it seems to pass,
  At once far off and near.

Though babbling only, to the vale,
  Of sunshine and of flowers,
Thou bringest unto me a tale
  Of visionary hours.

Thrice welcome, darling of the Spring!
  Even yet thou art to me
No Bird, but an invisible Thing,
  A voice, a mystery.

The same whom in my Schoolboy days
  I listened to; that cry
Which made me look a thousand ways,
  In bush, and tree, and sky.

To seek thee did I often rove
  Through woods and on the green,
And thou wert still a hope, a love,
  Still longed for, never seen.

And I can listen to thee yet;
  Can lie upon the plain
And listen till I do beget
  That golden time again.

O blessed Bird; the earth we pace
  Again appears to be
An unsubstantial, faery place,
  That is fit home for Thee!

WILLIAM WORDSWORTH

THE REDBREAST CHASING A BUTTERFLY

CAN this be the bird to man so good,
That, after their bewildering,
Covered with leaves the little children
So painfully in the wood?
What ailed thee, Robin, that thou couldst pursue
A beautiful creature
That is gentle by nature?
Beneath the summer sky,
From flower to flower let him fly;
'Tis all that he wishes to do.

The cheerer thou of our indoor sadness,
He is the friend of our summer gladness;
What hinders then that ye should be
Playmates in the sunny weather,
And fly about in the air together?
His beautiful wings in crimson are drest.
A crimson as bright as thine own:
If thou wouldst be happy in thy nest,
O pious bird! whom man loves best,
Love him, or leave him alone!

WILLIAM WORDSWORTH

THE TIGER

TIGER! Tiger! burning bright,
In the forests of the night,
What immortal hand or eye
Could frame thy fearful symmetry?

In what distant deeps or skies
Burnt the fire of thine eyes?
On what wings dare he aspire?
What the hand dare seize the fire?

And what shoulder, and what art,
Could twist the sinews of thy heart?
And, when thy heart began to beat,
What dread hand and what dread feet?

What the hammer? what the chain?
In what furnace was thy brain?
What the anvil? what dread grasp
Dare its deadly terrors clasp?

When the stars threw down their spears,
And watered heaven with their tears,
Did He smile His work to see?
Did He who made the Lamb, make thee?

Tiger! Tiger! burning bright,
In the forests of the night,
What immortal hand or eye
Dare frame thy fearful symmetry?

WILLIAM BLAKE

THE LARK AND THE NIGHTINGALE

'TIS sweet to hear the merry lark,
That bids a blithe good morrow;
But sweeter to hark, in the twinkling dark,
To the soothing song of sorrow.
O Nightingale! what doth she ail?
And is she sad or jolly?
For ne'er on earth was sound of mirth
So like to melancholy.

The merry lark, he soars on high,
No worldly thought o'ertakes him;
He sings aloud to the clear blue sky,
And the daylight that awakes him.

As sweet a lay, as loud, as gay,
The nightingale is trilling,
With feeling bliss, no less than his,
Her little heart is thrilling.

Yet ever and anon, a sigh
Peers through her lavish mirth;
For the lark's bold song is of the sky,
And hers is of the earth.
By day and night she tunes her lay,
To drive away all sorrow;
For bliss, alas! to-night must pass,
And woe may come to-morrow.

HARTLEY COLERIDGE

THE BIRDS OF PASSAGE

BIRDS, joyous birds of the wandering wing!
Whence is it ye come with the flowers of spring?
—"We come from the shores of the green old Nile,
From the land where the roses of Sharon smile,
From the palms that wave through the Indian sky,
From the myrrh trees of glowing Araby.

"We have swept o'er cities in song renowned,
Silent they lie with the desert round!
We have crossed the proud rivers whose tide hath rolled
All dark with the warrior blood of old;
And each worn wing hath regained its home
Under peasant's roof or monarch's dome."

And what have ye found in the monarch's dome,
Since last ye traversed the blue sea's foam?
—"We have found a change;—we have found a pall,
And a gloom o'ershadowing the banquet hall;
And a mark on the floor as of life drops spilt—
Nought looks the same save the nest we built."

Oh! joyous birds, it hath ever been so:
Through the halls of kings doth the tempest go,
But the huts of hamlets lie still and deep,
And the hills o'er their quiet a vigil keep:—
Say, what have ye found in the peasant's cot
Since last ye parted from that sweet spot?

"A change we have found there, and many a change,
Faces and footsteps, and all things strange;
Gone are the heads of the silvery hair,
And the young that were have a brow of care;
And the place is hushed where the children played;
Nought looks the same save the nest we made."

Sad is your tale of the beautiful earth,
Birds that o'ersweep it in power and mirth;
Yet through the wastes of the trackless air
Ye have a guide, and shall *we* despair?
Ye over desert and deep have passed,
So may *we* reach our bright home at last.

Felicia Dorothea Hemans

THE RETIRED CAT

A POET'S cat, sedate and grave
As poet well could wish to have,
Was much addicted to inquire
For nooks to which she might retire,
And where, secure as mouse in chink,
She might repose, or sit and think.

Sometimes ascending, debonair,
An apple tree, or lofty pear,
Lodged with convenience in the fork
She watched the gardener at his work;
Sometimes her ease and solace sought

In an old empty watering pot;
There, wanting nothing but a fan,
To seem some nymph in her sedan,
Appareled in exactest sort,
And ready to be borne to court.

But love of change it seems has place
Not only in our wiser race;
Cats also feel, as well as we,
That passion's force, and so did she.
Her climbing, she began to find,
Exposed her too much to the wind,
And the old utensil of tin
Was cold and comfortless within;
She therefore wished, instead of those,
Some place of more secure repose,
Where neither cold might come, nor air
Too rudely wanton with her hair,
And sought it in the likeliest mode
Within her master's snug abode.

A drawer, it chanced, at bottom lined
With linen of the softest kind—
A drawer impending o'er the rest,
Half open, in the topmost chest,
Of depth enough, and none to spare,
Inviting her to slumber there.
Puss, with delight beyond expression,
Surveyed the scene and took possession.
Then resting at her ease, ere long,
And lulled by her own humdrum song,
She left the cares of life behind,
And slept as she would sleep her last;
When in came, housewifely inclined,
The chambermaid, and shut it fast;
By no malignity impelled,
But all unconscious whom it held.
Awakened by the shock, cried Puss,
"Was ever cat attended thus!
The open drawer was left I see,
Merely to prove a nest for me;

For soon as I was well composed,
Then came the maid, and it was closed.
How smooth these kerchiefs and how sweet;
Oh! what a delicate retreat,
I will resign myself to rest,
Till Sol declining in the west,
Shall call to supper, when, no doubt,
Susan will come and let me out."

The evening came, the sun descended,
And Puss remained still unattended.
The night rolled tardily away
(With her, indeed, 'twas never day),
The sprightly moon her course renewed,
The evening gray again ensued;
And Puss came into mind no more
Than if entombed the day before.
With hunger pinched, and pinched for room,
She now presaged approaching doom,
Nor slept a single wink or purred,
Conscious of jeopardy incurred.

That night, by chance, the poet watching,
Heard an inexplicable scratching;
His noble heart went pit-a-pat,
And to himself he said, "What's that?"
He drew the curtain at his side,
And forth he peeped, but nothing spied;
Yet, by his ear directed, guessed
Something imprisoned in the chest,
And doubtful what, with prudent care,
Resolved it should continue there.
At length a voice which well he knew,
A long and melancholy mew,
Saluting his poetic ears,
Consoled him and dispelled his fears.
He left his bed, he trod the floor,
And 'gan in haste the drawers explore,
The lowest first, and without stop
The rest in order, to the top;
For 'tis a truth well known to most,

That whatsoever thing is lost,
We seek it ere it come to light
In every cranny but the right.

Forth skipped the cat, not now replete,
As erst, with airy self-conceit,
Nor in her own fond apprehension
A theme for all the world's attention;
But sober, modest, cured of all
Her notions so hyperbolical,
And wishing for her place of rest
Anything rather than a chest.
Then stepped the poet into bed
With this reflection in his head:

MORAL

Beware of too sublime a sense
Of your own worth and consequence!
The man who dreams himself so great,
And his importance of such weight,
That all around in all that's done,
Must move and act for *him* alone,
Will learn in school of tribulation,
The folly of his expectation.

William Cowper

THE EAGLE

He clasps the crag with crooked hands;
Close to the sun in lonely lands,
Ringed with the azure world, he stands.

The wrinkled sea beneath him crawls;
He watches from his mountain walls,
And like a thunderbolt he falls.

Alfred Tennyson

THE KITTEN AT PLAY

SEE the kitten on the wall,
Sporting with the leaves that fall,
Withered leaves, one, two, and three
Falling from the elder tree,
Through the calm and frosty air
Of the morning bright and fair.

See the kitten, how she starts,
Crouches, stretches, paws and darts;
With a tiger leap half way
Now she meets her coming prey.
Lets it go as fast and then
Has it in her power again.

Now she works with three and four,
Like an Indian conjurer;
Quick as he in feats of art,
Gracefully she plays her part;
Yet were gazing thousands there,
What would little Tabby care?

William Wordsworth

THE NIGHTINGALE AND GLOWWORM

A NIGHTINGALE, that all day long
Had cheered the village with his song,
Nor yet at eve his note suspended,
Nor yet when eventide was ended,
Began to feel, as well he might,
The keen demands of appetite;
When, looking eagerly around,
He spied far off, upon the ground,
A something shining in the dark,
And knew the glowworm by his spark;
So, stooping down from hawthorn top,
He thought to put him in his crop.

The worm, aware of his intent,
Harangued him thus, right eloquent—
"Did you admire my lamp," quoth he,
"As much as I your minstrelsy,
You would abhor to do me wrong,
As much as I to spoil your song;
For 'twas the self-same power divine,
Taught you to sing, and me to shine;
That you with music, I with light,
Might beautify and cheer the night."
The songster heard his short oration,
And warbling out his approbation,
Released him, as my story tells,
And found a supper somewhere else.

WILLIAM COWPER

THE DOG OF REFLECTION

A DOG growing thinner, for want of a dinner,
Once purloin'd a joint from a tray;
"How happy I am, with this shoulder of lamb!"
Thought the cur, as he trotted away.

But the way that he took, lay just over a brook,
Which he found it was needful to cross,
So, without more ado, he plunged in to go through,
Not dreaming of danger or loss.

But what should appear, in this rivulet clear,
As he thought upon coolest reflection,
But a cur like himself, who with ill-gotten pelf,
Had run off in that very direction.

Thought the dog, à propos! but that instant let go
(As he snatched at this same water-spaniel),
The piece he possess'd—so, with hunger distress'd,
He slowly walk'd home to his kennel.

Hence, when we are needy, don't let us be greedy
(Excuse me this line of digression),
Lest in snatching at all, like the dog, we let fall
The good that we have in possession.

JEFFREYS TAYLOR

THE LION AND THE MOUSE

A LION with the heat oppress'd,
One day composed himself to rest;
But whilst he dozed, as he intended,
A mouse his royal back ascended;
Nor thought of harm, as Æsop tells,
Mistaking him for some one else;
And travel'd over him, and round him,
And might have left him as he found him
Had he not—tremble when you hear—
Tried to explore the monarch's ear!
Who straightway woke, with wrath immense,
And shook his head to cast him thence.
"You rascal, what are you about?"
Said he, when he had turned him out.
"I'll teach you soon," the lion said,
"To make a mousehole in my head!"
So saying, he prepared his foot
To crush the trembling tiny brute;
But he (the mouse) with tearful eye,
Implored the lion's clemency,
Who thought it best at last to give
His little pris'ner a reprieve.

'Twas nearly twelve months after this,
The lion chanced his way to miss;
When pressing forward, heedless yet,
He got entangled in a net.
With dreadful rage, he stamped and tore,
And straight commenced a lordly roar;

When the poor mouse, who heard the noise,
Attended, for she knew his voice.
Then what the lion's utmost strength
Could not effect, she did at length;
With patient labor she applied
Her teeth, the network to divide;
And so at last forth issued he,
A *lion*, by a mouse set free.

Few are so small or weak, I guess,
But may assist us in distress,
Nor shall we ever, if we're wise,
The meanest, or the least despise.

JEFFREYS TAYLOR

TO A BEE

THOU wert out betimes, thou busy, busy bee!
As abroad I took my early way,
Before the cow from her resting place
Had risen up, and left her trace
On the meadow, with dew so gay,
Saw I thee, thou busy, busy bee!

Thou wert working late, thou busy, busy bee!
After the fall of the cistus flower,
When the primrose of evening was ready to burst,
I heard thee last, as I saw thee first;
In the silence of the evening hour,
Heard I thee, thou busy, busy bee!

Thou art a miser, thou busy, busy bee!
Late and early at employ;
Still on thy golden stores intent,
Thy summer in keeping and hoarding is spent,
What thy winter will never enjoy.
Wise lesson this for me, thou busy, busy bee!

Little dost thou think, thou busy, busy bee!
  What is the end of thy toil,
When the latest flowers of the ivy are gone,
And all thy work for the year is done,
  Thy master comes for the spoil;
Woe then for thee, thou busy, busy bee!

Robert Southey

TO AN INSECT

I LOVE to hear thine earnest voice,
  Wherever thou art hid,
Thou testy little dogmatist,
  Thou pretty Katydid!
Thou mindest me of gentlefolks,—
  Old gentlefolks are they,—
Thou say'st an undisputed thing
  In such a solemn way.

Thou art a female, Katydid!
  I know it by the trill
That quivers through thy piercing notes,
  So petulant and shrill;
I think there is a knot of you
  Beneath the hollow tree,—
A knot of spinster Katydids,—
  Do Katydids drink tea?

Oh, tell me where did Katy live,
  And what did Katy do?
And was she very fair and young,
  And yet so wicked, too?
Did Katy love a naughty man,
  Or kiss more cheeks than one?
I warrant Katy did no more
  Than many a Kate has done.

Dear me! I'll tell you all about
  My fuss with little Jane,
And Ann, with whom I used to walk
  So often down the lane,
And all that tore their locks of black,
  Or wet their eyes of blue,—
Pray tell me, sweetest Katydid,
  What did poor Katy do?

Ah no! the living oak shall crash,
  That stood for ages still,
The rock shall rend its mossy base
  And thunder down the hill,
Before the little Katydid
  Shall add one word, to tell
The mystic story of the maid
  Whose name she knows so well.

Peace to the ever-murmuring race!
  And when the latest one
Shall fold in death her feeble wings
  Beneath the autumn sun,
Then shall she raise her fainting voice,
  And lift her drooping lid,
And then the child of future years
  Shall hear what Katy did.

OLIVER WENDELL HOLMES

THE GRASSHOPPER AND THE CRICKET

THE poetry of earth is never dead:
  When all the birds are faint with the hot sun,
And hide in cooling trees, a voice will run
From hedge to hedge about the new-mown mead:
That is the grasshopper's—he takes the lead
In summer luxury—he has never done
With his delights, for when tired out with fun,
He rests at ease beneath some pleasant weed.

The poetry of earth is ceasing never:
On a lone winter evening, when the frost
Has wrought a silence, from the stove there shrills
The cricket's song, in warmth increasing ever,
And seems to one in drowsiness half lost,
The grasshopper's among the grassy hills.

JOHN KEATS

TO A BUTTERFLY

I'VE watched you now a full half-hour,
Self-poised upon that yellow flower;
And, little butterfly, indeed,
I know not if you sleep or feed.

How motionless!—not frozen seas
More motionless; and then,
What joy awaits you when the breeze
Hath found you out among the trees,
And calls you forth again!

This plot of orchard ground is ours,
My trees they are, my sister's flowers;
Here rest your wings when they are weary,
Here lodge as in a sanctuary!

Come to us often, fear no wrong,
Sit near us on the bough!
We'll talk of sunshine and of song,
And summer days when we were young;
Sweet childish days that were as long
As twenty days are now.

WILLIAM WORDSWORTH

FLOWERS AND SEASONS

GLIMPSE IN AUTUMN

LADIES at a ball
Are not so fine as these
Richly brocaded trees
That decorate the fall.

They stand against a wall
Of crisp October sky,
Their plumèd heads held high,
Like ladies at a ball.

JEAN STARR UNTERMEYER

NOVEMBER'S PARTY

NOVEMBER gave a party,
The leaves by hundreds came,
The Chestnuts, Oaks, and Maples,
And leaves of every name;
The sunshine spread a carpet,
And everything was grand;
Miss Weather led the dancing,
Professor Wind, the band.

The Chestnuts came in yellow,
The Oaks in crimson drest;
The lovely Misses Maple
In scarlet looked their best.
All balanced to their partners,
And gayly fluttered by;
The sight was like a rainbow,
New fallen from the sky.

Then, in the rusty hollows,
  At hide-and-seek they played;
The party closed at sundown,
  And everybody stayed.
Professor Wind played louder.
  They flew along the ground,
And there the party ended
  In "hands across, all round."

UNKNOWN

THE DAISY

(On finding one in bloom on Christmas Day)

THERE is a flower, a little flower,
  With silver crest and golden eye,
That welcomes every changing hour
  And weathers every sky;
The prouder beauties of the field
  In gay but quick succession shine;
Race after race their honors yield,
  They flourish and decline.

But this small flower, to Nature dear,
  While moons and stars their courses run,
Wreathes the whole circle of the year,
  Companion of the sun.
It smiles upon the lap of May,
  To sultry August spreads its charms,
Lights pale October on its way,
  And twines December's arms.

The purple heath and golden broom,
  On moory mountains catch the gale.
O'er lawns the lily sheds perfume,
  The violet in the vale;
But this bold floweret climbs the hill,
  Hides in the forest, haunts the glen,
Plays on the margin of the rill,
  Peeps round the fox's den.

Within the garden's cultured round
It shares the sweet carnation's bed;
And blooms on consecrated ground,
In honor of the dead.
The lambkin crops its crimson gem,
The wild bee murmurs on its breast,
The blue fly bends its pensile stem
Light o'er the skylark's nest.

'Tis Flora's page: in every place,
In every season, fresh and fair,
It opens with perennial grace,
And blossoms everywhere.
On waste and woodland, rock and plain,
The humble buds unheeded rise;
The rose has but a summer reign,
The daisy never dies.

JAMES MONTGOMERY

TREES *

I THINK that I shall never see
A poem lovely as a tree.

A tree whose hungry mouth is pressed
Against the earth's sweet flowing breast;

A tree that looks at God all day
And lifts her leafy arms to pray;

A tree that may in summer wear
A nest of robins in her hair;

Upon whose bosom snow has lain;
Who intimately lives with rain.

Poems are made by fools like me,
But only God can make a tree.

JOYCE KILMER

* From "Trees and Other Poems," by Joyce Kilmer, copyright, 1914, George H. Doran Company, Publishers.

TO DAFFODILS

FAIR daffodils, we weep to see
You haste away so soon;
As yet the early rising sun
Has not attained his noon:
Stay, stay
Until the hastening day
Has run
But to the evensong;
And having prayed together, we
Will go with you along!

We have short time to stay, as you,
We have as short a spring,
As quick a growth to meet decay,
As you or anything.
We die
As your hours do; and dry
Away,
Like to the summer's rain,
Or as the pearls of morning dew,
Ne'er to be found again.

Robert Herrick

VIOLETS

WELCOME, maids of honor!
You do bring
In the Spring,
And wait upon her.

She hath virgins many,
Fresh and fair;
Yet you are
More sweet than any.

You're the maiden posies;
And so graced,
To be placed
'Fore damask roses.

Yet, though thus respected,
By and by
Ye do lie,
Poor girls, neglected.

ROBERT HERRICK

SWEET PEAS

HERE are sweet peas, on tiptoe for a flight:
With wings of gentle flush o'er delicate white,
And taper fingers catching at all things,
To bind them all about with tiny rings.
Linger a while upon some bending planks
That lean against a streamlet's rushy banks,
And watch intently Nature's gentle doings:
They will be found softer than ring-dove's cooings.
How silent comes the water round that bend!
Not the minutest whisper does it send
To the o'erhanging sallows: blades of grass
Slowly across the chequer'd shadows pass.

JOHN KEATS

BUTTERCUPS AND DAISIES

BUTTERCUPS and daisies,
Oh, the pretty flowers;
Coming ere the spring time,
To tell of sunny hours.
While the trees are leafless,
While the fields are bare,
Buttercups and daisies
Spring up here and there.

Ere the snowdrop peepeth,
  Ere the crocus bold,
Ere the early primrose
  Opes its paly gold,—
Somewhere on the sunny bank
  Buttercups are bright;
Somewhere 'mong the frozen grass
  Peeps the daisy white.

Little hardy flowers,
  Like to children poor,
Playing in their sturdy health
  By their mother's door.
Purple with the north wind,
  Yet alert and bold;
Fearing not, and caring not,
  Though they be a-cold!

What to them is winter!
  What are stormy showers!
Buttercups and daisies
  Are these human flowers!
He who gave them hardships
  And a life of care,
Gave them likewise hardy strength
  And patient hearts to bear.

MARY HOWITT

A ROSEBUD

A ROSEBUD by my early walk,
  Adown a corn-enclosed bawk,
Sae gently bent its thorny stalk,
    All on a dewy morning.

Ere twice the shades o' dawn are fled,
In a' its crimson glory spread,
And drooping rich the dewy head,
    It scents the early morning.

Within the bush, her covert nest
A little linnet fondly prest,
The dew sat chilly on her breast
Sae early in the morning.

So thou, dear bird, young Jenny fair,
On trembling string, or vocal air,
Shall sweetly pay the tender care
That tents thy early morning.

So thou sweet rosebud, young and gay,
Shalt beauteous blaze upon the day,
And bless the parents' evening ray
That watch thy early morning.

Robert Burns

A GARDEN

A SENSITIVE plant in a garden grew,
And the young winds fed it with silver dew,
And it open'd its fanlike leaves to the light,
And closed them beneath the kisses of night.

And the Spring arose on the garden fair,
And the Spirit of Love fell everywhere;
And each flower and herb on Earth's dark breast
Rose from the dreams of its wintry nest.

The snowdrop, and then the violet,
Arose from the ground with warm rain wet,
And their breath was mix'd with fresh odor, sent
From the turf, like the voice and the instrument.

Then the pied windflowers and the tulip tall,
And narcissi, the fairest among them all,
Who gaze on their eyes in the stream's recess,
Till they die of their own dear loveliness.

And the Naiad-like lily of the vale,
Whom youth makes so fair and passion so pale,
That the light of its tremulous bell is seen,
Through their pavilions of tender green.

And the hyacinth, purple and white and blue,
Which flung from its bells a sweet peal anew,
Of music so delicate, soft, and intense,
It was felt like an odor within the sense.

And the jessamine faint, and the sweet tuberose,
The sweetest flower for scent that blows;
And all rare blossoms from every clime
Grew in that garden in perfect prime.

PERCY BYSSHE SHELLEY

THE CORN SONG

HEAP high the farmer's wintry board!
  Heap high the golden corn!
No richer gift has autumn poured
  From out her lavish horn!

Let other lands, exulting, glean
  The apple from the pine,
The orange from its glossy green,
  The cluster from the vine.

We better love the hardy gift
  Our rugged vales bestow,
To cheer us when the storm shall drift
  Our harvest fields with snow.

Through vales of grass and meads of flowers,
  Our plow their furrows made,
While on the hills the sun and showers
  Of changeful April played.

We dropped the seed o'er hill and plain
  Beneath the sun of May,
And frightened from our sprouting grain
  The robber crows away.

All through the long, bright days of June
  Its leaves grew green and fair,
And waved in hot midsummer's noon
  Its soft and yellow hair.

And now with autumn's moonlit eyes,
  Its harvest time has come,
We pluck away the frosted leaves,
  And bear the treasure home.

There richer than the fabled gift
  Apollo showered of old,
Fair hands the broken grain shall sift,
  And knead its meal of gold.

Let vapid idlers loll in silk
  Around their costly board;
Give us the bowl of samp and milk,
  By homespun beauty poured!

Where'er the wide old kitchen hearth
  Sends up its smoky curls,
Who will not thank the kindly earth,
  And bless our farmer girls!

Then shame on all the proud and vain,
  Whose folly laughs to scorn
The blessing of our hardy grain,
  Our wealth of golden corn!

Let earth withhold her goodly root,
  Let mildew blight the rye,
Give to the worm the orchard's fruit,
  The wheat field to the fly:

But let the good old crop adorn
The hills our fathers trod;
Still let us for His golden corn,
Send up our thanks to God!

John Greenleaf Whittier

THE FROST

THE Frost looked forth, one still, clear night,
And he said, "Now I shall be out of sight;
So through the valley and over the height
In silence I'll take my way.
I will not go like that blustering train,
The wind and the snow, the hail and the rain,
Who make so much bustle and noise in vain,
But I'll be as busy as they!"

Then he went to the mountain, and powdered its crest,
He climbed up the trees, and their boughs he dressed
With diamonds and pearls, and over the breast
Of the quivering lake he spread
A coat of mail, that it need not fear
The downward point of many a spear
That he hung on its margin, far and near,
Where a rock could rear its head.

He went to the windows of those who slept,
And over each pane like a fairy crept;
Wherever he breathed, wherever he stepped,
By the light of the moon were seen
Most beautiful things. There were flowers and trees,
There were bevies of birds and swarms of bees,
There were cities, thrones, temples, and towers, and these
All pictured in silver sheen!

But he did one thing that was hardly fair,—
He peeped in the cupboard, and, finding there

That all had forgotten for him to prepare,—
"Now, just to set them a-thinking,
I'll bite this basket of fruit," said he;
"This costly pitcher I'll burst in three,
And the glass of water they've left for me
Shall *'tchick!'* to tell them I'm drinking."

HANNAH FLAGG GOULD

THE PROCESSION OF THE FLOWERS

FIRST came the primrose,
On the bank high,
Like a maiden looking forth
From the window of a tower
When the battle rolls below,
So look'd she,
And saw the storms go by.

Then came the windflower
In the valley left behind,
As a wounded maiden, pale
With purple streaks of woe,
When the battle has roll'd by
Wanders to and fro,
So totter'd she,
Dishevell'd in the wind.

Then came the daisies,
On the first of May,
Like a banner'd show's advance
While the crowd runs by the way,
With ten thousand flowers about them
They came trooping through the fields.

As a happy people come,
So came they,
As a happy people come

When the war has roll'd away,
With dance and tabor, pipe and drum,
And all make holiday.

Then came the cowslip,
Like a dancer in the fair,
She spread her little mat of green,
And on it danced she.
With a fillet bound about her brow,
A fillet round her happy brow,
A golden fillet round her brow,
And rubies in her hair.

SYDNEY DOBELL

THE MONTHS

JANUARY brings the snow,
Makes our feet and fingers glow.

February brings the rain,
Thaws the frozen lake again.

March brings breezes loud and shrill,
Stirs the dancing daffodil.

April brings the primrose sweet,
Scatters daisies at our feet.

May brings flocks of pretty lambs,
Skipping by their fleecy dams.

June brings tulips, lilies, roses,
Fills the children's hands with posies.

Hot July brings cooling showers,
Apricots and gillyflowers.

August brings the sheaves of corn,
Then the harvest home is borne.

Warm September brings the fruit,
Sportsmen then begin to shoot.

Fresh October brings the pheasant,
Then to gather nuts is pleasant.

Dull November brings the blast,
Then the leaves are whirling fast.

Chill December brings the sleet,
Blazing fire and Christmas treat.

SARA COLERIDGE

MY HEART LEAPS UP WHEN I BEHOLD

MY heart leaps up when I behold
A rainbow in the sky;
So was it when my life began;
So it is now I am a man;
So be it when I shall grow old,
Or let me die!
The child is father of the man;
And I could wish my days to be
Bound each to each by natural piety.

WILLIAM WORDSWORTH

EVENING

OH, Hesperus! thou bringest all good things—
Home to the weary, to the hungry cheer,
To the young bird the parent's brooding wings,
The welcome stall to the o'erlabored steer!
Whate'er of peace about our hearthstone clings,
Whate'er our household gods protect of dear,
Are gathered round us by thy look of rest;
Thou bring'st the child, too, to the mother's breast.

Soft hour! which wakes the wish and melts the heart
  Of those who sail the seas, on the first day
When they from their sweet friends are torn apart
  Or fills with love the pilgrim on his way,
As the far bell of vesper makes him start,
  Seeming to weep the dying day's decay;
Is this a fancy which our reason scorns?
Ah, surely nothing dies but something mourns!

GEORGE GORDON BYRON

THE LIGHT OF STARS

THE night is come, but not too soon;
  And sinking silently,
All silently, the little moon
  Drops down behind the sky.

There is no light in earth or heaven,
  But the cold light of stars;
And the first watch of night is given
  To the red planet Mars.

Is it the tender star of love?
  The star of love and dreams?
O no! from that blue tent above,
  A hero's armor gleams.

And earnest thoughts within me rise,
  When I behold afar,
Suspended in the evening skies,
  The shield of that red star.

O star of strength! I see thee stand
  And smile upon my pain;
Thou beckonest with thy mailèd hand,
  And I am strong again.

Within my breast there is no light,
  But the cold light of stars;
I give the first watch of the night
  To the red planet Mars.

The star of the unconquered will,
  He rises in my breast,
Serene, and resolute, and still,
  And calm, and self-possessed.

And thou, too, whosoe'er thou art
  That readest this brief psalm,
As one by one thy hopes depart,
  Be resolute and calm.

O, fear not, in a world like this,
  And thou shalt know ere long,
Know how sublime a thing it is,
  To suffer and be strong.

HENRY WADSWORTH LONGFELLOW

THE BROOK

I COME from haunts of coot and hern,
  I make a sudden sally,
And sparkle out among the fern,
  To bicker down a valley.

By thirty hills I hurry down,
  Or slip between the ridges,
By twenty thorps, a little town,
  And half a hundred bridges.

Till last by Philip's farm I flow
  To join the brimming river,
For men may come and men may go,
  But I go on for ever.

I chatter over stony ways,
  In little sharps and trebles,
I bubble into eddying bays,
  I babble on the pebbles.

With many a curve my banks I fret
  By many a field and fallow,
And many a fairy foreland set
  With willow weed and mallow.

I chatter, chatter, as I flow
  To join the brimming river,
For men may come and men may go,
  But I go on for ever.

I wind about, and in and out,
  With here a blossom sailing,
And here and there a lusty trout,
  And here and there a grayling.

And here and there a foamy flake
  Upon me, as I travel
With many a silvery waterbreak
  Above the gravel,

And draw them all along, and flow
  To join the brimming river,
For men may come and men may go,
  But I go on for ever.

I steal by lawns and grassy plots,
  I slide by hazel covers;
I move the sweet forget-me-nots
  That grow for happy lovers.

I slip, I slide, I gloom, I glance,
  Among my skimming swallows;
I make the netted sunbeam dance
  Against my sandy shallows.

I murmur under moon and stars
  In brambly wildernesses;
I linger by my shingly bars;
  I loiter round my cresses;

And out again I curve and flow
  To join the brimming river,
For men may come and men may go,
  But I go on for ever.

ALFRED TENNYSON

JACK-IN-THE-PULPIT

FOUR of us went to the woods one day,
  Keeping the trail in the Indian way,
    Creeping, crawling
    Sometimes sprawling,
Pushing through bushes; and there we found
A little green pulpit stuck in the ground
And in the pulpit a brown man stood,
Preaching to all the folk in the wood.

We lay as quiet as Indians do,
Because each one of the four of us knew,
    At any sound,
    The creatures 'round,
The squirrels and chipmunks, birds and bees,
Would fly away through the ring of trees,
And Jack-in-the-Pulpit would stop his speech
If he knew we four were in easy reach.

We listened as hard as ever we could,
But not a one of us understood,
    Or even heard,
    A single word,
Though I saw a chipmunk nod his head
As if he knew what the preacher said,
And a big gray squirrel clapped his paws
When he thought it was time for some applause.

Many and many a Jack we've found,
But none of us ever heard a sound;
So I suppose
That Jackie knows
When children try to hear him preach,
And talks in some peculiar speech;
I wonder if we could find a way
To hear what Jacks-in-the-Pulpit say?

Rupert Sargent Holland

FOOLISH FLOWERS

WE'VE Foxgloves in our garden;
How careless they must be
To leave their gloves out hanging
Where every one can see!

And Bachelors leave their Buttons
In the same careless way,
If I should do the same with mine,
What would my Mother say?

We've lots of Larkspurs in the yard—
Larks only fly and sing—
Birds surely don't need spurs because
They don't ride anything!

And as for Johnny-Jump-Ups—
I saw a hornet light
On one of them the other day;
He didn't jump a mite!

Rupert Sargent Holland

THE VIOLET

DOWN in a green and shady bed
A modest violet grew;
Its stalk was bent, it hung its head,
As if to hide from view.

And yet it was a lovely flower,
  Its color bright and fair;
It might have graced a rosy bower,
  Instead of hiding there.

Yet there it was content to bloom,
  In modest tints arrayed;
And there diffused a sweet perfume,
  Within the silent shade.

Then let me to the valley go,
  This pretty flower to see;
That I may also learn to grow
  In sweet humility.

JANE TAYLOR

HUMOR

EXTINGUISHED *

"THE boy stood on the burning deck, whence all but him had fled"—
When Tommy Gibbs stood up to speak he had it in his head,
But when he saw the schoolroom full of visitors, he knew,
From his weak knees and parching tongue, the words had all fled, too.

"The boy stood on the burning deck"—a second time he tried,
But he forgot about the boy, or if he lived or died;
He only knew the burning deck was something nice and cool
Beside the rostrum where he stood that awful day in school.

"The boy stood on the burning deck"—he felt the flames and smoke.
His tongue was thick, his mouth was dry, he felt that he would choke.
And from the far back seats he heard a whisper run about:
"Come back here, Tom, and take your seat. They've put the fire out!"

JAMES W. FOLEY

A LESSON IN GRAMMAR

ONE night an owl was prowling round
Looking for mice, when on the ground
He spied a cat, and straightway flew
Quite close to it. "Tu whit, tu whoo!"
Quoth he, "may I again ne'er stir,
If here, dressed in a coat of fur,

I do not see a four-legged owl.
Oh, what a very funny fowl!
It makes me laugh, so droll—Ha! ha!
Ha! ha!—it are,—ha! ha! ha! ha!
It are, it are, it really are
The drollest thing I've seen by far!"

"You're much mistaken, scornful sir,"
The cat said, as she ceased to purr;
"For though, like one, I often prowl
About at night, I am no owl.
And if I were, why, still would you
Be queerer creature of the two;
For you look, there's no doubt of that,
Extremely like a two-legged cat.
As for your grammar, 'pon my word
(Excuse this giggle), he-he-he-he,
It be, it be, it really be
The very worst I ever heard."

MARGARET EYTINGE

TOMMY LOOKS AHEAD

WHEN I'm as big as my Papa, the thing that puzzles me
Is what I'll do to make my bread, and just what shall I be.
I used to think conducting on a horse-car was the thing,
With naught to do but take up fares and pull the ting-a-ling.
But Papa says they cannot keep the money that they make.
They have to give to some one else each nickel that they take.
And where there's profit in that work is more than I can tell,
Unless it's in the fun one gets in playing with the bell.

And then I thought policeman's work was just the thing for me.
I'm fond of hitting things with clubs and leaning 'gainst a tree;

But I am told that if one's caught asleep he has to go—
Though how a man can live without his sleep I do not
know.

And as I'm very fond of rest, I'll never join the force.
A sailor I could never be, because, you see, of course
I'd have to be away from home so much upon the sea,
I'd hardly ever have a chance to meet my family.
I couldn't quite get used to that, for really half the fun
A man gets out of life is got from playing with his son
At night when supper's over—so my father's often said—
Before the Sandman comes around and sends me off to bed.

However, with this subject I'll no longer vex my mind,
Until I get through boying; and, perhaps, then I shall find
Somebody who will pay me well to do just what I please,
So that my little boy and I may live a life of ease.

John Kendrick Bangs

POOR JACK-IN-THE-BOX

FRIGHTEN the children, do I? Pop with too sudden
a jump?
Well, how do you think *I* felt, all shut in there in a lump?
And didn't *I* get a shock when the lid came down on my
head?
And if *you* were squeezed up and locked in, wouldn't *you*
get ugly and red?
If you think I'm so dreadful, my friend, suppose you just
try it yourself;
Let someone shut *you* in a box, and set you away on a
shelf—
And then, when the lid is unhooked, if *you* don't leap out
with a whack,
And look like a fright when you spring, I'll give in, or
my name isn't Jack.

Mary Mapes Dodge

WHAT MOTHER DOESN'T KNOW *

SOMETIMES w'en I got to pile wood in the yard,
'Ist wringin' with sweat 'cuz I'm workin' so hard,
An' see all the neighbors' boys startin' to fish,
I can't hardly work any more, an' I wish
'At I wuz a-goin' an' 'en right away
I run an' ast Ma if I can't go to-day,
An' she says to me 'en: "Johnny Jones, you can run
Off an' fish 'ist as soon as your work is all done.

You must work while you work,
You must play while you play
An' 'en you'll be happy for many a day."
An' mebbe it's so,
But my goodness! to go
With the boys 'at's gone fishin'!—I guess she dunno!

Sometimes w'en I got to hoe garden an' hear
The boys playin' ball in the next lot, so near
I hear 'em all cheerin' an' see 'em all score,
I can't hardly stand it to hoe any more.
So 'en I ast Ma if I can't go an' play
An' promise to hoe twict as much the next day,
But she says to me 'en: "Johnny Jones, you can run
Off an' play 'ist as soon as your work is all done.

You must work while you work,
You must play while you play
An' 'en you'll be happy for many a day."
An' mebbe it's so,
But, my goodness! to hoe
W'en you hear 'em a-playin'!—I guess she dunno.

Sometimes w'en the snow gets all piled up so deep
On the walk 'at she tells me to go out an' sweep
It all off, an' Sam Russell comes by with his sled,
My broom 'at I'm usin' gets heavy as lead.
An' I can't hardly sweep, an' I ast Ma if I
Can't go out a-slidin' an' sweep by an' by,
But she says to me 'en: "Johnny Jones, you can run
Off an' slide 'ist as soon as your work is all done.

You must work while you work,
You must play while you play
An' 'en you'll be happy for many a day."
An' mebbe it's so,
But to have to sweep snow
W'en the boys are a-slidin'!—I guess she dunno.

JAMES W. FOLEY

THE WISH OF PRISCILLA PENELOPE POWERS

PRISCILLA PENELOPE POWERS one day,
Took tea at a neighbor's just over the way.
Two pieces of pie they urged her to take.
And seven whole slices of chocolate cake!
"Oh dear," sighed Priscilla Penelope Powers,
"I wish I was your little girl 'stead of ours!"

MRS. JOHN T. VAN SANT

A STORY OF SELF-SACRIFICE *

POP took me to the circus 'cause it disappoints me so
To have to stay at home, although he doesn't care to go;
He's seen it all so many times, the wagons and the tents;
The cages of wild animals and herds of elephants;
This morning he went down with me to watch the big parade,
He was so dreadful busy that he oughtn't to have stayed,
He said he'd seen it all before and all the reason he
Went down and watched it coming was because it's new to me.

Then we walked to the circus grounds and Pop he says: "I guess
You want a glass of lemonade, of course," and I says: "Yes."

And he bought one for each of us, and when he drank his he
Told me he drank it only just to keep me company;
And then he says, "The sideshow is, I s'pose, the same old sell,
But everybody's goin' in, so we might just as well."
He said he'd seen it all before, and all the reason he
Went in and saw it was because it was all new to me.

Well, by and by we both came out and went in the big tent,
And saw the lions and tigers and the bigges' elephant
With chains on his front corner and an awful funny nose
That looks around for peanuts that the crowd of people throws;
And Pop, he bought some peanuts and it curled its nose around
Until it found 'most every one that he threw on the ground;
He said he'd seen it all before, and all the reason he
Stayed there and threw 'em was because it was all new to me.

Well, then the band began to play the liveliestest tune,
And Pop, he says he guessed the show would open pretty soon;
So we went in the other tent, and Pop, he says to me:
"I guess we'll get some reserved seats so you will surely see."
And then some lovely ladies came and stood there on the ground,
And jumped up on the horses while the horses ran around,
Pop said he'd seen it all before, and all the reason he
Looked at the ladies was because it was all new to me.

Well, finally it's over, but a man came out to say
That they're going to have a concert, and Pop said we'd better stay;
He said they're always just the same and always such a sell,
But lots of folks was staying and he guessed we might as well.

Then by and by we're home again, and Mamma wants to
know
What kind of circus was it, and Pop said, "The same old
show,"
And said he'd seen it all before and all the reason he
Had stayed and seen it all was 'cause it's all so new to me.

JAMES W. FOLEY

THE WELL-DIGGER

COME, listen all, while I relate
What recently befell
Unto a farmer down in Maine
While digging of a well.

Full many a yard he dug and delved,
And still he dug in vain:
"Alack!" quoth he, "e'en water seems
Prohibited in Maine!"

And still he dug and delved away.
And still the well was dry;
The only water to be found
Was in the farmer's eye.

For, by the breaking of the bank
That tumbled from the station,
All suddenly his hopes were dashed
Of future liquidation.

And now his sands were running fast,
And he had died, no doubt—
But that just when the earth caved in
He happened to be out!

"Ah, ah! I have a happy thought!"
Exclaimed this wicked man:
"To dig away this cursed well,
I see a pretty plan.

"I'll hide me straight; and when my wife
  And eke the neighbors know
What's happened to the digging here,
  They'll think that I'm below.

"And so to save my precious life,
  They'll dig the well, no doubt,
E'en deeper than it was at first,
  Before they find me out!"

And so he hid him in the barn
  Through all the hungry day,
To bide the digging of his well
  In this deceitful way.

But list what grief and shame befell
  The false, ungrateful man,
The while he slyly watched to see
  The working of his plan.

The neighbors all, with one accord,
  Unto each other said,
"With such a weight of earth above,
  The man is surely dead!"

And the wife, with pious care,
  All needless cost to save,
Said, "Since the Lord has willed it,
  E'en let it be his grave!"

JOHN G. SAXE

BABY IN CHURCH

AUNT NELLIE had fashioned a dainty thing
  Of hamburg and ribbon and lace,
And mamma had said, as she settled it round
  Our Baby's beautiful face,

Where the dimples play and the laughter lies
Like sunbeams hid in her violet eyes,—
"If the day is pleasant, and Baby is good,
She may go to church and wear her new hood."

Then Ben, aged six, began to tell,
  In elder-brotherly way,
How very, very good she must be
  If she went to church next day.
He told of the church, the choir, and the crowd,
And the man up front who talked so loud;
But she must not talk, nor laugh, nor sing,
But just sit as quiet as anything.

And so, on a beautiful Sabbath in May,
  When the fruit buds burst into flowers
(There wasn't a blossom on bush or tree
  So fair as this blossom of ours),
All in her white dress, dainty and new,
Our Baby sat in the family pew;
The grand, sweet music, the reverend air,
The solemn hush, and the voice of prayer,

Filled all her baby soul with awe,
  As she sat in her little place,
And the holy look that the angels wear
  Seemed pictured upon her face.
And the sweet words uttered so long ago
Came into my mind with a rhythmic flow,—
"Of such is the kingdom of heaven," said He,
And I knew He spake of such as she.

The sweet-voiced organ pealed forth again,
  The collection box came around,
And Baby dropped her penny in,
  And smiled at the chinking sound.
Alone in the choir Aunt Nellie stood,
Waiting the close of the soft prelude,
To begin her solo. High and strong
She struck the first note; clear and long

She held it, and all were charmed, but one
  Who, with all the might she had
Sprang to her little feet and cried,
  "Aunt Nellie, you's being bad!"
The audience smiled, the minister coughed,
The little boys in the corner laughed,
The tenor shook like an aspen leaf,
And hid his face in his handkerchief.

And poor Aunt Nellie could never tell
  How she finished that terrible strain,
But says nothing on earth could tempt
  Her to go through the scene again.
So we have decided, perhaps 'tis best,
For her sake, and ours, and all the rest,
That we wait, maybe a year or two,
Ere our Baby reënter the family pew.

UNKNOWN

THE MONKEY'S SCHEME

THE monkey said to the chimpanzee,
  In a monkey's original way:
"Come, let us start a peanut stand,
We'll surely make it pay.

The boys would buy the nuts of you
As you sit your stall beside;
And every one as he passed along
With me would his nuts divide.

So you could sell and I could feast
And both would be so gay;
For you would handle all the cash
And I would stock the nuts away."

UNKNOWN

THE FAVORITE

SAID the rubber dog with the long straight tail
  To the duck with the emerald breast,
"You are very lovely to look upon,
  But the baby loves me best.

"For she takes my whole head in her mouth,
  And I patiently let her chew,
And suck and bite with all her might,
  To help her teeth come through."

Said the emerald duck, "She would never dare
  Do such a thing to me,
But she finds me floating in her bath,
  And laughs and crows with glee."

"I'll tell you what," said the rubber dog,
  "Let us together stand
On the bureau top, and see which one
  She first takes in her hand."

So they took their stand on the bureau top,
  And stood there side by side,
The dog held his tail up straight and high,
  And the green duck swelled with pride.

Then the baby came on her nurse's arm,
  And their hearts went pit-a-pat,
The baby did not glance at them,
  She was hugging the worsted cat!

MILDRED WHITNEY STILLMAN

AND JUST THEN *

DON'T you remember when the ship, the pirate ship, that flew
The black flag with the gleaming skull, in the fierce gale that blew,

Went on the rocks? I think it was upon the Spanish Main;
The sails were torn to tatters and there fell a driving rain,
The air was pierced with cries of fear, shocks followed upon shocks,
"Come, man the lifeboats," called the mate, "the ship is on the rocks!"
And just when lightnings rent the air and all the sky was red,
Your mother said, "You've read enough, my boy! It's time for bed!"

Don't you remember when the score stood six to six, until
The very ending of the game and every heart stood still?
The Red Sox pitcher took his place, while not a watcher stirred,
A hit, a pass, an error and a runner got to third.
Don't you remember, as you read, you almost heard the crack
As bat met ball and you could feel cold chills go down your back?
And just as you had but a page to find which players led,
Your mother said, "You've read enough, my boy! It's time for bed!"

Don't you remember when Wild Bill and Deadshot Dick, the scout,
Were prisoned in the rocky cave with redskins all about,
With all their ammunition gone, nor food to eat, as they
Had been a thousand times before, but always got away?
The war whoops rang out fierce and shrill. Said Dick, "I have a plan;
We will escape or sell our lives as dearly as we can."
And just as you turned o'er the page to see what plans they'd lay,
The clock struck nine—your mother came and took the book away.

Oh, Captain Kidd, it seemed to me when you went on the rock
You always timed the hour of it to be at nine o'clock!

And Dick, the scout, the redskins came and fell on you
with rage
Just when my boyhood bedtime came and I turned down
the page!
And Spike, the wizard of the slab, who mowed the batsmen
down
Like blades of grass, the hero of the little country town,
You seemed to time the crisis of your fiercest game, some
way,
At nine o'clock, when Mother came and took the book
away!

JAMES W. FOLEY

CASTOR OIL

I DON'T mind lickin's, now an' then,
An' I can even stand it when
My mother calls me in from play
To run some errand right away.
There's things 'bout bein' just a boy
That ain't all happiness an' joy,
But I suppose I've got to stand
My share o' trouble in this land,
An' I ain't kickin' much—but, say,
The worst of parents is that they
Don't realize just how they spoil
A feller's life with castor oil.

Of all the awful stuff, gee whiz!
That is the very worst there is.
An' every time if I complain,
Or say I've got a little pain,
There's nothing else that they can think
'Cept castor oil for me to drink.
I notice, though, when Pa is ill,
That he gets fixed up with a pill,
An' Pa don't handle Mother rough
An' make her swallow nasty stuff;
But when I've got a little ache,
It's castor oil I've got to take.

I don't mind goin' up to bed
Afore I get the chapter read;
I don't mind being scolded, too,
For lots of things I didn't do;
But, Gee! I hate it when they say,
"Come! Swallow this--an' right away!"
Let poets sing about the joy
It is to be a little boy,
I'll tell the truth about my case:
The poets here can have my place,
An' I will take their life of toil
If they will take my castor oil.

EDGAR A. GUEST

NOTHING TO LAUGH AT

'TAIN'T nothin' to laugh at as I can see!
If you'd been stung by a bumble bee,
An' your nose wuz swelled an' it smarted, too,
You wouldn't want people to laugh at you.
If you had a lump that wuz full of fire,
Like you'd been touched by a red hot wire,
An' your nose spread out like a load of hay,
You wouldn't want strangers who come your way
To ask you to let 'em see the place
An' laugh at you right before your face.

What's funny about it, I'd like to know?
It isn't a joke to be hurted so!
An' how wuz I ever on earth to tell
'At the pretty flower which I stooped to smell
In our backyard wuz the very one
Which a bee wuz busily working on?
An' jus' as I got my nose down there,
He lifted his foot an' kicked for fair,
An' he planted his stinger right into me,
But it's nothin' to laugh at as I can see.

I let out a yell an' my Maw came out
To see what the trouble wuz all about.
She says from my shriek she wuz sure 'at I
Had been struck by a motor car passin' by;
But when she found what the matter wuz
She laughed just like ever'body does
An' she made me stand while she poked about
To pull his turrible stinger out.
An' my Pa laughed, too, when he looked at me,
But it's nothin' to laugh at as I can see.

My Maw put witch hazel on the spot
To take down the swellin' but it has not.
It seems to git bigger as time goes by
An' I can't see good out o' this one eye;
An' it hurts clean down to my very toes
Whenever I've got to blow my nose.
An' all I can say is when this gits well
There ain't any flowers I'll stoop to smell.
I'm through disturbin' a bumble bee,
But it's nothin' to laugh at as I can see.

EDGAR A. GUEST

WHEN FATHER PLAYED BASEBALL

THE smell of arnica is strong,
And mother's time is spent
In rubbing father's arms and back
With burning liniment.
The house is like a druggist's shop;
Strong odors fill the hall,
And day and night we hear him groan,
Since father played baseball.

He's forty past, but he declared
That he was young as ever;
And in his youth, he said, he was
A baseball player clever.

So when the business men arranged
  A game, they came to call
On dad and asked him if he thought
  That he could play baseball.

"I haven't played in fifteen years,"
  Said father, "but I know
That I can stop the grounders hot,
  And I can make the throw.
I used to play a corking game;
  The curves, I know them all;
And you can count on me, you bet,
  To join your game of ball."

On Saturday the game was played,
  And all of us were there;
Dad borrowed an old uniform,
  That Casey used to wear.
He paid three dollars for a glove,
  Wore spikes to save a fall;
He had the make-up on all right,
  When father played baseball.

At second base they stationed him;
  A liner came his way;
Dad tried to stop it with his knee,
  And missed a double play.
He threw into the bleachers twice,
  He let a pop fly fall;
Oh, we were all ashamed of him,
  When father played baseball.

He tried to run, but tripped and fell,
  He tried to take a throw;
It put three fingers out of joint,
  And father let it go.
He stopped a grounder with his face;
  Was spiked, nor was that all;
It looked to us like suicide,
  When father played baseball.

At last he limped away, and now
  He suffers in disgrace;
His arms are bathed in liniment;
  Court plaster hides his face.
He says his back is breaking, and
  His legs won't move at all;
It made a wreck of father when
  He tried to play baseball.

The smell of arnica abounds;
  He hobbles with a cane;
A row of blisters mar his hands;
  He is in constant pain.
But lame and weak as father is,
  He swears he'll lick us all
If we dare even speak about
  The day he played baseball.

EDGAR A. GUEST

WHEN THE SOAP GETS IN YOUR EYE

MY father says that I ought to be
A man when anything happens to me.
An' he says that a man will take a blow
An' never let on it hurts him so;
He'll grit his teeth an' he'll set his chin
An' bear his pain with a manly grin.
But I'll bet that the bravest man would cry
If ever the soap gets into his eye.

I'm brave enough when I'm playin' ball,
An' I can laugh when I've had a fall.
With the girls around I'd never show
That I was scared if the blood should flow
From my banged up nose or a battered knee.
As brave as the bravest I can be,
But it's different pain, an' I don't know why,
Whenever the soap gets into your eye.

I can set my teeth an' I can grin
When I scrape my cheek or I bark my shin,
An' once I fell from our apple tree
An' the wind was knocked right out of me,
But I never cried an' the gang all said
That they thought for sure I was really dead.
But it's worse than thinking you're going to die
Whenever the soap gets into your eye.

When your mother's holding your neck, and you
Couldn't get away if you wanted to,
An' she's latherin' hard with her good right hand,
It's more than the bravest man could stand.
If you open your mouth to howl, you get
A taste of the wash rag, cold and wet,
But you got to yell till your face gets dry
Whenever the soap gets into your eye.

Edgar A. Guest

THE RADIO

SINCE Pa put in the radio we have a lot of fun,
We hustle to my room upstairs as soon as supper's done
And Pa he tinkers with the disks to get it loud and clear,
Then says: "Wait just a minute now, there's nothing yet to hear.
Oh, now it's coming! Silence there! Now don't you move a thing.
Say Ma, this is a marvelous age—a lady's going to sing!"

Then Ma she listens for a while, as pleased as she can be,
And when I want to hear it, too, she says, "Don't bother me!
Your turn comes next and sister's, too; don't jump around that way,
I want to hear the orchestra—it's just begun to play.
I wish you children wouldn't fuss, I'm sure I cannot hear
While you are trying all the time to snatch it from my ear."

Then Pa takes up the thing awhile and says: "Oh, that's just great!
A man is telling stories now. You kids will have to wait.
It's wonderful to think his voice is floating in the air
And people sitting in their homes can hear it everywhere—
All right, all right! It's your turn now. Perhaps this man will teach
You youngsters how you should behave. A parson's going to preach."

Pa put that radio in for me—at least he told me so,
But if it's really mine or not, is something I don't know,
'Coz Pa he wants it all himself, to hear the funny things,
An' Ma must hear the concerts through when some great artist sings,
But when the parson starts to talk on Selfishness an' Sin,
Pa says: "Now it has come the time for you to listen in."

EDGAR A. GUEST

BEING BRAVE AT NIGHT

THE other night 'bout two o'clock, or maybe it was three,
An elephant with shining tusks came chasing after me.
His trunk was wavin' in the air an' spoutin' jets of steam
An' he was out to eat me up, but still I didn't scream
Or let him see that I was scared—a better thought I had,
I just escaped from where I was and crawled in bed with dad.

One time there was a giant who was horrible to see,
He had three heads and twenty arms, an' he come after me
And red hot fire came from his mouths and every hand was red
And he declared he'd grind my bones and make them into bread.
But I was just too smart for him, I fooled him mighty bad,
Before his hands could collar me I crawled in bed with dad.

I ain't scared of nothing that comes pesterin' me at night.
Once I was chased by forty ghosts all shimmery an' white,
An' I just raced 'em round the room an' let 'em think maybe
I'd have to stop an' rest awhile, when they could capture me.
Then when they leapt onto my bed, Oh Gee! but they were mad
To find that I had slipped away an' crawled in bed with dad.

No giants, ghosts or elephants have dared to come in there
'Coz if they did he'd beat 'em up and chase 'em to their lair.
They just hang 'round the children's rooms an' snap an' snarl an' bite
An' laugh if they can make 'em yell for help with all their might,
But I don't ever yell out loud. I'm not that sort of lad,
I slip from out the covers, and I crawl in bed with dad.

EDGAR A. GUEST

PARTRIDGE TIME

WHEN Pa came home last night he had a package in his hand;
"Now, Ma," said he, "I've something here which you will say is grand.
A friend of mine got home to-day from hunting in the woods,
He's been away a week or two, and got back with the goods.
He had a corking string of birds—I wish you could have seen 'em!"
"If you've brought any partridge home," said Ma, "you'll have to clean 'em."

"Now listen, Ma," said Pa to her, "these birds are mighty rare.
I know a lot of men who'd pay a heap to get a pair.

But it's against the law to sell this splendid sort of game,
And if you bought 'em you would have to use a different
name.
It isn't every couple has a pair to eat between 'em."
"If you got any partridge there," says Ma, "you'll have
to clean 'em."

"Whenever kings want something fine, it's partridge that
they eat,
And millionaires prefer 'em, too, to any sort of meat.
About us everywhere to-night are folks who'd think it fine
If on a brace of partridge they could just sit down to dine.
They've got a turkey skinned to death, they're sweeter than
a chicken."
"If that's what you've brought home," says Ma, "you'll
have to do the pickin'."

And then Pa took the paper off and showed Ma what he
had.
"There, look at those two beauties! Don't they start you
feelin' glad?
An' ain't your mouth a-waterin' to think how fine they'll be
When you've cooked 'em up for dinner, one for you an'
one for me?"
But Ma just turned her nose up high, an' said, when she
had seen 'em,
"You'll never live to eat 'em if you wait for me to clean
'em."

EDGAR A. GUEST

THE LOST PURSE

I REMEMBER the excitement and the terrible alarm
That worried everybody when William broke his arm;
An' how frantic Pa and Ma got only jes' the other day
When they couldn't find the baby 'coz he'd up an' walked
away;

But I'm sure there's no excitement that our house has ever shook
Like the times Ma can't remember where she's put her pocketbook.

When the laundry man is standin' at the door an' wants his pay
Ma hurries in to get it, an' the fun starts right away.
She hustles to the sideboard, 'coz she knows exactly where
She can put her hand right on it, but alas! it isn't there.
She tries the parlor table an' she goes upstairs to look,
An' once more she can't remember where she put her pocketbook.

She tells us that she had it just a half an hour ago,
An' now she cannot find it though she's hunted high and low;
She's searched the kitchen cupboard an' the bureau drawers upstairs,
An' it's not behind the sofa nor beneath the parlor chairs.
She makes us kids get busy searching every little nook,
An' this time says she's certain that she's lost her pocketbook.

She calls Pa at the office an' he laughs I guess, for then
She always mumbles something 'bout the heartlessness of men.
She calls to mind a peddler who came to the kitchen door,
An' she's certain from his whiskers an' the shabby clothes he wore
An' his dirty shirt an' collar that he must have been a crook,
An' she's positive that feller came and got her pocketbook.
But at last she allus finds it in some queer an' funny spot,
Where she'd put it in a hurry, an' had somehow clean forgot;

An' she heaves a sigh of gladness, an' she says, "Well, I declare,
I would take an oath this minute that I never put it there."

An' we're peaceable an' quiet till next time Ma goes to
 look
An' finds she can't remember where she put her pocketbook.

EDGAR A. GUEST

THE FUNNIEST THING IN THE WORLD

THE funniest thing in the world, I know,
 Is watchin' the monkeys 'at's in the show!—
Jumpin' an' runnin' an' racin' roun',
'Way up the top o' the pole; nen down!
First they're here, an' nen they're there,
An' ist a'most any an' ever'where!—
Screechin' an' scratchin' wherever they go,
They're the funniest things in the world, I know!

They're the funniest things in the world, I think:—
Funny to watch 'em eat an' drink;
Funny to watch 'em a-watchin' us,
An' actin' 'most like grown folks does!—
Funny to watch 'em p'tend to be
Skeered at their tail 'at they happen to see—
But the funniest thing in the world they do
Is never to laugh, like me an' you!

JAMES WHITCOMB RILEY

A MEETING ON THE RAIL

HE was walking on the railroad, and the track he closely
 scanned,
With a red flag, neatly folded, and a lantern in his hand;
And, happening to pass him as I journeyed on my way,
We paused a moment to exchange the greetings of the day.

"My friend, will you inform me," in an anxious tone he said,
"If you have seen a broken rail or misplaced switch ahead?"
And, when I told him I had not, with wonder in my eye,
He showed his disappointment by a plaintive little sigh.

"I'm a hero by profession," he proceeded to explain,
"And it's always been the hobby of my life to save a train;
But, though I've gone on foot across the continent and back,
I never yet have found a thing the matter with the track!

"I've a red flag for the day time and a lantern for the night,
To wave the very moment that the engine comes in sight;
But, in spite of my endeavors, it's a melancholy fact
That I haven't had a chance yet to perform a noble act!"

And, bidding me good-by, he slowly sauntered up the ties,
While downward at the shining rails he bent his eager eyes;
And now, whene'er in newspapers a hero's name I see,
I think about my little friend and wonder if it's he!

MALCOLM DOUGLAS

ELEGY WRITTEN IN A COUNTRY COAL BIN *

THE furnace tolls the knell of falling steam,
The coal supply is virtually done,
And at this price, indeed it does not seem
As though we could afford another ton.

Now fades the glossy, cherished anthracite;
The radiators lose their temperature:
How ill avail, on such a frosty night,
The "short and simple flannels of the poor."

Though in the ice box, fresh and newly laid,
The rude forefathers of the omelet sleep,
No eggs for breakfast till the bill is paid:
We cannot cook again till coal is cheap.

* From "Songs for a Little House," by Christopher Morley, copyright, 1917, George H. Doran Company, Publishers.

Can Morris chair or papier-mâché bust
  Revivify the failing pressure gauge?
Chop up the grand piano if you must,
  And burn the East Aurora parrot cage!

Full many a can of purest kerosene
  The dark unfathomed tanks of Standard Oil
Shall furnish me, and with their aid I mean
  To bring my morning coffee to a boil.

The village collier (flinty-hearted beast)
  Who tried to hold me up in such a pinch
May soon be numbered with the dear deceased:
  I give him to the mercy of Judge Lynch.

CHRISTOPHER MORLEY

THE MILKMAN *

EARLY in the morning, when the dawn is on the roofs,
  You hear his wheels come rolling, you hear his horse's
      hoofs;
You hear the bottles clinking, and then he drives away:
You yawn in bed, turn over, and begin another day!

The old-time dairy maids are dear to every poet's heart—
I'd rather be the dairy *man* and drive a little cart,
And bustle round the village in the early morning blue.
And hang my reins upon a hook, as I've seen Casey do.

CHRISTOPHER MORLEY

THE BUMBLEBEE

YOU better not fool with a Bumblebee!—
  Ef you don't think they can sting—you'll see!
They're lazy to look at, an' kindo' go
Buzzin' an' hummin' aroun' so slow,

* From "Songs for a Little House," by Christopher Morley, copyright, 1917, George H. Doran Company, Publishers.

An' ac' so slouchy an' all fagged out,
Danglin' their legs as they drone about
The hollyhocks 'at they can't climb in
'Ithout ist a-tumble-un out ag'in!
Wunst I watched one climb clean 'way
In a jim'son-blossom, I did, one day,—
An' I ist grabbed it—an' nen let go—
An' *"Ooh-ooh! Honey! I told ye so!"*
Says The Raggedy Man; an' he ist run
An' pullt out the stinger, an' don't laugh none
An' says: "They *has* ben folks, I guess,
'At thought I wuz predjudust, more er less,—
Yit I still maintain 'at a Bumblebee
Wears out his welcome too quick fer me!"

James Whitcomb Riley

AN OVERWORKED ELOCUTIONIST

ONCE there was a little boy, whose name was Robert Reece;
And every Friday afternoon he had to speak a piece.
So many poems thus he learned, that soon he had a store
Of recitations in his head and still kept learning more.
And now this is what happened; he was called upon one week
And totally forgot the piece he was about to speak.
His brain he cudgeled. Not a word remained within his head!
And so he spoke at random, and this is what he said:
"My Beautiful, my beautiful, who standest proudly by,
It was the schooner Hesperus—the breaking waves dashed high!
Why is this Forum crowded? What means this stir in Rome?
Under a spreading chestnut tree, there is no place like home!
When freedom from her mountain height cried 'Twinkle little star.'

Shoot, if you must, this old gray head, King Henry of
Navarre!
Roll on, thou deep and dark blue castled crag of Drachen-
fels,
My name is Norval, on the Grampian hills, ring out wild
bells!
If you're waking, call me early, to be or not to be,
The curfew must not ring to-night! Oh, woodman, spare
that tree!
Charge, Chester, Charge! On, Stanley, on! and let who
will be clever!
The boy stood on the burning deck, but I go on forever!"
His elocution was superb, his voice and gestures fine;
His schoolmates all applauded as he finished the last line.
"I see it doesn't matter," Robert thought, "what words I
say,
So long as I declaim with oratorical display."

CAROLYN WELLS

A BOY'S COMPLAINT

HERE are questions in physics and grammar
That would puzzle you somewhat I know,
Can you tell what is meant by inertia?
Can you clearly define rain and snow?

Do you know there's a valve in the bellows?
Can you tell why your clock is too slow?
Why the pendulum needs looking after?
Perhaps it is swinging too low.

"They was going uptown in the evening,"
Do you call that bad grammar, I say?
I'm sure Mary Jones and her mother
Say worse things than that every day.

But I s'pose "*was*" should be in the plural,
To agree with its old subject "*they*,"

According to rule—my! I've lost it,
There's two per cent gone right away.

And now, only look at the parsing,
It will surely take in every rule;
And down at the end more false syntax.
With authorities given "in full."

Arithmetic, my! how I hate it,
I'm stupid at that in the class,
So, how, in the name of creation,
Can I be expected to pass?

Here's a ten-acre lot to be fenced in,
Here is duty to find on some tea;
Here's a problem in old alligation,
And a monstrous square root one I see.

Can you tell who defeated the Indians?
Do you know who was killed in a duel?
Do you know what the first tax was raised on?
And how some just thought it was cruel?

Perhaps I may pass on an average,
If three-fourths are right I'll get through;
But my teacher calls such standing shabby,
So what is a poor boy to do?

Annie H. Streeter

THE BOY TO THE SCHOOLMASTER

YOU'VE quizzed me often and puzzled me long,
  You've asked me to cipher and spell,
You've called me a dunce if I answered wrong,
  Or a dolt if I failed to tell
Just when to say *lie* and when to say *lay,*
  Or what nine sevens may make,
Or the longitude of Kamschatka Bay,

Or the I-forget-what's-its-name lake,
So I think it's *my* turn, I do,
To ask a question or so of you.
The schoolmaster then opened wide his eyes,
But said not a word for sheer surprise.

Can you tell what "phen-dubs" means? I can.
Can you say all off by heart
The "onery towery ickery ann,"
Or tell "alleys" and "commons" apart?
Can *you* fling a top, I would like to know,
Till it hums like a bumble bee?
Can you make a kite yourself that will go
'Most as high as the eye can see,
Till it sails and soars like a hawk on the wing,
And the little birds come and light on its string?
The schoolmaster looked, oh! very demure,
But his mouth was twitching, I'm almost sure.

Can you tell where the nest of the oriole swings,
Or the color its eggs may be?
Do you know the time when the squirrel brings
Its young from their nest in the tree?
Can you tell when the chestnuts are ready to drop,
Or where the best hazel-nuts grow?
Can you climb a high tree to the very tiptop,
Then gaze without trembling below?
Can you swim and dive, can you jump and run,
Or do anything else we boys call fun?
The master's voice trembled as he replied,
"You are right, my lad, I'm the dunce," he sighed.

E. J. Wheeler

THE BOY'S COMPLAINT

"Oh! never mind, they're only boys";
'Tis thus the people say,
And they hustle us and jostle us,
And drive us out the way.

They never give us half our rights:
  I know that this is so;
Ain't I a boy? and can't I see
  The way that these things go?

The little girls are petted all,
  Called "honey," "dear," and "sweet,"
But boys are cuffed at home and school,
  And knocked about the street.

My sister has her rags and dolls
  Strewn all about the floor,
While old dog Growler dares not put
  His nose inside the door.

And if I go upon the porch
  In hopes to have a play,
Some one calls out, "Hollo, young chap,
  Take that noisy dog away!"

My hoop is used to build a fire,
  My ball is thrown aside;
And mother let the baby have
  My top, because it cried.

If company should come at night,
  The boys can't sit up late;
And if they come to dinner, then
  The boys, of course, must wait.

If anything is raw or burned
  It falls to us, no doubt;
And if the cake or pudding's short,
  We have to go without.

If there are fireworks, we can't get
  A place to see at all;
And when the soldiers come along
  We're crowded to the wall.

Whoever wants an errand done,
We always have to scud;
Whoever wants the sidewalk, we
Are crowded in the mud.

'Tis hurry-scurry, here and there,
Without a moment's rest,
And we scarcely get a "Thank you," if
We do our very best.

But never mind, boys—we will be
The grown men by and by;
Then I suppose 'twill be our turn
To snub the smaller boy.

UNKNOWN

THE FUNNY SMALL BOY

THE room it was hot,
Of a far-away school;
So the schoolmaster got
Fast asleep on his stool,
While the scholars were having a frolic,
Bereft of all reason and rule.

When a ball, badly aimed,
Struck the schoolmaster's nose,
Which was long and quite famed
For its terrible blows;
Then he scowled on those innocent scholars,
In a way he could scowl when he chose.

"Come hither, my child,
Thou art writing, I see";
And the schoolmaster smiled,
"Come, now, right on my knee;
The up-strokes, you see, are made lightly,
The down-strokes are heavy and free."

When that small boy was tanned,
He laughed in great glee;
And the teacher so bland,
Much astonished was he
At the way the boy giggled;
He thought, "How can this thing be?"

The teacher was beat
And deprived of his wind,
So he stood on his feet
That small boy, who just grinned,
And who shook with a mirth that was jolly,
And felt of his back which was skinned.

"Now tell me, my son,
E'er this rod I employ
Once again for thy fun,
Why this wonderful joy?"
"Such a joke," cried the lad, "don't you see,
You're whipping—ha, ha—the wrong boy."

H. C. Dodge

MUMPS

I HAD a feeling in my neck,
And on the sides were two big bumps;
I couldn't swallow anything
At all because I had the mumps.

And Mother tied it with a piece,
And then she tied up Will and John,
And no one else but Dick was left
That didn't have a mump rag on.

He teased at us and laughed at us,
And said, whenever he went by,
"It's vinegar and lemon drops
And pickles!" just to make us cry.

But Tuesday Dick was very sad
  And cried because his neck was sore,
And not a one said sour things
  To anybody any more.

ELIZABETH MADOX ROBERTS

IT WON'T STAY BLOWED

TO the sniffing pickaninny once his good old mammy said,
"Yo' lil' black nose am drippin' from de cold dat's in yo' head,
An' yo' sleeve am slick and shiny like de hillside when it snows.
Why doan' you pump de bellers from de inside ob yo' nose?"
"Ain't I been," the child replied to her, "a-doin' ob jes' dat
Twel I's got a turble empty feel right whur I wears muh hat?
De traffic soht o' nacherly keeps gittin' in de road.
I blow muh nose a-plenty, but
it
won't
stay
blowed.

"What's de use ob raisin' chickens ef dey won't stay riz?
What's de use ob freezin' sherbet ef it won't stay friz?
What's de use ob payin' debts off ef dey's gwine stay owed?
What's de use ob blowin' noses ef dey won't stay blowed?"

This old world is sometimes jealous of the chap who means to rise;
It sneers at what he's doing or it bats him 'twixt the eyes;
It trips him when he's careless, and it makes his way so hard
What's left of him is sinew, not a walking tub of lard;

But it's only wasting effort, for by George, the guy keeps on
When his hopes have crumbled round him and you'd think his faith was gone,
Till the world at last knocks under and it passes him a crown:
Once, twice, thrice it has upset him, but
he
won't
stay
down.

What cares he when out he's flattened by the cruel blow it deals?
He has rubber in his shoulders and a mainspring in his heels.
Let the world uncork its buffets till he's bruised from toe to crown;
Let it thump him, bump him, dump him, but he won't stay down.

St. Clair Adams

A POOR UNFORTUNATE

His hoss went dead an' his mule went lame;
He lost six cows in a poker game;
A harricane came on a summer's day,
An' carried the house whar' he lived away;
Then a airthquake come when that wuz gone,
An' swallered the lan' that the house stood on!
An' the tax collector, *he* come roun'
An' charged him up fer the hole in the groun'!
An' the city marshal—he come in view
An' said he wanted his street tax, too!

Did he moan an' sigh? Did he set an' cry
An' cuss the harricane sweepin' by?
Did he grieve that his ol' friends failed to call
When the airthquake come an' swallered all?

Never a word o' blame he said,
With all them troubles on top his head!
Not *him*. . . . He clumb to the top o' the hill—
Whar' standin' room wuz left him still,
An', barin' his head, here's what he said:
"I reckon it's time to git up an' git;
But, Lord, I hain't had the measels yit!"

FRANK L. STANTON

THE NEW DUCKLING

"I WANT to be new," said the duckling.
"O ho!" said the wise old owl,
While the guinea hen cluttered off chuckling
To tell all the rest of the fowl.

"I should like a more elegant figure,"
That child of a duck went on.
"I should like to grow bigger and bigger,
Until I could swallow a swan.

"I *won't* be the bond slave of habit,
I *won't* have these webs on my toes.
I want to run round like a rabbit,
A rabbit as red as a rose.

"I *don't* want to waddle like mother,
Or quack like my silly old dad.
I want to be utterly other,
And *frightfully* modern and mad."

"Do you know," said the turkey, "you're quacking!
There's a fox creeping up thro' the rye;
And, if you're not utterly lacking,
You'll make for that duck pond. Good-by!"

But the duckling was perky as perky.
"Take care of your stuffing!" he called.

(This was horribly rude to a turkey!)
"But you aren't a real turkey," he bawled.

"You're an Early-Victorian Sparrow!
A fox is more fun than a sheep!
I shall show that *my* mind is not narrow
And give him my feathers—to keep."

Now the curious end of this fable,
So far as the rest ascertained,
Though they searched from the barn to the stable,
Was that *only his feathers remained.*

So he *wasn't* the bond slave of habit,
And he *didn't* have webs on his toes;
And *perhaps* he runs round like a rabbit,
A rabbit as red as a rose.

ALFRED NOYES

BORROWED FEATHERS

A ROOSTER one morning was preening his feathers
That glistened so bright in the sun;
He admired the tints of the various colors
As he laid them in place one by one.
Now as roosters go he was a fine bird,
And he should have been satisfied;
But suddenly there as he marched along,
Some peacock feathers he spied.
They had beautiful spots and their colors were gay—
He wished that his own could be green;
He dropped his tail, tried to hide it away;
Was completely ashamed to be seen.

Then his foolish mind hatched up a scheme—
A peacock yet he could be;
So he hopped behind a bush to undress
Where the other fowls could not see.

He caught his own tail between his bill,
  And pulled every feather out;
And into the holes stuck the peacock plumes;
  Then proudly strutted about.
The other fowls rushed to see the queer sight;
  And the peacocks came when they heard;
They could not agree just what he was,
  But pronounced him a funny bird.
Then the chickens were angry that one of their kind
  Should try to be a peacock;
And the peacocks were mad that one with their tail
  Should belong to a common fowl flock.
So the chickens beset him most cruelly behind,
  And yanked his whole tail out together;
The peacocks attacked him madly before,
  And pulled out each chicken feather.
And when he stood stripped clean down to the skin,
  A horrible thing to the rest,
He learned this sad lesson when it was too late—
  As his own simple self he was best.

JOSEPH MORRIS

THE PLAINT OF THE CAMEL

CANARY birds feeds on sugar and seed,
    Parrots have crackers to crunch;
And as for poodles, they tell me the noodles
  Have chickens and cream for their lunch.
    But there's never a question
    About MY digestion—
  ANYTHING does for me!

Cats, you're aware, can repose in a chair,
  Chickens can roost upon rails;
Puppies are able to sleep in a stable,
  And oysters can slumber in pails.
    But no one supposes
    A poor camel dozes—
  ANY PLACE does for me!

Lambs are enclosed where it's never exposed,
  Coops are constructed for hens;
Kittens are treated to houses well heated,
  And pigs are protected by pens.
    But a camel comes handy
    Wherever it's sandy—
  ANYWHERE does for me!

People would laugh if you rode a giraffe,
  Or mounted the back of an ox;
It's nobody's habit to ride on a rabbit,
  Or try to bestraddle a fox.
    But as for a camel, he's
    Ridden by families—
  ANY LOAD does for me!

A snake is as round as a hole in the ground,
  And weasels are wavy and sleek;
And no alligator could ever be straighter
  Than lizards that live in a creek,
    But a camel's all lumpy
    And bumpy and humpy—
  ANY SHAPE does for me!

CHARLES EDWARD CARRYL

MY SORE THUMB

I JABBED a jackknife in my thumb—
Th' blood just *spurted* when it come!
  The cook got faint, an' nurse she yelled
  And showed me how it should be held,
An' Gran'ma went to get a rag,
An' couldn't find one in th' bag;
  An' all the rest was just struck *dumb*
  To see my thumb!

Since I went an' jabbed my thumb
I go around a-lookin' glum,

And Aunt, she pats me on the head
An' gives me extra gingerbread;
But brother's *mad*, an' says he'll go
An' take an ax, an' chop his toe:
An' *then* he guesses I'll keep mum
About my *thumb!*

At school they as't to see my thumb,
But I just showed it to my chum,
An' any else that wants to see
Must divvy up their cake with me!
It's gettin' well so fast, I think
I'll fix it up with crimson ink,
An' that'll keep up *int'rest* some
In my poor thumb!

BURGES JOHNSON

THE DUEL *

THE gingham dog and the calico cat
Side by side on the table sat;
'Twas half-past twelve, and (what do you think!)
Nor one nor t'other had slept a wink!
The old Dutch clock and the Chinese plate
Appeared to know as sure as fate
There was going to be a terrible spat.
(I wasn't there; I simply state
What was told to me by the Chinese plate!)

The gingham dog went "bow-wow-wow!"
And the calico cat replied "mee-ow!"
The air was littered, an hour or so,
With bits of gingham and calico,
While the old Dutch clock in the chimney place
Up with its hands before its face,
For it always dreaded a family row!

* "The Duel," by Eugene Field (1850-95), is almost the most popular humorous poem that has come under my notice In making such a collection as this it is not easy to find poems at once delicate, witty, and graphic.

(Now mind: I'm only telling you
What the old Dutch clock declares is true!)

The Chinese plate looked very blue,
And wailed, "Oh, dear! what shall we do!"
But the gingham dog and the calico cat
Wallowed this way and tumbled that,
Employing every tooth and claw
In the awfullest way you ever saw—
And, oh! how the gingham and calico flew!
(Don't fancy I exaggerate!
I got my views from the Chinese plate!)

Next morning where the two had sat
They found no trace of the dog or cat;
And some folks think unto this day
That burglars stole the pair away!
But the truth about the cat and the pup
Is this: they ate each other up!
Now what do you really think of that!
(The old Dutch clock it told me so,
And that is how I came to know.)

EUGENE FIELD

A MORTIFYING MISTAKE

I STUDIED my tables over and over, and backward and forward, too;
But I couldn't remember six times nine, and I didn't know what to do,
Till sister told me to play with my doll, and not to bother my head.
"If you call her 'Fifty-four' for a while, you'll learn it by heart," she said.

So I took my favorite, Mary Ann (though I thought 'twas a dreadful shame
To give such a perfectly lovely child such a perfectly horrid name),

And I called her my dear little "Fifty-four" a hundred times, till I knew
The answer of six times nine as well as the answer of two times two.

Next day Elizabeth Wigglesworth, who always acts so proud,
Said, "Six times nine is fifty-two," and I nearly laughed aloud!
But I wished I hadn't when teacher said, "Now, Dorothy, tell if you can."
For I thought of my doll and—sakes alive!—I answered, "*Mary Ann!*"

ANNA MARIA PRATT

A TRAGIC STORY

THERE lived a sage in days of yore,
And he a handsome pigtail wore;
But wondered much, and sorrowed more,
Because it hung behind him.

He mused upon this curious case,
And swore he'd change the pigtail's place,
And have it hanging at his face,
Not dangling there behind him.

Says he, "The mystery I've found,—
I'll turn me round,"—he turned him round;
But still it hung behind him.

Then round and round, and out and in,
All day the puzzled sage did spin;
In vain—it mattered not a pin—
The pigtail hung behind him.

And right and left, and round about,
And up and down and in and out
He turned; but still the pigtail stout
Hung steadily behind him.

And though his efforts never slack,
And though he twist, and twirl, and tack,
Alas! still faithful to his back,
  The pigtail hangs behind him.

WILLIAM MAKEPEACE THACKERAY

ODE ON THE DEATH OF A FAVORITE CAT DROWNED IN A TUB OF GOLD FISHES

'TWAS on a lofty vase's side
  Where China's gayest art had dyed
  The azure flowers that blow;
Demurest of the tabby kind,
The pensive Selima, reclin'd,
  Gaz'd on the lake below.

Her conscious tail her joy declar'd;
The fair round face, the snowy beard,
  The velvet of her paws,
Her coat that with the tortoise vies,
Her ears of jet and emerald eyes,
  She saw: and purred applause.

Still had she gaz'd; but midst the tide
Two angel forms were seen to glide,
  The genii of the stream:
Their scaly armor's Tyrian hue,
Through richest purple to the view,
  Betray'd a golden gleam.

The hapless Nymph with wonder saw;
A whisker first, and then a claw,
  With many an ardent wish,
She stretch'd, in vain, to reach the prize:
What female heart can gold despise?
  What cat's averse to fish?

Presumptuous Maid! with looks intent,
Again she stretch'd, again she bent,
Nor knew the gulf between
(Malignant Fate sat by, and smil'd).
The slipp'ry verge her feet beguiled,
She tumbled headlong in.

Eight times emerging from the flood
She mew'd to every wat'ry god
Some speedy aid to send.
No Dolphin came, no Nereid stirr'd;
Nor cruel Tom, nor Susan heard.
A fav'rite has no friend!

From hence, ye beauties, undeceived,
Know, one false step is ne'er retriev'd,
And be with caution bold.
Not all that tempts your wand'ring eyes
And heedless hearts, is lawful prize,
Nor all that glitters gold.

THOMAS GRAY

THE LOBSTER AND THE MAID

HE was a gentle lobster
(The boats had just come in),
He did not love the fishermen,
He could not stand their din;
And so he quietly stole off,
As if it were no sin.

She was a little maiden,
He met her on the sand,
"And how d'you do?" the lobster said,
"Why don't you give your hand?"
For why she edged away from him
He *could* not understand.

"Excuse me, sir," the maiden said:
"Excuse me, if you please,"
And put her hands behind her back,
And doubled up her knees;
"I always thought that lobsters were
A little apt to squeeze."

"Your ignorance," the lobster said,
"Is natural, I fear;
Such scandal is a shame," he sobbed,
"It is not true, my dear,"
And with his pocket handkerchief
He wiped away a tear.

So out she put her little hand,
As though she feared him not,
When some one grabbed him suddenly
And put him in a pot,
With water which, I think he found
Uncomfortably hot.

It may have been the water made
The blood flow to his head,
It may have been that dreadful fib
Lay on his soul like lead;
This much is true—he went in gray,
And came out very red.

Frederick Edward Weatherly

WHY BETTY DIDN'T LAUGH

"WHEN I was at the party,"
Said Betty (aged just four),
"A little girl fell off her chair
Right down upon the floor;
And all the other little girls
Began to laugh but me—
I didn't laugh a single bit,"
Said Betty, seriously.

"Why not?" her mother asked her,
  Full of delight to find
That Betty—bless her little heart!—
  Had been so sweetly kind.
"Why didn't you laugh, darling?
  Or don't you like to tell?"
"I didn't laugh," said Betty,
  "'Cause it was me that fell!"

UNKNOWN

AN ELEGY ON THE DEATH OF A MAD DOG

GOOD people all, of every sort,
  Give ear unto my song,
And if you find it wondrous short,
  It cannot hold you long.

In Islington there was a man
  Of whom the world might say,
That still a godly race he ran,
  Whene'er he went to pray.

A kind and gentle heart he had,
  To comfort friends and foes;
The naked every day he clad,
  When he put on his clothes.

And in that town a dog was found,
  As many dogs there be,
Both mongrel, puppy, whelp, and hound
  And curs of low degree.

This dog and man at first were friends,
  But when a pique began,
The dog, to gain some private ends,
  Went mad and bit the man.

Around from all the neighboring streets
  The wondering neighbors ran,
And swore the dog has lost his wits,
  To bite so good a man.

The wound it seemed both sore and sad
  To every Christian eye;
And while they swore the dog was mad,
  They swore the man would die.

But soon a wonder came to light,
  That show'd the rogues they lied;
The man recovered of the bite,
  The dog it was that died.

OLIVER GOLDSMITH

WHEN FATHER CARVES THE DUCK

WE all look on with anxious eyes
  When father carves the duck,
And mother almost always sighs
  When father carves the duck;
Then all of us prepare to rise,
And hold our bibs before our eyes,
And be prepared for some surprise
  When father carves the duck.

He braces up and grabs a fork
  Whene'er he carves a duck,
And won't allow a soul to talk,
  Until he's carved the duck.
The fork is jabbed into the sides,
Across the breast the knife he slides,
While every careful person hides
  From flying chips of duck.

The platter's always sure to slip
  When father carves a duck,
And how it makes the dishes skip!
  Potatoes fly amuck!
The squash and cabbage leap in space,
We get some gravy in our face,
And father mutters Hindoo grace
  Whene'er he carves a duck.

We then have learned to walk around
  The dining room and pluck
From off the window sills and walls
  Our share of father's duck,
While father growls and blows and jaws,
And swears the knife was full of flaws,
And mother laughs at him because
  He couldn't carve a duck.

E. V. Wright

HOW THE SERMON SOUNDED TO BABY

I KNOW a little darling
  With lovely golden curls,
With cheeks like apple blossoms,
  And teeth like rows of pearls.

His ways are dear and winning,
  And though he is not three,
He's very good at meeting—
  As sweet as sweet can be.

But one day when the sermon
  Seemed rather long (he thought),
His eyes went straight to mamma's
  And her attention sought.

And then he softly whispered,
  With just a little fret—
"Say, mamma, ain't dat preacher
  Dot froo *hollerin* yet?"

Mrs. J. M. Hunter

BETSY'S BATTLE FLAG

FROM dusk till dawn the livelong night
She kept the tallow dips alight,
And fast her nimble fingers flew
To sew the stars upon the blue.
With weary eyes and aching head
She stitched the stripes of white and red,
And when the day came up the stair
Complete across a carven chair
Hung Betsy's battle flag.

Like shadows in the evening gray
The Continentals filed away,
With broken boots and ragged coats,
But hoarse defiance in their throats;
They bore the marks of want and cold,
And some were lame and some were old,
And some with wounds untended bled,
But floating bravely overhead
Was Betsy's battle flag.

When fell the battle's leaden rain,
The soldier hushed his moans of pain
And raised his dying head to see
King George's troopers turn and flee.
Their charging column reeled and broke,
And vanished in the rolling smoke,
Before the glory of the stars,
The snowy stripes, and scarlet bars
Of Betsy's battle flag.

The simple stone of Betsy Ross
Is covered now with mold and moss,
But still her deathless banner flies,
And keeps the color of the skies.

A nation thrills, a nation bleeds,
A nation follows where it leads,
And every man is proud to yield
His life upon a crimson field
For Betsy's battle flag!

MINNA IRVING

LEADER OF MEN

"ROOSEVELT is dead." Why should that line
Strike to my heart, as if it told
The death of some close kin of mine,
Father or brother, friend of old?

I never saw him face to face—
But once, some fourteen years ago,
Outside the crowded meeting place,
When he addressed the overflow;

The fearless eyes, the firm-set chin,
A man who loved the nobler fight—
The short, swift gestures, driving in
The things he knew were just and right;

A newer, deeper reverence
For things that never can grow old;
Judgments so filled with common sense
Fools did not realize their gold;

And things which statesmen scorn to preach—
The love of children, home, and wife;
Old-fashioned laws, yet those whose breach
May sap the proudest nation's life.

So with his passing now it seems
The old, old order too is dead;
The new, with all its restless dreams,
Revolt and chaos, lowers ahead.

The coming storm in rage assaults
  The rocks that bulwarked all our past;
And yet that age, with all its faults,
  Held things to which we must hold fast.

The outworn temples we thought good,
  False gods, may well be overthrown;
The broad foundations where he stood
  We still will cherish as our own.

"Roosevelt is dead." Our leader gone!
  To-day there stands his vacant chair—
Not in that island home alone—
  By myriad firesides everywhere.

He loved us! Swift our torches light
  With the bright fire his courage gives;
We shall not falter in the fight—
  "Roosevelt is dead." His spirit lives.

ROBERT GORDON ANDERSON

WITH THE TIDE

SOMEWHERE I read, in an old book whose name
Is gone from me, I read that when the days
Of a man are counted, and his business done,
There comes up the shore at evening, with the tide,
To the place where he sits, a boat—
And in the boat, from the place where he sees,
Dim in the dusk, dim and yet so familiar,
The faces of his friends long dead; and knows
They come for him, brought in upon the tide,
To take him where men go at set of day.
Then rising, with his hands in theirs, he goes
Between them his last steps, that are the first
Of the new life—and with the ebb they pass,
Their shaken sail grown small upon the moon.

Often I thought of this, and pictured me
How many a man who lives with throngs about him,
Yet straining through the twilight for that boat
Shall scarce make out one figure in the stern,
And that so faint its features shall perplex him
With doubtful memories—and his heart hang back.
But others, rising as they see the sail
Increase upon the sunset, hasten down,
Hands out and eyes elated; for they see
Head over head, crowding from bow to stern,
Repeeping their long loneliness with smiles,
The faces of their friends; and such go forth
Content upon the ebb tide, with safe hearts.

But never
To worker summoned when his day was done
Did mounting tide bring in such freight of friends,
As stole to you up the white wintry shingle
That night while they watched you though you slept,
Softly they came, and beached the boat, and gathered
In the still cove under the icy stars,
Your last born, and the dear loves of your heart,
And all men that have loved right more than ease,
And honor above honors; all who gave
Free handed of their best for other men,
And thought their giving taking; they who knew
Man's natural state is effort, up and up—
All these were there, so great a company
Perchance you marveled, wondering what great ship
Had brought that throng unnumbered to the cove
Where the boys used to beach their light canoe
After old happy picnics—

But these, your friends and children, to whose hands
Committed, in the silent night you rose
And took your last faint steps—
These led you down, O great American,
Down to the winter night and the white beach,
And there you saw that the huge hull that waited
Was not as are the boats of the other dead,
Frail craft for a brief passage; no, for this

Was first of a long line of towering transports,
Storm worn and ocean weary every one,
The ships you launched, the ships you manned, the ships
That now, returning from their sacred quest
With the thrice-sacred burden of their dead,
Lay waiting there to take you forth with them,
Out with the ebb tide, on some farther quest.

EDITH WHARTON

THEODORE ROOSEVELT—PILOT AND PROPHET!

I

ON what divine adventure has he gone?
Beyond what peaks of dawn
Is he now faring? On what errand blest
Has his impulsive heart now turned? No rest
Could be the portion of his tireless soul.
He seeks some frenzied goal
Where he can labor on till Time is not,
And earth is nothing but a thing forgot.

II

Pilot and Prophet! as the years increase
The sorrow of your passing will not cease.
We love to think of you still moving on
From sun to blazing sun,
From planet to far planet, to some height
Of clear perfection in the Infinite,
Where with the wise Immortals you can find
The Peace you fought for with your heart and mind.
Yet from that bourne where you are journeying
Sometimes we think we hear you whispering,
"I went away, O world, so false and true,
I went away—with still so much to do!"

CHARLES HANSON TOWNE

PREAMBLE TO THE CONSTITUTION OF THE UNITED STATES OF AMERICA

WE, the people of the United States, in order to form a more perfect union, establish justice, insure domestic tranquillity, provide for the common defense, promote the general welfare, and secure the blessings of liberty to ourselves and our posterity, do ordain and establish this Constitution.

COLUMBUS DAY

DO you wonder to see him in chains
Whom once the King rose from his throne to greet?
At Barcelona—the city decked herself
To meet me, roared my name; the King and Queen
Bade me be seated, speak, and tell them all
The story of my voyage, and while I spoke
The crowd's roar fell,
And when I ceased to speak, the King and Queen
Sank from their thrones, and melted into tears,
And knelt, and lifted hand and voice
In praise to God who led me thro' the waste.

And now you see me in chains!
Chains for him who gave a new heaven, a new earth,
Gave glory and more empire to the Kings
Of Spain than did all their battles! Chains for him
Who pushed his prows into the setting sun,
And made West East, and sail'd into the Dragon's mouth,
And came upon the Mountain of the World,
And saw the rivers fall from Paradise!

Eighteen long years of waste, seven in your Spain,
Lost, showing courts and King a truth,—the earth a sphere.
At Salamanca we fronted the learning of all Spain,
All their cosmogonies, their astronomies;
No guesswork! I was certain of my goal;

At last their Highnesses were half-assured this earth might
be a sphere.
Last night a dream I had—I sail'd
On my first voyage, harass'd by the frights
Of my first crew, their curses and their groans.
The compass, like an old friend false at last
In our most need, appall'd them, and the wind
Still westward, and the weedy seas—at length
The landbird, and the branch with berries on it,
The carven staff—and at last the light, the light on Sal-
vador.

All glory to God!
I have accomplished what I came to do.
I pray you tell King Ferdinand
That I am loyal to him even unto death.

Alfred Tennyson

THE PILGRIM FATHERS

HERE, on this rock, and on this sterile soil,
Began the kingdom, not of kings, but men;
Began the making of the world again.
Here centuries sank, and from the hither brink,
A new world reached and raised an old world link,
When English hands, by wider vision taught,
Threw down the feudal bars the Normans brought
And here revived, in spite of sword and stake,
Their ancient freedom of the Wapentake;
Here struck the see—the Pilgrim's roofless town,
Where equal rights and equal bonds were set;
Where all the people, equal franchised, met;
Where doom was writ of privilege and crown;
Where human breath blew all the idols down;
Where crests were naught, where vulture flags were furled,
And common men began to own the world!

John Boyle O'Reilly

BANNER OF THE FREE

BEHOLD, its streaming rays unite,
One mingling flood of braided light;
The red that fires the southern rose,
With spotless white from northern snows,
And, spangled o'er its azure, see,
The sister stars of liberty.
Then hail the Banner of the Free,
The starry flower of Liberty!

OLIVER WENDELL HOLMES

INDEPENDENCE BELL

THERE was tumult in the city,
In the quaint old Quaker town,
And the streets were rife with people,
Pacing restless up and down;
People gathering at corners,
Where they whispered, each to each,
And the sweat stood on their temples,
With the earnestness of speech.

As the bleak Atlantic currents
Lash the wild Newfoundland shore,
So they beat against the State House,
So they surged against the door;
And the mingling of their voices
Made a harmony profound,
Till the quiet street of chestnuts
Was all turbulent with sound.

"Will they do it?" "Dare they do it?"
"Who is speaking?" "What's the news?"
"What of Adams?" "What of Sherman?"
"Oh, God grant they won't refuse!"

"Make some way, there!" "Let me nearer!"
  "I am stifling!"—"Stifle, then:
When a nation's life's at hazard,
  We've no time to think of men!"

So they beat against the portal—
  Man and woman, maid and child;
And the July sun in heaven
  On the scene looked down and smiled;
The same sun that saw the Spartan
  Shed his patriot blood in vain,
Now beheld the soul of freedom,
  All unconquered, rise again.

Aloft in that high steeple
  Sat the bellman, old and gray;
He was weary of the tyrant
  And his iron-sceptered sway;
So he sat with one hand ready
  On the clapper of the bell,
Till his eye should catch the signal
  Of the happy news to tell.

See! Oh, see! the dense crowd quivers
  All along the lengthening line,
As the boy from out the portal
  Rushes forth to give the sign!
With his little hands uplifted,
  Breezes dallying with his hair,
Hark! with deep, clear intonation,
  Breaks his young voice on the air.

Hushed the people's swelling murmur,
  List the boy's exultant cry.
"Ring!" he shouts aloud; "ring! Grandpa!
  Ring! Oh, ring for Liberty!"
Instantly, upon the signal,
  The old bellman lifts his hand,
Forth he sends the good news, making
  Iron music through the land.

How they shouted! What rejoicing!
  How the old bell shook the air,
Till the clang of freedom ruffled
  The calm-gliding Delaware!
How the bonfires and the torches
  Lighted up the night's repose;
And from out the flames, like Phœnix,
  Glorious Liberty arose!

That old State House bell is silent,
  Hushed is now its clamorous tongue,
But the spirit is awakened
  Still is living—ever young.
And whene'er we greet the sunlight
  On the Fourth of each July,
We will ne'er forget the bellman
  Who, betwixt the earth and sky,
Rung out our independence,
  Which, please God, shall never die!

ANONYMOUS

THEY SHALL NOT PASS

THEY shall not pass,
    While Britain's sons draw breath,
  While strength is theirs to strike with shining sword.
They shall not pass,
Except they pass to Death—
  For British fighting men have pledged their word.

They shall not pass—
For France knows no defeat,
  Nor hesitates to nobly pay the price.
They shall not pass
Till brave hearts cease to beat,
  And none shall stand to fall in sacrifice.

They shall not pass—
America will stand
  As long as lips can answer her, "I come."
They shall not pass,
To strike the lovéd land,
  That freedom's children rise to call their home.

ALISON BROWN

SAINT JEANNE

THERE is a little church in France to-day
  Where once a simple maiden knelt, who now
  Wears God's insignia upon her brow—
First of all the saints to whom her people pray.
Maid of the Lilies, warrior of the Sword,
    Jeanne d'Arc,
True soldier in the service of the Lord
    Shall you not hark?

To-day the candles burn before your shrine,
  Your banner glows within the sacred space,
  But not alone, for with it, by God's grace,
There does another of its color shine;
Two and yet one—a holy thing enshrined,
    Sainte Jeanne,
Two banners at Domremy are entwined,
    Bless them as one.

There is a little church in France to-day;
  How many prayers have risen thence to you!
  For their sake heed another prayer and new,
Strange words yet beautiful your people say.
Bend down between the lilies and the lance,
  Sainte Jeanne.
"For those Americans who died for France"
    Light their souls on!

There is a little church in France to-day;
Your people kneel about the altar there.
You who were warrior and woman, hear
With hands of very love this prayer they pray:
A simple prayer for those souls chivalrous
Who dared the dark,
"*For those Americans who died for us,*"
Jeanne d'Arc.

THEODOSIA GARRISON

JEAN DESPREZ

OH ye whose hearts are resonant, and ring to War's romance,
Hear ye the story of a boy, a peasant boy of France;
A lad uncouth and warped with toil, yet who, when trial came,
Could feel within his soul upleap and soar, the sacred flame;
Could stand upright, and scorn and smite, as only heroes may:
Oh, harken! Let me try to tell the tale of Jean Desprez.

With fire and sword the Teuton horde was ravaging the land,
And there was darkness and despair, grim death on every hand;
Red fields of slaughter sloping down to ruin's black abyss;
The wolves of war ran evil fanged, and little did they miss.
And on they came with fear and flame, to burn and loot and slay,
Until they reached the red-roofed croft, the home of Jean Desprez.

"Rout out of the village, one and all!" the Uhlan Captain said.
"Behold! Some hand has fired a shot. My trumpeter is dead.

Now shall they Prussian vengeance know; now shall they rue the day,
For by this sacred German slain, ten of these dogs shall pay."

They drove the cowering peasants forth, women and babes and men,
And from the last, with many a jeer, the Captain chose he ten;
Ten simple peasants, bowed with toil; they stood, they knew not why
Against the gray wall of the church, hearing their children cry;
Hearing their wives and mothers wail, with faces dazed they stood.
A moment only. . . . *Ready! Fire!* They weltered in their blood.

But there was one who gazed unseen, who heard the frenzied cries,
Who saw these men in sabots fall before their children's eyes;
A Zouave wounded in a ditch, and knowing death was nigh,
He laughed with joy: "Ah! here is where I settle ere I die."
He clutched his rifle once again, and long he aimed and well. . . .
A shot! Beside his victims ten the Uhlan Captain fell.

They dragged the wounded Zouave out; their rage was like a flame.
With bayonets they pinned him down, until their Major came.
A blond, full-blooded man he was, and arrogant of eye.
He stared to see with shattered skull his favorite Captain lie.
"Nay, do not finish him so quick, this foreign swine," he cried;
"Go nail him to the big church door: he shall be crucified."

With bayonets through hands and feet they nailed the
Zouave there,
And there was anguish in his eyes, and horror in his stare;
"Water! A single drop!" he moaned; but how they jeered
at him,
And mocked him with an empty cup, and saw his sight
grow dim;
And as in agony of death with blood his lips were wet,
The Prussian Major gayly laughed, and lit a cigarette.

But 'mid the white-faced villagers who cowered in horror by,
Was one who saw the woeful sight, who heard the woeful cry:
"Water! One little drop, I beg! For love of Christ who
died. . . ."
It was the little Jean Desprez who turned and stole aside;
It was the little barefoot boy who came with cup abrim
And walked up to the dying man, and gave the drink to
him.

A roar of rage! They seize the boy; they tear him fast
away.
The Prussian Major swings around; no longer is he gay.
His teeth are wolfishly agleam; his face all dark with spite:
"Go, shoot the brat," he snarls, "that dare defy our Prussian might.

Yet stay! I have another thought. I'll kindly be, and
spare.
Quick! give the lad a rifle charged, and set him squarely
there,
And bid him shoot, and shoot to kill. Haste! Make him
understand
The dying dog he fain would save shall perish by his
hand.
And all his kindred they shall see, and all shall curse his
name,
Who bought his life at such a cost, the price of death and
shame."

They brought the boy, wild eyed with fear; they made him understand;
They stood him by the dying man, a rifle in his hand.
"Make haste!" said they; "the time is short, and you must kill or die."
The Major puffed his cigarette, amusement in his eye.
And then the dying Zouave heard, and raised his weary head:
"Shoot, son, 'twill be the best for both; shoot swift and straight," he said.
"Fire first and last, and do not flinch; for lost to hope am I;
And I will murmur: Vive la France! and bless you ere I die."

Half blind with blows the boy stood there; he seemed to swoon and sway;
Then in that moment woke the soul of little Jean Desprez.
He saw the woods go sheening down; the larks were singing clear;
And, oh! the scents and sounds of spring, how sweet they were! how dear!
He felt the scent of new-mown hay, a soft breeze fanned his brow;
O God! the paths of peace and toil! How precious were they now!

The summer days and summer ways, how bright with hope and bliss!
The autumn such a dream of gold; and all must end in this:
This shining rifle in his hand, that shambles all around;
The Zouave there with dying glare; the blood upon the ground;
The brutal faces round him ringed, the evil eyes aflame;
That Prussian bully standing by as if he watched a game.
"Make haste and shoot," the Major sneered; a minute more I give;
A minute more to kill your friend, if you yourself would live."

They only saw a barefoot boy, with blanched and twitching face;
They did not see within his eyes the glory of his race;
The glory of a million men who for fair France have died,
The splendor of self-sacrifice that will not be denied.
Yet he was but a peasant lad, and, oh! but life was sweet.
"Your minute's nearly gone, my lad," he heard a voice repeat.
"Shoot! Shoot!" the dying Zouave moaned; "Shoot! Shoot!" the soldier said.
Then Jean Desprez reached out and shot . . . *the Prussian Major dead!*

ROBERT W. SERVICE

THE MAN BEHIND

THE band is on the quarter-deck, the starry flag unfurled;
The air is mad with music and with cheers.
The ship is bringing home to us the homage of the world
And writing new our name upon the years.
Her officer is on the bridge; we greet him with hurrahs;
But some one says, "Not he the glory won;
Not he alone who wears the braid, deserves the loud applause,
Oh, don't forget the man behind the gun!"
'Tis said that to embattled seas our ship sailed forth at dawn,
Unheeding shot, unheeding hidden mine;
And through the thunders of the fight went steaming bravely on,
The nation's floating fortress on the brine.
And never throbbing engine stopped, nor parted plate or seam
In all that bloody day from sun to sun;
The good ship sang her battle cry in hissing clouds of steam
To cheer anew the man behind the gun.

I look upon her shining bore, her engine's pulsing heart,
I look upon her bulwarks shaped of steel;
I know there is another art, as great as gunner's art,
That makes the world at arms in homage kneel.
This ship, defying shot and shell, defying winds and seas,
Is fruit of honest labor, rightly done;
The man who built the ship, my lads, remember him, for he's
The man behind the man behind the gun!

DOUGLAS MALLOCH

OUR SOLDIER DEAD

"IN Flanders fields, where poppies blow,"
In France where beauteous roses grow,
There let them rest—forever sleep,
While we eternal vigil keep
With our heart's love—with our soul's pray'r,
For all our Fallen "Over There."

The sounding sea between us rolls
And in perpetual requiem tolls—
Three thousand miles of cheerless space
Lie 'twixt us and their resting place;
'Twas God who took them by the hand
And left them in the stranger land.

The earth is sacred where they fell—
Forever on it lies the spell
Of hero deeds in Freedom's cause,
And men unborn shall come and pause
To say a prayer, or bow the head,
So leave these graves to hold their dead.

Let not our sighing nor our tears
Fall on them through the coming years
Who on the land, on sea, in air,

With dauntless courage everywhere,
Their homes and country glorified—
Stood to their arms and smiling died.

Great France will leave no need nor room
That we place flowers on their tomb—
And proudly o'er their resting place,
Will float forever in its grace,
O'er cross, and star, and symbol tag,
Their own beloved country's flag.

ANNETTE KOHN

EPITAPH FOR THE UNKNOWN SOLDIER

WITHIN this nation-hallowed tomb
An unknown soldier lies asleep,
Symbolic comrade of all those
Who, on the land, on sea, in air,
In that red death across the seas,
Sealed with their blood the sacred truths
For which our country ever stands:
That righteousness is all the law—
That justice is true government—
Man's liberty the gift of God.
In memory of the faith they kept,
Here through the ages all the land
As honor guard on watch will stand!

ANNETTE KOHN

THE FLAG

WHY do I love our flag? Ask why
Flowers love the sunshine. Or, ask why
The needle turns with eager eye
Toward the great stars in northern sky.

I love Old Glory, for it waved
Where loyal hearts the Union saved.
I love it, since it shelters me
And all most dear, from sea to sea.
I love it, for it bravely flies
In freedom's cause, 'neath foreign skies.

I love it for its blessed cheer,
Its starry hopes and scorn of fear;
For good achieved and good to be
To us and to humanity.

It is the people's banner bright,
Forever guiding toward the light;
Foe of the tyrant, friend of right,
God give it leadership and might!

Edward A. Horton

NOVEMBER ELEVENTH

A THOUSAND whistles break the bonds of sleep
With swift exultant summons wild and shrill;
Impassioned tongues of flames toward heaven leap
To tell us peace has come. The guns are still.

A thousand flags have blossomed in the air
Like poppies in a garden by the sea.
Beyond the eastern hills a golden flare
Foretells the day that broke on Calvary.

Long-darkened Liberty uplifts once more
Her torch on Belgium, Poland and Alsace
And Flanders—on each desecrated shore,
Slow dawns the sun; and on my mother's face
The look, I think, that Mary must have worn
In Galilee on Resurrection morn.

Elizabeth Hanly

ABRAHAM LINCOLN, THE MASTER

WE need him now—his rugged faith that held
Fast to the rock of Truth through all the days
Of moil and strife, the sleepless nights; upheld
By very God was he—that God who stays
All hero souls who will but trust in Him,
And trusting, labor as if God were not.
His eyes beheld the stars, clouds could not dim
Their glory; but his task was not forgot—
To keep his people one; to hold them true
To that fair dream their fathers willed to them—
Freedom for all; to spur them; to renew
Their hopes in bitter days; strife to condemn.
Such was his task, and well his work was done—
Who willed us greater tasks, when set his sun.

THOMAS CURTIS CLARK

COLUMBUS

BEHIND him lay the gray Azores,
Behind the gates of Hercules;
Before him not the ghost of shores,
Before him only shoreless seas.
The good mate said: "Now must we pray,
For lo! the very stars are gone;
Speak, Admiral, what shall I say?"
"Why say, sail on! and on!"

"My men grow mut'nous day by day;
My men grow ghastly wan and weak."
The stout mate thought of home; a spray
Of salt wave wash'd his swarthy cheek.
"What shall I say, brave Admiral,
If we sight naught but seas at dawn?"
"Why, you shall say, at break of day:
'Sail on! sail on! and on!'"

They sailed and sailed, as winds might blow,
  Until at last the blanch'd mate said:
"Why, now, not even God would know
  Should I and all my men fall dead.
These very winds forget their way,
  For God from these dread seas is gone.
Now speak, brave Admiral, and say——"
  He said: "Sail on! and on!"

They sailed, they sailed, then spoke his mate:
  "This mad sea shows his teeth to-night,
He curls his lip, he lies in wait,
  With lifted teeth as if to bite!
Brave Admiral, say but one word;
  What shall we do when hope is gone?"
The words leaped as a leaping sword:
  "Sail on! sail on! and on!"

Then, pale and worn, he kept his deck,
  And thro' the darkness peered that night
Ah, darkest night! and then a speck—
  A light! a light! a light! a light!
It grew—a star-lit flag unfurled!
  It grew to be Time's burst of dawn;
He gained a world! he gave that world
  Its watch-word: "On! and on!"

JOAQUIN MILLER

AMERICA

MY country, 'tis of thee,
  Sweet land of liberty,
  Of thee I sing;
Land where my fathers died,
Land of the pilgrim's pride,
From every mountain side
  Let freedom ring.

My native country, thee,
Land of the noble free,
  Thy name I love;
I love thy rocks and rills,
Thy woods and templed hills;
My heart with rapture thrills
  Like that above.

Let music swell the breeze,
And ring from all the trees
  Sweet freedom's song;
Let mortal tongues awake,
Let all that breathe partake,
Let rocks their silence break,
  The sound prolong.

Our fathers' God, to Thee,
Author of liberty,
  To Thee we sing;
Long may our land be bright
With freedom's holy light:
Protect us by Thy might,
  Great God, our King.

SAMUEL FRANCIS SMITH

THE STAR-SPANGLED BANNER

OH, say, can you see, by the dawn's early light,
  What so proudly we hailed at the twilight's last gleaming?
Whose broad stripes and bright stars, through the perilous fight,
  O'er the ramparts we watched, were so gallantly streaming?
And the rockets' red glare, the bombs bursting in air,
Gave proof through the night that our flag was still there:
Oh, say, does that star-spangled banner yet wave
O'er the land of the free and the home of the brave?

On the shore, dimly seen through the mists of the deep,
  Where the foe's haughty host in dread silence reposes,
What is that which the breeze, o'er the towering steep,
  As it fitfully blows, half conceals, half discloses?
Now it catches the gleam of the morning's first beam;
In full glory reflected, now shines on the stream:
'Tis the star-spangled banner; oh, long may it wave
O'er the land of the free and the home of the brave!

And where is the band who so vauntingly swore,
  'Mid the havoc of war and the battle's confusion,
A home and a country they'd leave us no more?
  Their blood hath washed out their foul footsteps' pollution:
No refuge could save the hireling and slave
From the terror of flight, or the gloom of the grave;
And the star-spangled banner in triumph doth wave
O'er the land of the free and the home of the brave.

Oh, thus be it ever, when freemen shall stand
  Between their loved home and the war's desolation!
Blest with victory and peace, may the Heaven-rescued land
  Praise the Power that hath made and preserved us a nation.
Then conquer we must, for our cause it is just;
And this be our motto, "In God is our trust;"
And the star-spangled banner in triumph shall wave
O'er the land of the free and the home of the brave.

FRANCIS SCOTT KEY

THE LEAGUE OF LOVE IN ACTION

O LEAGUE of Kindness, woven in all lands,
  You bring Love's tender mercies in your hands;
Above all flags you lift the conquering sign,
And hold invincible Love's battle line.

O League of Kindness, in your far-flung bands,
You weave a chain that reaches to God's hands;
And where blind guns are plotting for the grave,
Yours are the lips that cheer, the arms that save.

O League of Kindness, in your flag we see
A foregleam of the brotherhood to be
In ages when the agonies are done,
When all will love and all will lift as one.

EDWIN MARKHAM

RECESSIONAL

GOD of our fathers, known of old—
  Lord of our far-flung battle line—
Beneath whose awful Hand we hold
  Dominion over palm and pine—
Lord God of Hosts, be with us yet,
Lest we forget—lest we forget!

The tumult and the shouting dies—
  The Captains and the Kings depart—
Still stands Thine ancient sacrifice,
  An humble and a contrite heart.
Lord God of Hosts, be with us yet,
Lest we forget—lest we forget!

Far-called, our navies melt away—
  On dune and headland sinks the fire—
Lo, all our pomp of yesterday
  Is one with Nineveh and Tyre!
Judge of the Nations, spare us yet,
Lest we forget—lest we forget!

If, drunk with sight of power, we loose
  Wild tongues that have not Thee in awe—
Such boasting as the Gentiles use,
  Or lesser breeds without the Law—

Lord God of Hosts, be with us yet,
Lest we forget—lest we forget!

For heathen heart that puts her trust
In reeking tube and iron shard—
All valiant dust that builds on dust,
And guarding calls not Thee to guard,—
For frantic boast and foolish word,
Thy Mercy on Thy People, Lord! Amen.

RUDYARD KIPLING

PEACE

WERE half the power that fills the world with terror,
Were half the wealth bestowed on camps and courts,
Given to redeem the human mind from error,
There were no need of arsenal or forts.
The warrior's name would be a name abhorred;
And every nation that should lift again
Its hand against a brother, on its forehead
Would wear forevermore the curse of Cain!

HENRY WADSWORTH LONGFELLOW

CHARGE OF THE LIGHT BRIGADE

HALF a league, half a league,
Half a league onward,
Into the valley of death
Rode the six hundred.
"Forward, the Light Brigade!
Charge for the guns!" he said.
Into the valley of death,
Rode the six hundred.

"Forward, the Light Brigade!
Was there a man dismayed?
Not though the soldiers knew
  Some one had blundered:
Theirs not to make reply,
Theirs not to reason why,
Theirs but to do and die;
Into the valley of death,
  Rode the six hundred.

Cannon to right of them,
Cannon to left of them,
Cannon in front of them,
  Volleyed and thundered:
Stormed at with shot and shell,
Boldly they rode and well;
Into the jaws of death,
Into the mouth of hell,
  Rode the six hundred.

Flashed all their sabres bare,
Flashed as they turned in air,
Sab'ring the gunners there,
Charging an army, while
  All the world wondered:
Plunged in the battery smoke,
Right through the line they broke,
Cossack and Russian
Reeled from the sabre-stroke,
  Shattered and sundered.
Then they rode back—but not,
  Not the six hundred.

Cannon to right of them,
Cannon to left of them,
Cannon behind them,
  Volleyed and thundered.
Stormed at with shot and shell,
While horse and hero fell,
They that had fought so well,
Came through the jaws of death,

Back from the mouth of hell,
All that was left of them,
  Left of six hundred.

When can their glory fade?
O, the wild charge they made!
  All the world wondered.
Honor the charge they made!
Honor the Light Brigade,
  Noble six hundred!

ALFRED TENNYSON

SHERIDAN'S RIDE

(October 19, 1864)

UP from the South, at break of day,
  Bringing to Winchester fresh dismay,
The affrighted air with a shudder bore,
Like a herald in haste, to the chieftain's door,
The terrible grumble, and rumble, and roar,
Telling the battle was on once more,
  And Sheridan twenty miles away.

And wider still those billows of war
Thundered along the horizon's bar;
And louder yet into Winchester rolled
The roar of that red sea uncontrolled,
Making the blood of the listener cold,
As he thought of the stake in that fiery fray,
  And Sheridan twenty miles away.

But there is a road from Winchester town,
A good, broad highway leading down:
And there, through the flush of the morning light,
A steed as black as the steeds of night
Was seen to pass as with eagle flight;

As if he knew the terrible need,
He stretched away with his utmost speed;
Hills rose and fell, but his heart was gay,
With Sheridan fifteen miles away.

Still sprang from those swift hoofs, thundering south,
The dust, like smoke from the cannon's mouth,
Or the trail of a comet, sweeping faster and faster,
Foreboding to traitors the doom of disaster.
The heart of the steed and the heart of the master
Were beating like prisoners assaulting their walls,
Impatient to be where the battle field calls;
Every nerve of the charger was strained to full play,
With Sheridan only ten miles away.

Under his spurning feet, the road
Like an arrowy Alpine river flowed,
And the landscape sped away behind
Like an ocean flying before the wind;
And the steed, like a bark fed with furnace ire,
Swept on, with his wild eye full of fire;
But, lo! he is nearing his heart's desire;
He is snuffing the smoke of the roaring fray,
With Sheridan only five miles away.

The first that the general saw were the groups
Of stragglers, and then the retreating troops;
What was done? what to do? a glance told him both,
Then, striking his spurs, with a terrible oath,
He dashed down the line, 'mid a storm of huzzas,
And the wave of retreat checked its course there, because
The sight of the master compelled it to pause.
With foam and with dust the black charger was gray;
By the flash of his eye, and the red nostril's play,
He seemed to the whole great army to say:
"I have brought you Sheridan all the way
From Winchester town to save the day!"

Hurrah! hurrah for Sheridan!
Hurrah! hurrah for horse and man!

And when their statues are placed on high,
Under the dome of the Union sky,
The American soldier's Temple of Fame,
There, with the glorious general's name,
Be it said, in letters both bold and bright:
"Here is the steed that saved the day
By carrying Sheridan into the fight,
From Winchester—twenty miles away!"

THOMAS BUCHANAN READ

THE RED CROSS SPIRIT SPEAKS

I

WHENEVER war, with its red woes,
Or flood, or fire or famine goes,
There, too, go I;
If earth in any quarter quakes,
Or pestilence its ravage makes,
Thither I fly.

II

I kneel behind the soldier's trench,
I walk 'mid shambles' smear and stench,
The dead I mourn;
I bear the stretcher and I bend
O'er Fritz and Pierre and Jack to mend
What shells have torn.

III

I go wherever men may dare,
I go wherever woman's care
And love can live,
Wherever strength and skill can bring
Surcease to human suffering
Or solace give.

IV

I helped upon Haldora's shore,
With Hospitaller Knights I bore
The first red cross;
I was the Lady of the Lamp
I saw in Colferino's camp
The crimson loss.

V

I am your pennies and your pounds,
I am your bodies on their rounds
Of pain afar;
I am *you* doing what you would
If you were only where you could—
Your avatar.

VI

The cross which on my arm I wear,
The flag which o'er my breast I bear,
Is but the sign
Of what you'd sacrifice for him
Who suffers on the hellish rim
Of war's red line.

JOHN E. FINLEY

THE RED CROSS CHRISTMAS SEAL

OH, happy folk, contented folk, and ye that go with gold
To seek within the noisy mart the gifts to mark the day—
Jolly toys and gems and lace and trinkets manifold—
Here be better wares to buy along the crowded way.

Buy a pair of red cheeks to give a little lad again,
Buy a pallid woman's face the bright eyes of health,

Buy a broken man a hope, buy the strength he had again,
Here are bargains wonderful awaiting on your wealth.

Oh, happy folk and careless folk, the world's bazaar is piled
With lovely gifts and lasting gifts to mark a holiday.
You who seek the fairest thing for lover, friend, and child,
Surely ye shall pause awhile and buy the while ye stay.

Buy a mother back her bairn, buy a man his wife again,
Buy a lad the right to love, a child the right to play,
Buy the wistful kindred all, home and health and life again,
And God be with you gentle folk who purchase these to-day.

THEODOSIA GARRISON

WASHINGTON'S BIRTHDAY

THE birthday of the Father of his Country! May it ever be freshly remembered by American hearts! May it ever reawaken in them a filial veneration for his memory; ever rekindle the fires of patriotic regard for the country which he loved so well, to which he gave his youthful vigor and his youthful energy; to which he devoted his life in the maturity of his powers, in the field; to which again he offered the counsels of his wisdom and his experience as president of the convention that framed our Constitution, which he guided and directed while in the chair of state, and for which the last prayer of his earthly supplication was offered up, when it came the moment for him so well, and so grandly, and so calmly, to die. He was the first man of the time in which he grew. His memory is first and most sacred in our love, and ever hereafter, till the last drop of blood shall freeze in the last American heart, his name shall be a spell of power and of might.

ANONYMOUS

WASHINGTON'S ADDRESS TO HIS TROOPS

THE time is now near at hand which must probably determine whether Americans are to be freemen or slaves; whether they are to have any property they can call their own; whether their houses and farms are to be pillaged and destroyed, and themselves consigned to a state of wretchedness, from which no human efforts will deliver them. The fate of unborn millions will now depend, under God, on the courage and conduct of this army. Our cruel and unrelenting enemy leaves us only the choice of a brave resistance, or the most abject submission. We have, therefore, to resolve to conquer or to die.

Our own, our country's honor, calls upon us for a vigorous and manly exertion; and if we now shamefully fail, we shall become infamous to the whole world. Let us then rely on the goodness of our cause, and the aid of the Supreme Being, in whose hands victory is, to animate and encourage us to great and noble actions. The eyes of all our countrymen are now upon us, and we shall have their blessings and praises, if happily we are the instruments of saving them from the tyranny meditated against them. Let us animate and encourage each other, and show the whole world that a freeman contending for liberty on his own ground is superior to any slavish mercenary on earth.

Liberty, property, life, and honor are all at stake; upon your courage and conduct rest the hopes of our bleeding and insulted country; our wives, children, and parents expect safety from us, only; and they have every reason to believe that Heaven will crown with success so just a cause.

The enemy will endeavor to intimidate by show and appearance; but, remember, they have been repulsed on various occasions by a few brave Americans. Their cause is bad—their men are conscious of it; and, if opposed with firmness and coolness on their first onset, with our advantage of works, and knowledge of the ground, the victory is most assuredly ours. Every good soldier will be silent and attentive—wait for orders, and reserve his fire until he is sure of doing execution.

George Washington

THE GLORY OF WASHINGTON

TO Americans the name of Washington will be forever dear,—a savor of sweet incense, descending to every succeeding generation. The things which he has done are too great, too interesting, ever to be forgotten. Every object which we see, every employment in which we are engaged, every comfort which we enjoy, reminds us daily of his character.

Every ship bears the fruit of his labors on its wings and exultingly spreads its streamers to his honor. The student meets him in the still and peaceful walk; the traveler sees him in all the smiling and prosperous scenes of his journey; and our whole country, in her thrift, order, safety, and morals, bears inscribed in sunbeams, on all her hills and plains, the name and glory of Washington.

TIMOTHY DWIGHT

OUR MARTYR-CHIEF

SUCH was he, our Martyr-Chief,
  Whom late the Nation he had led,
  With ashes on her head,
Wept with the passion of an angry grief:
Forgive me, if from present things I turn
To speak what in my heart will beat and burn,
And hang my wreath on his world-honored urn.
  Nature, they say, doth dote,
  And cannot make a man
  Save on some worn-out plan,
  Repeating us by rote;
For him her Old World molds aside she threw,
  And, choosing sweet clay from the breast
  Of the unexhausted West,
With stuff untainted shaped a hero new,
Wise, steadfast in the strength of God, and true.
  How beautiful to see,

Once more a shepherd of mankind indeed,
Who loved his charge, but never loved to lead:
One whose meek flock the people joyed to be,
  Not lured by any cheat of birth,
  But by his clear-grained human worth,
And brave old wisdom of sincerity!
  They knew that outward grace is dust;
  They could not choose but trust
In the sure-footed mind's unfaltering skill,
  And supple-tempered will
That bent like perfect steel to spring again and thrust
  His was no lonely mountain peak of mind,
Thrusting to thin air o'er our cloudy bars,
  A sea mark now, now lost in vapors blind;
  Broad prairie rather, genial, level lined,
  Fruitful and friendly for all human kind,
Yet also nigh to heaven and loved of loftiest stars.

Great captains, with their guns and drums,
Disturb our judgment for the hour,
  But at last silence comes;
These all are gone, and standing like a tower,
  Our children shall behold his fame,
  The kindly, earnest, brave, foreseeing man,
Sagacious, patient, dreading praise, not blame,
New birth of our new soil, the first American.

JAMES RUSSELL LOWELL

WASHINGTON'S BIRTHDAY

WELCOME to the day returning,
  Dearer still as ages flow,
While the torch of Faith is burning,
  Long as Freedom's altars glow!
See the hero whom it gave us
  Slumbering on a mother's breast;
For the arm he stretched to save us,
  Be its morn forever blest!

Hear the tale of youthful glory,
  While of Britain's rescued band
Friend and foe repeat the story,
  Spread his fame o'er sea and land,
Where the red cross, proudly streaming,
  Flaps above the frigate's deck,
Where the golden lilies, gleaming,
  Star the watch towers of Quebec.

Look! The shadow on the dial
  Marks the hour of deadlier strife;
Days of terror, years of trial,
  Scourge a nation into life.
Lo, the youth, becomes her leader!
  All her baffled tyrants yield;
Through his arms the Lord hath freed her;
  Crown him on the tented field!

Vain is Empire's mad temptation!
  Not for him an earthly crown!
He whose sword hath freed a nation
  Strikes the offered scepter down.
See the throneless Conqueror seated,
  Ruler by a people's choice;
See the Patriot's task completed;
  Hear the Father's dying voice!

"By the name that you inherit,
  By the sufferings you recall,
Cherish the fraternal spirit;
  Love your country first of all!
Listen not to idle questions
  If its bands may be untied;
Doubt the patriot whose suggestions
  Strive a nation to divide!"

Father! We, whose ears have tingled
  With the discord notes of shame,—
We, whose sires their blood have mingled
  In the battle's thunder flame,—

Gathering, while this holy morning
  Lights the land from sea to sea,
Hear thy counsel, heed thy warning;
  Trust us, while we honor thee!

Oliver Wendell Holmes

LINCOLN'S ADDRESS AT GETTYSBURG

FOUR score and seven years ago our fathers brought forth on this continent a new nation, conceived in liberty and dedicated to the proposition that all men are created equal.

Now we are engaged in a great civil war, testing whether that nation, or any nation so conceived and so dedicated, can long endure. We are met on a great battlefield of that war. We have come to dedicate a portion of that field as a final resting place for those who here gave their lives that that nation might live. It is altogether fitting and proper that we should do this.

But, in a larger sense, we cannot dedicate, we cannot consecrate, we cannot hallow this ground. The brave men, living and dead, who struggled here, have consecrated it far above our poor power to add or detract. The world will little note, nor long remember, what we say here, but it can never forget what they did here. It is for us, the living, rather to be dedicated here to the unfinished work which they who fought here have thus far so nobly advanced. It is rather for us to be here dedicated to the great task remaining before us: that from the same honored dead we take increased devotion to that cause for which they gave the last full measure of devotion; that we here highly resolve that these dead should not have died in vain; that this nation, under God, shall have a new birth of freedom, and that government of the people, by the people, for the people, shall not perish from the earth.

Abraham Lincoln

WHICH GENERAL?

(*For Washington's Birthday or any patriotic exercises*)

SOMETIMES mamma calls me "general";
I wish I knew which one;
But I always try to tell the truth,
So I *hope* it's Washington.

But when I tell my papa that,
He laughs loud as he can,
And says if she calls me "general"
She must mean Sheridan;

Because whenever she wants me,
And I am out at play,
I nearly always seem to be
'Bout "twenty miles away."

KATE W. HAMILTON

LIKE WASHINGTON

WE cannot all be Washingtons,
And have our birthdays celebrated;
But we can love the things he loved,
And we can hate the things he hated.

He loved the truth, he hated lies,
He minded what his mother taught him,
And every day he tried to do
The simple duties that it brought him.

Perhaps the reason little folks
Are sometimes great when they grow taller,
Is just because, like Washington,
They do their best when they are smaller.

UNKNOWN

GEORGE WASHINGTON

(A recitation for five small boys. Let each boy hold in his right hand a card with date, lifting it high during his recitation)

1732.—IN seventeen hundred thirty-two
George Washington was born;
Truth, goodness, skill, and glory high,
His whole life did adorn.

1775.—In seventeen hundred seventy-five,
The chief command he took
Of all the army in the State,
And ne'er his flag forsook.

1783.—In seventeen hundred eighty-three,
Retired to private life,
He saw his much-loved country free
From battle and from strife.

1789.—In seventeen hundred eighty-nine
The country with one voice,
Proclaimed him President to shine,
Blessed by the people's choice.

1799.—In seventeen hundred ninety-nine
The Nation's tears were shed,
To see the Patriot life resign,
And sleep among the dead.

All.—As "first in war, and first in peace,"
As patriot, father, friend,
He will be blessed till time shall cease,
And earthly life shall end.

UNKNOWN

GEORGE WASHINGTON

WHEN great and good George Washington
Was a little boy like me,
He took his little hatchet
And chopped down a cherry tree.

And when his papa called him,
He then began to cry,
"I did it, oh, I did it,
I cannot tell a lie."

His papa did not scold at all,
But said, "You noble youth,
I'd gladly lose ten cherry trees
And have you tell the truth."

But I myself am not quite clear;
For, if I took my hatchet
And chopped my papa's cherry tree,
Oh, wouldn't I just catch it!

UNKNOWN

FEBRUARY TWENTY-SECOND

IN seventeen hundred thirty-two,
This very month and day,
Winking and blinking at the light,
A little baby lay.

No doubt they thought the little man
A goodly child enough;
But time has proved that he was made
Of most uncommon stuff.

The little babe became a man
That everybody knew
Would finish well what he began,
And prove both firm and true.

So when the Revolution came,
That made our nation free,
They couldn't find a better man
For general, you see.

As general, he never failed
  Or faltered; so they thought
He ought to be the President,
  And so I'm sure he ought.

And then he did his part so well
  As President—'twas plain
They couldn't do a better thing
  Than choose him yet again.

Through all his life they loved him well,
  And mourned him when he died;
And ever since his noble name
  Has been our nation's pride.

The lesson of his life is clear,
  And easy quite to guess,
Be firm and true, if you would make
  Your life a grand success.

JOY ALLISON

OUR COUNTRY AND OUR HOME

THERE is a land, of every land the pride,
  Beloved by heaven o'er all the world beside,
Where brighter suns dispense serener light,
And milder moons imparadise the night.
A land of beauty, virtue, valor, truth,
Time-tutored age, and love-exalted youth:
The wandering mariner, whose eye explores
The wealthiest isles, the most enchanting shores,
Views not a realm so bountiful and fair,
Nor breathes the spirit of a purer air;
In every clime the magnet of his soul,
Touched by remembrance trembles to that pole;
For in this land of heaven's peculiar grace,
The heritage of nature's noblest race,
There is a spot of earth supremely blest,

A dearer, sweeter spot than all the rest,
Where man, creation's tyrant, casts aside
His sword and scepter, pageantry and pride,
While in his softened looks benignly blend
The sire, the son, the husband, brother, friend;
Here woman reigns; the mother, daughter, wife,
Strews with fresh flowers the narrow way of life!
In the clear heaven of her delightful eye
An angel guard of loves and graces lie;
Around her knees domestic duties meet,
And fireside pleasures gambol at her feet;
Where shall that land, that spot of earth be found!
Art thou a man?—a patriot?—look around;
Oh thou shalt find, howe'er thy footsteps roam,
That land *thy country*, and that spot *thy home.*

MONTGOMERY

OUR DEAD HEROES

REST on, O heroes! in your silent slumber!
Hail and farewell, ye mighty, moveless dead!
Long as her centuries Earth shall know and number,
Green be the laurel boughs above ye spread.

Your course is spread; your record man remembers,
And God's own hand your sacred dust shall keep;
Though all the flame hath left those mortal embers,
Upward it sprang, with bright, immortal leap.

Sleep in your country's heart; forever holy
Your memory shines along the slopes we tread;
Another hundred years their incense lowly
Ere long shall o'er your sculptured honors shed.

And we who bring you grace and salutation,
We, too, shall sleep; and nobler tribes of men
Shall offer here the homage of a nation
Rich with a wisdom far beyond our ken.

But still, as years return, shall man returning
Fight, fall, despair, or chant the conqueror's psalm
Still the same light in patriot hearts be burning,
And Heaven, still just, bestow the martyr's palm.

ROSE TERRY COOKE

A PATRIOTIC BOY

(A small boy with flag)

YOU see I am a little boy,
But I can wave a flag,
And when the other boys all march
I'm sure I do not lag.

And when the others shout out loud,
As loud as they, shout I;
I wave my flag and say,
Hurrah, hurrah for Fourth o' July!

MRS. E. J. H. GOODFELLOW

THE RED, WHITE AND BLUE

WELCOME, bright flag! welcome to-day!
Above the schoolhouse float for aye.
Our country's pride, our country's boast,
From Maine to the Pacific coast.
Thy starry folds we raise on high
And vow for thee to live or die.

Banner all glorious, float ever o'er us!
Every star shining there steadfast and true;
Holding the lesson of Union before us,
Written for aye in the red, white and blue.

UNKNOWN

DECORATION DAY

HERE is a lily and here is a rose,
And here is a heliotrope,
And here is the woodbine sweet that grows
On the garden's sunny slope.

Here is a bit of mignonette,
And here's a geranium red,
A pansy bloom and a violet
I found in a mossy bed.

These are the flowers I love the best,
And I've brought them all to lay
With loving hands where soldiers rest,
On Decoration Day.

SUSIE M. BEST

MY COUNTRY'S FLAG

(*With flag in hand*)

THIS is my country's flag,
And I am my country's boy!
To love and serve her well
Will ever be my joy.

JUNIATA STAFFORD

A ZEALOUS PATRIOT

(*A boy's recitation for Washington's Birthday*)

IF there was a war I'd get my gun
And I'd be like General Washington;
I'd sling it over my shoulder—so—
And forth to the contest I would go.

I'd ride on a stately snow-white horse
In the very thick of the fight, of course;
I'd keep the hearts of my soldiers true,
For that is the way he used to do.

If there was a war I'd try to be
A brave defender of liberty,
I'd think of the way that Washington
Fought and conquered in days long done.

I'd be so full of a patriot's zeal
The hardships of war I would not feel;
If I died in battle, my wounds should show
I fell on the field fronting the foe.

But, oh! to be good from day to day
Is a harder task than to lead the fray;
Yet I'll do my examples and fetch the wood,
For heroes begin by being good!

SUSIE M. BEST

WORKING FOR OUR FLAG

(A recitation for Flag Day)

WE'RE working for our flag each day,
Though we are very small,
And you will hear some big folks say
We cannot work at all.

We're working for our flag each day,
And each good deed we do
Is like a little budding flower
Around our flag so true.

We're working for our flag each day,
Our bright and starry flag;
We'll spend our lives without a fear,
In working for our flag.

F. URSULA PAYNE

OUR FLAG

(A recitation for Flag Day or any patiotic occasion. The speaker holds a flag)

YOU may talk about the countries
  That lie beyond the sea,
But America's the country
  That's good enough for me!

The stars and stripes! The stars and stripes!
  Oh! that's the flag I love.
(Waves a flag.)
Long may we see it proudly float
  Our schools and homes above.

Our country! It shall ever be
  More dear to me than any other—
A home for all that are oppressed,
  Where the rich man to the poor is brother.

Red, white and blue is our country's flag—
  The flag of the brave and free;
Red, white, and blue, wherever we go,
  Is the flag for you and me.

M. D. STERLING

THE AMERICAN FLAG

(A recitation for a flag-raising)

LIFT it high, our glorious banner;
  Let it wave upon the breeze;
Freedom's starry emblem ever,
  Lift it high o'er land and seas.

Many conflicts it has witnessed,
  Many stories it could tell
Of the brave who fought around it,
  Of the brave who 'neath it fell.

Scenes of woe and desolation,
Scenes of joy o'er vict'ries won;
Scenes of rest and peaceful union;
Freedom now for every one.

Lift the flag, then, high above us,
May it wave till time shall cease,
And its record for the future
Be of happiness and peace!

LENA E. FAULDS

TO AMERICA

WHAT is the voice I hear
On the winds of the western sea?
Sentinel, listen from out Cape Clear
And say what the voice may be.
'Tis a proud free people calling loud to a people proud and free.

And it says to them: "Kinsmen, hail!
We severed have been too long.
Now let us have done with a worn-out tale—
The tale of an ancient wrong—
And our friendship last long as our love doth last and be stronger than death is strong."

Answer them, sons of the self-same race,
And blood of the self-same clan;
Let us speak with each other face to face
And answer as man to man,
And loyally love and trust each other as none but free men can.

Now fling them out to the breeze,
Shamrock, Thistle, and Rose,
And the Star-spangled Banner unfurl with these—
A message to friends and foes
Wherever the sails of peace are seen and wherever the war wind blows—

A message to bond and thrall to wake,
For wherever we come, we twain,
The throne of the tyrant shall rock and quake,
And his menace be void and vain;
For you are lords of a strong land and we are lords of the main.

Yes, this is the voice of the bluff March gale;
We severed have been too long,
But now we have done with a worn-out tale—
The tale of an ancient wrong—
And our friendship last long as love doth last and stronger than death is strong.

Alfred Austin

MARCO BOZZARIS

At midnight, in his guarded tent,
The Turk lay dreaming of the hour
When Greece, her knee in suppliance bent,
Should tremble at his power:
In dreams, through camp and court, he bore
The trophies of a conqueror;
In dreams his song of triumph heard;
Then wore his monarch's signet ring:
Then pressed that monarch's throne—a king;
As wild his thoughts, and gay of wing,
As Eden's garden bird.

At midnight, in the forest shades,
Bozzaris ranged his Suliote band,
True as the steel of their tried blades,
Heroes in heart and hand.
There had the Persian's thousands stood,
There had the glad earth drunk their blood
On old Platæa's day;

And now there breathed that haunted air
The sons of sires who conquered there,
With arm to strike and soul to dare,
As quick, as far as they.

An hour passed on—the Turk awoke;
That bright dream was his last;
He woke—to hear his sentries shriek,
"To arms! they come; the Greek! the Greek!"
He woke—to die midst flame, and smoke,
And shout, and groan, and saber stroke,
And death shots falling thick and fast
As lightnings from the mountain cloud;
And heard, with voice as trumpet loud,
Bozzaris cheer his band:
"Strike—till the last armed foe expires;
Strike—for your altars and your fires;
Strike—for the green graves of your sires;
God—and your native land!"

They fought—like brave men, long and well;
They piled that ground with Moslem slain,
They conquered—but Bozzaris fell,
Bleeding at every vein.
His few surviving comrades saw
His smile when rang their proud hurrah,
And the red field was won;
Then saw in death his eyelids close
Calmly, as to a night's repose,
Like flowers at set of sun.

Come to the bridal chamber, Death!
Come to the mother's, when she feels,
For the first time, her first-born's breath;
Come when the blessed seals
That close the pestilence are broke,
And crowded cities wail its stroke;
Come in consumption's ghastly form,
The earthquake shock, the ocean storm;
Come when the heart beats high and warm
With banquet song, and dance, and wine;

And thou art terrible—the tear,
The groan, the knell, the pall, the bier,
And all we know, or dream, or fear
Of agony, are thine.

But to the hero, when his sword
Has won the battle for the free,
Thy voice sounds like a prophet's word;
And in its hollow tones are heard
The thanks of millions yet to be.
Come, when his task of fame is wrought—
Come, with her laurel leaf, blood-bought—
Come in her crowning hour—and then
Thy sunken eye's unearthly light
To him is welcome as the sight
Of sky and stars to prisoned men;
Thy grasp is welcome as the hand
Of brother in a foreign land;
Thy summons welcome as the cry
That told the Indian isles were nigh
To the world-seeking Genoese,
When the land wind, from woods of palm,
And orange groves, and fields of balm,
Blew o'er the Haytian seas.

Bozzaris! with the storied brave
Greece nurtured in her glory's time,
Rest thee—there is no prouder grave,
Even in her own proud clime.
She wore no funeral weeds for thee,
Nor bade the dark hearse wave its plume
Like torn branch from death's leafless tree
In sorrow's pomp and pageantry,
The heartless luxury of the tomb;
But she remembers thee as one
Long loved and for a season gone;
For thee her poet's lyre is wreathed,
Her marble wrought, her music breathed;
For thee she rings the birthday bells;
Of thee her babe's first lisping tells;
For thine her evening prayer is said

At palace couch and cottage bed:
Her soldier, closing with the foe,
Gives for thy sake a deadlier blow,
His plighted maiden, when she fears
For him the joy of her young years,
Thinks of thy fate, and checks her tears;
  And she, the mother of thy boys,
Though in her eye and faded cheek
Is read the grief she will not speak,
  The memory of her buried joys,
And even she who gave thee birth,
Will, by their pilgrim-circled hearth,
  Talk of thy doom without a sigh;
For thou art Freedom's now, and Fame's:
One of the few, the immortal names,
  That were not born to die.

FITZ-GREENE HALLECK

A BALLAD OF HEROES

BECAUSE you passed, and now are not,—
  Because, in some remoter day,
Your sacred dust from doubtful spot
  Was blown of ancient airs away,—
  Because you perished,—must men say
Your deeds were naught, and so profane
  Your lives with that cold burden? Nay,
The deeds you wrought are not in vain!

Though, it may be, above the plot
  That hid your once imperial clay,
No greener than o'er men forgot
  The unregarding grasses sway;—
  Though there no sweeter is the lay
From careless bird,—though you remain
  Without distinction of decay,—
The deeds you wrought are not in vain!

No. For while yet in tower or cot
  Your story stirs the pulses' play;
And men forget the sordid lot—
  The sordid care, of cities gray;
  While yet, beset in homelier fray,
They learn from you the lesson plain
  That Life may go, so Honor stay,—
The deeds you wrought are not in vain!

ENVOY

Heroes of old! I humbly lay
  The laurel on your graves again;
Whatever men have done, men may,—
  The deeds you wrought are not in vain!

Austin Dobson

THE BATTLE OF BLENHEIM

IT was a summer's evening,
    Old Kaspar's work was done,
And he before his cottage door
  Was sitting in the sun;
And by him sported on the green
His little grandchild Wilhelmine.

She saw her brother Peterkin
  Roll something large and round,
Which he, beside the rivulet,
  In playing there, had found.
He came to ask what he had found,
That was so large, and smooth, and round.

Old Kaspar took it from the boy,
  Who stood expectant by;
And then the old man shook his head,
  And, with a natural sigh,
" 'Tis some poor fellow's skull," said he,
"Who fell in the great victory!

"I find them in the garden,
  For there's many hereabout;
And often when I go to plow,
  The plowshare turns them out;
For many thousand men," said he,
"Were slain in that great victory!"

"Now tell us what 'twas all about,"
  Young Peterkin he cries;
And little Wilhelmine looks up
  With wonder-waiting eyes;
"Now tell us all about the war,
And what they killed each other for."

"It was the English," Kaspar cried,
  "Who put the French to rout;
But what they killed each other for
  I could not well make out.
But everybody said," quoth he,
"That 'twas a famous victory!

"My father lived at Blenheim then,
  Yon little stream hard by:
They burned his dwelling to the ground
  And he was forced to fly;
So with his wife and child he fled,
Nor had he where to rest his head.

"With fire and sword the country round
  Was wasted far and wide;
And many a childing mother then
  And new-born baby died.
But things like that, you know, must be
At every famous victory.

"They say it was a shocking sight
  After the field was won;
For many thousand bodies here
  Lay rotting in the sun.
But things like that, you know, must be
After a famous victory.

"Great praise the Duke of Marlborough won,
And our good Prince Eugene."
"Why, 'twas a very wicked thing!"
Said little Wilhelmine.
"Nay, nay, my little girl," quoth he,
"It was a famous victory!

"And everybody praised the Duke
Who this great fight did win."
"But what good came of it at last?"
Quoth little Peterkin.
"Why, that I cannot tell," said he,
"But 'twas a famous victory."

ROBERT SOUTHEY

THE LOST COLORS

(1843)

FROWNING, the mountain stronghold stood,
Whose front no mortal could assail;
For more than twice three hundred years
The terror of the Indian vale.
By blood and fire the robber band
Answered the helpless village wail.

Hot was his heart and cool his thought,
When Napier from his Englishmen
Up to the bandits' rampart glanced,
And down upon his ranks again.
Summoned to dare a deed like that,
Which of them all would answer then?

What sullen regiment is this
That lifts its eyes to dread Cutchee?
Abased, its standard bears no flag.
For thus the punishment shall be
That England metes to Englishmen
Who shame her once by mutiny.

From out the disgraced Sixty-Fourth
There stepped a hundred men of might.
Cried Napier: "Now prove to me
I read my soldiers' hearts aright!
Form! Forward! Charge, my volunteers!
Your colors are on yonder height!"

So sad is shame, so wise is trust!
The challenge echoed bugle-clear.
Like fire along the Sixty-Fourth
From rank to file rang cheer on cheer.
In death and glory up the pass
They fought for all to brave men dear.

Old is the tale, but read anew
In every warring human heart,
What rebel hours, what coward shame,
Upon the aching memory start!
To find the ideal forfeited,
—What tears can teach the holy art?

Thou great Commander! leading on
Through weakest darkness to strong light;
By any anguish, give us back
Our life's young standard, pure and bright.
O fair, lost Colors of the soul!
For your sake storm we any height.

ELIZABETH STUART PHELPS WARD

FARRAGUT

(*Mobile Bay, August 5, 1864*)

FARRAGUT, Farragut,
Old Heart of Oak,
Daring Dave Farragut,
Thunderbolt stroke,

Watches the hoary mist
    Lift from the bay,
Till his flag, glory-kissed,
    Greets the young day.

Far, by gray Morgan's walls,
    Looms the black fleet.
Hark, deck to rampart calls
    With the drums' beat!
Buoy your chains overboard,
    While the steam hums;
Men! to the battlement,
    Farragut comes.

See, as the hurricane
    Hurtles in wrath
Squadrons of clouds amain
    Back from its path!
Back to the parapet,
    To the guns' lips,
Thunderbolt Farragut
    Hurls the black ships.

Now through the battle's roar
    Clear the boy sings,
"By the mark fathoms four,"
    While his lead swings.
Steady the wheelman five
    "Nor' by East keep her,"
"Steady," but two alive:
    How the shells sweep her!

Lashed to the mast that sways
    Over red decks,
Over the flame that plays
    Round the torn wrecks,
Over the dying lips
    Framed for a cheer,
Farragut leads his ships,
    Guides the line clear.

On by heights cannon-browed,
While the spars quiver;
Onward still flames the cloud
Where the hulks shiver.
See, yon fort's star is set,
Storm and fire past.
Cheer him, lads—Farragut,
Lashed to the mast!

Oh! while Atlantic's breast
Bears a white sail,
While the Gulf's towering crest
Tops a green vale,
Men thy bold deeds shall tell,
Old Heart of Oak,
Daring Dave Farragut,
Thunderbolt stroke!

William Tuckey Meredith

WARREN'S ADDRESS AT BUNKER HILL

(*June 16-17, 1775*)

STAND! the ground's your own, my braves!
Will ye give it up to slaves?
Will ye look for greener graves?
Hope ye mercy still?
What's the mercy despots feel?
Hear it in that battle-peal!
Read it on yon bristling steel!
Ask it,—ye who will.

Fear ye foes who kill for hire?
Will ye to your homes retire?
Look behind you!—they're afire!
And, before you, see
Who have done it! From the vale
On they come—and will ye quail?
Leaden rain and iron hail
Let their welcome be!

In the God of battles trust!
Die we may,—and die we must:
But, oh, where can dust to dust
  Be consigned so well,
As where heaven its dews shall shed
On the martyred patriot's bed,
And the rocks shall raise their head,
  Of his deeds to tell?

JOHN PIERPONT

IVRY

(March 14, 1590)

NOW glory to the Lord of Hosts, from whom all glories
  are!
And glory to our Sovereign Liege, King Henry of Navarre!
Now let there be the merry sound of music and of dance,
Through thy cornfields green, and sunny vines, oh, pleasant
  land of France!
And thou, Rochelle, our own Rochelle, proud city of the
  waters,
Again let rapture light the eyes of all thy mourning
  daughters.
As thou wert constant in our ills, be joyous in our joy;
For cold, and stiff, and still are they who wrought thy
  walls annoy.
Hurrah! hurrah! a single field hath turned the chance of
  war.
Hurrah! hurrah! for Ivry, and Henry of Navarre.

Oh! how our hearts were beating, when, at the dawn of
  day,
We saw the army of the League drawn out in long array;
With all its priest-led citizens, and all its rebel peers,
And Appenzel's stout infantry, and Egmont's Flemish
  spears.
There rode the brood of false Lorraine, the curses of our
  land;

And dark Mayenne was in the midst, a truncheon in his hand;
And, as we looked on them, we thought of Seine's empurpled flood,
And good Coligni's hoary hair all dabbled with his blood;
And we cried unto the living God, who rules the fate of war,
To fight for His own holy name, and Henry of Navarre.

The King is come to marshal us, in all his armor dressed;
And he has bound a snow-white plume upon his gallant crest.
And looked upon his people, and a tear was in his eye;
He looked upon the traitors, and his glance was stern and high.
Right graciously he smiled on us, as rolled from wing to wing,
Down all our line, a deafening shout: "God save our Lord the King!"
"And if my standard bearer fall, as fall full well he may,
For never saw I promise yet of such a bloody fray,
Press where ye see my white plume shine, amidst the ranks of war,
And be your oriflamme to-day the helmet of Navarre."

Hurrah! the foes are moving. Hark to the mingled din,
Of fife, and steed, and trump, and drum, and roaring culverin.
The fiery Duke is pricking fast across Saint André's plain,
With all the hireling chivalry of Guelders and Almayne.
Now by the lips of those ye love, fair gentlemen of France,
Charge for the Golden Lilies,—upon them with the lance!
A thousand spurs are striking deep, a thousand spears in rest,
A thousand knights are pressing close behind the snow-white crest;
And in they burst, and on they rushed, while, like a guiding star,
Amidst the thickest carnage blazed the helmet of Navarre.

Now, God be praised, the day is ours. Mayenne hath turned his rein;
D'Aumale hath cried for quarter; the Flemish count is slain.
Their ranks are breaking like thin clouds before a Biscay gale;
The field is heaped with bleeding steeds, and flags, and cloven mail.
And then we thought on vengeance, and, all along our van,
"Remember Saint Bartholomew!" was passed from man to man.
But out spake gentle Henry, "No Frenchman is my foe:
Down, down with every foreigner, but let your brethren go."
Oh! was there ever such a knight, in friendship or in war,
As our Sovereign Lord, King Henry, the soldier of Navarre?

Right well fought all the Frenchmen who fought for France to-day;
And many a lordly banner God gave them for a prey.
But we of the religion have borne us best in fight;
And the good Lord of Rosny hath ta'en the cornet white
Our own true Maximilian the cornet white hath ta'en,
The cornet white with crosses black, the flag of false Lorraine.
Up with it high; unfurl it wide; that all the host may know
How God hath humbled the proud house which wrought His Church such woe.
Then on the ground, while trumpets sound their loudest point of war,
Fling the red shreds, a footcloth meet for Henry of Navarre.

Ho! maidens of Vienna; ho! matrons of Lucerne;
Weep, weep, and rend your hair for those who never shall return.
Ho! Philip, send, for charity, thy Mexican pistoles,
That Antwerp monks may sing a mass for thy poor spearmen's souls.

Ho! gallant nobles of the League, look that your arms be bright;
Ho! burghers of St. Genevieve, keep watch and ward to-night;
For our God hath crushed the tyrant, our God hath raised the slave,
And mocked the counsel of the wise, and the valor of the brave.
Then glory to His holy name, from whom all glories are;
And glory to our Sovereign Lord, King Henry of Navarre!

THOMAS BABINGTON MACAULAY

THE FLAG GOES BY

HATS off!
Along the street there comes
A blare of bugles, a ruffle of drums,
A flash of color beneath the sky:
Hats off!
The flag is passing by!

Blue and crimson and white it shines,
Over the steel-tipped, ordered lines.
Hats off!
The colors before us fly;
But more than the flag is passing by:

Sea fights and land fights, grim and great,
Fought to make and to save the State:
Weary marches and sinking ships;
Cheers of victory on dying lips;

Days of plenty and years of peace;
March of a strong land's swift increase;
Equal justice, right and law,
Stately honor and reverend awe;

Sign of a nation, great and strong,
To ward her people from foreign wrong:
Pride and glory and honor,—all
Live in the colors to stand or fall.

Hats off!
Along the street there comes
A blare of bugles, a ruffle of drums;
And loyal hearts are beating high:
Hats off!
The flag is passing by!

HENRY HOLCOMB BENNETT

CONCORD HYMN

BY the rude bridge that arched the flood,
Their flag to April's breeze unfurled,
Here once the embattled farmers stood,
And fired the shot heard round the world.

The foe long since in silence slept;
Alike the conqueror silent sleeps;
And Time the ruined bridge has swept
Down the dark stream which seaward creeps.

On this green bank, by this soft stream,
We set to-day a votive stone;
That memory may their deed redeem,
When, like our sires, our sons are gone.

Spirit, that made those heroes dare
To die, and leave their children free,
Bid Time and Nature gently spare
The shaft we raise to them and thee.

RALPH WALDO EMERSON

PAUL REVERE'S RIDE

LISTEN, my children, and you shall hear
Of the midnight ride of Paul Revere,
On the eighteenth of April, in seventy-five;
Hardly a man is now alive
Who remembers that famous day and year.

He said to his friend, "If the British march
By land or sea from the town to-night,
Hang a lantern aloft in the belfry arch
Of the North Church tower as a signal light,—
One, if by land, and two, if by sea;
And I on the opposite shore will be,
Ready to ride and spread the alarm
Through every Middlesex village and farm,
For the country folk to be up and to arm."

Then he said, "Good night!" and with muffled oar
Silently rowed to the Charlestown shore,
Just as the moon rose over the bay,
Where swinging wide at her moorings lay
The *Somerset*, British man-of-war;
A phantom ship, with each mast and spar
Across the moon like a prison bar,
And a huge black hulk, that was magnified
By its own reflection in the tide.

Meanwhile, his friend, through alley and street,
Wanders and watches with eager ears,
Till in the silence around him he hears
The muster of men at the barrack door,
The sound of arms, and the tramp of feet,
And the measured tread of the grenadiers,
Marching down to their boats on the shore.

Then he climbed the tower of the Old North Church,
By the wooden stairs, with stealthy tread,
To the belfry chamber overhead,

And startled the pigeons from their perch
On the somber rafters, that round him made
Masses and moving shapes of shade,—
By the trembling ladder, steep and tall,
To the highest window in the wall,
Where he paused to listen and look down
A moment on the roofs of the town,
And the moonlight flowing over all.

Beneath, in the churchyard, lay the dead,
In their night encampment on the hill,
Wrapped in silence so deep and still
That he could hear, like a sentinel's tread,
The watchful night wind, as it went
Creeping along from tent to tent,
And seeming to whisper, "All is well!"
A moment only he feels the spell
Of the place and the hour, and the secret dread
Of the lonely belfry and the dead;
For suddenly all his thoughts are bent
On a shadowy something far away,
Where the river widens to meet the bay,—
A line of black that bends and floats
On the rising tide, like a bridge of boats.

Meanwhile, impatient to mount and ride,
Booted and spurred, with a heavy stride
On the opposite shore walked Paul Revere.
Now he patted his horse's side,
Now gazed at the landscape far and near,
Then, impetuous, stamped the earth,
And turned and tightened his saddle-girth;
But mostly he watched with eager search
The belfry-tower of the Old North Church,
As it rose above the graves on the hill,
Lonely and spectral and somber and still.
And lo! as he looks, on the belfry's height
A glimmer, and then a gleam of light!
He springs to the saddle, the bridle he turns,
But lingers and gazes, till full on his sight
A second lamp in the belfry burns!

A hurry of hoofs in a village street,
A shape in the moonlight, a bulk in the dark,
And beneath, from the pebbles, in passing, a spark
Struck out by a steed flying fearless and fleet:
That was all! And yet, through the gloom and the light,
The fate of a nation was riding that night;
And the spark struck out by that steed, in his flight,
Kindled the land into flame with its heat.

He has left the village and mounted the steep,
And beneath him, tranquil and broad and deep,
Is the *Mystic*, meeting the ocean tides;
And under the alders that skirt its edge,
Now soft on the sand, now loud on the ledge,
Is heard the tramp of his steed as he rides.

It was twelve by the village clock,
When he crossed the bridge into Medford town.
He heard the crowing of the cock,
And the barking of the farmer's dog,
And felt the damp of the river fog,
That rises after the sun goes down.

It was one by the village clock,
When he galloped into Lexington.
He saw the gilded weathercock
Swim in the moonlight as he passed.
And the meeting-house windows, blank and bare,
Gaze at him with a spectral glare,
As if they already stood aghast
At the bloody work they would look upon.

It was two by the village clock,
When he came to the bridge in Concord town.
He heard the bleating of the flock,
And the twitter of birds among the trees,
And felt the breath of the morning breeze
Blowing over the meadows brown.
And one was safe and asleep in his bed
Who at the bridge would be first to fall,

Who that day would be lying dead,
Pierced by a British musket-ball.
You know the rest. In the books you have read,
How the British Regulars fired and fled,—
How the farmers gave them ball for ball,
From behind each fence and farmyard wall,
Chasing the red-coats down the lane,
Then crossing the fields to emerge again
Under the trees at the turn of the road,
And only pausing to fire and load.

So through the night rode Paul Revere;
And so through the night went his cry of alarm
To every Middlesex village and farm,—
A cry of defiance and not of fear,
A voice in the darkness, a knock at the door,
And a word that shall echo forevermore!
For, borne on the night wind of the Past,
Through all our history, to the last,
In the hour of darkness and peril and need,
The people will waken and listen to hear
The hurrying hoof beats of that steed,
And the midnight message of Paul Revere.

HENRY WADSWORTH LONGFELLOW

THE CAPTAIN STOOD ON THE CARRONADE

THE captain stood on the carronade—"First lieutenant," says he,
"Send all my merry men aft here, for they must list to me:
I haven't the gift of the gab, my sons—because I'm bred to the sea,
That ship there is a Frenchman, who means to fight with we.
Odds blood, hammer and tongs, long as I've been to sea,
I've fought 'gainst every odds—but I've gained the victory.

"That ship there is a Frenchman, and if we don't take *she*,
'Tis a thousand bullets to one, that she will capture *we;*

I haven't the gift of the gab, my boys, so each man to his gun,
If she's not mine in half-an-hour, I'll flog each mother's son.
Odds bobs, hammer and tongs, long as I've been to sea,
I've fought 'gainst every odds—and I've gained the victory."

We fought for twenty minutes, when the Frenchman had enough,
"I little thought," said he, "that your men were of such stuff."
The captain took the Frenchman's sword, a low bow made to he—
"I haven't the gift of the gab, Monsieur, but polite I wish to be.
Odds bobs, hammer and tongs, long as I've been to sea,
I've fought 'gainst every odds—and I've gained the victory."

Our captain sent for all of us; "My merry men," said he,
"I haven't the gift of the gab, my lads, but yet I thankful be;
You've done your duty handsomely, each man stood to his gun,
If you hadn't, you villains, as sure as day, I'd have flogged each mother's son.
Odds bobs, hammer and tongs, as long as I'm at sea,
I'll fight 'gainst every odds—and I'll gain the victory."

FREDERICK MARRYAT

BROWN OF OSSAWATOMIE

(December 2, 1859)

JOHN BROWN of Ossawatomie spake on his dying day:
"I will not have to shrive my soul a priest in Slavery's pay.
But let some poor slave mother whom I have striven to free,
With her children, from the gallows-stair put up a prayer for me!"

John Brown of Ossawatomie, they led him out to die;
And lo! a poor slave mother with her little child pressed nigh.
Then the bold, blue eye grew tender, and the old harsh face grew mild,
As he stooped between the jeering ranks and kissed the negro's child!

The shadows of his stormy life that moment fell apart;
And they who blamed the bloody hand forgave the loving heart.
That kiss from all its guilty means redeemed the good intent,
And round the grisly fighter's hair the martyr's aureole bent!

Perish with him the folly that seeks through evil good!
Long live the generous purpose unstained with human blood!
Not the raid of midnight terror, but the thought which underlies;
Not the borderer's pride of daring, but the Christian's sacrifice.

Nevermore may yon Blue Ridges the Northern rifle hear,
Nor see the light of blazing homes flash on the negro's spear;
But let the free-winged angel Truth their guarded passes scale,
To teach that right is more than might, and justice more than mail!

So vainly shall Virginia set her battle in array;
In vain her trampling squadrons knead the winter snow with clay.
She may strike the pouncing eagle, but she dares not harm the dove;
And every gate she bars to Hate, shall open wide to Love!

John Greenleaf Whittier

INCIDENT OF THE FRENCH CAMP

YOU know, we French stormed Ratisbon:
  A mile or so away
On a little mound, Napoleon
  Stood on our storming day;
With neck outthrust, you fancy how,
  Legs wide, arms locked behind,
As if to balance the prone brow
  Oppressive with its mind.

Just as, perhaps, he mused, "My plans
  That soar, to earth may fall,
Let once my army leader Lannes
  Waver at yonder wall,"—
Out 'twixt the battery smokes there flew
  A rider, bound on bound
Full-galloping; nor bridle drew
  Until he reached the mound.

Then off there flung in smiling joy,
  And held himself erect
By just his horse's mane, a boy:
  You hardly could suspect—
(So tight he kept his lips compressed,
  Scarce any blood came through),
You looked twice ere you saw his breast
  Was all but shot in two.

"Well," cried he, "Emperor, by God's grace
  We've got you Ratisbon!
The Marshal's in the market place,
  And you'll be there anon
To see your flag bird flap his vans,
  Where I, to heart's desire,
Perched him!" The Chief's eye flashed; his plans
  Soared up again like fire.

The Chief's eye flashed; but presently
  Softened itself, as sheathes
A film the mother eagle's eye

When her bruised eaglet breathes:
"You're wounded!" "Nay," his soldier's pride
Touched to the quick, he said:
"I'm killed, sire!" And, his Chief beside,
Smiling the boy fell dead.

ROBERT BROWNING

COLUMBIA, THE LAND OF THE BRAVE

O COLUMBIA, the gem of the ocean,
The home of the brave and the free,
The shrine of each patriot's devotion,
A world offers homage to thee.
Thy mandates make heroes assemble,
When liberty's form stands in view,
Thy banners make tyranny tremble,
When borne by the Red, White and Blue.

Chorus

When borne by the Red, White and Blue,
When borne by the Red, White and Blue,
Thy banners make tyranny tremble,
When borne by the Red, White and Blue.

When war winged its wide desolation,
And threatened the land to deform,
The ark then of freedom's foundation,
Columbia, rode safe through the storm,
With the garlands of victory around her,
When so proudly she bore her brave crew,
With her flag proudly floating before her,
The boast of the Red, White, and Blue.

Chorus

The wine cup, the wine cup bring hither,
And fill you it true to the brim.
May the wreaths they have won never wither,

Nor the stars of their glory grow dim.
May the service united ne'er sever,
But they to their colors prove true!
The Army and Navy forever!
Three cheers for the Red, White, and Blue!

David T. Shaw

THE SONG IN CAMP

"Give us a song!" the soldiers cried,
The outer trenches guarding,
When the heated guns of the camps allied
Grew weary of bombarding.

The dark Redan, in silent scoff,
Lay, grim and threatening, under;
And the tawny mound of the Malakoff
No longer belched its thunder.

There was a pause. A guardsman said,
"We storm the forts to-morrow;
Sing while we may, another day
Will bring enough of sorrow."

They lay along the battery's side,
Below the smoking cannon:
Brave hearts, from Severn and from Clyde
And from the banks of Shannon.

They sang of love, and not of fame;
Forgot was Britain's glory:
Each heart recalled a different name,
But all sang "Annie Laurie."

Voice after voice caught up the song,
Until its tender passion
Rose like an anthem, rich and strong,—
Their battle eve confession.

Dear girl, her name he dared not speak,
  But, as the song grew louder,
Something upon the soldier's cheek
  Washed off the stains of powder.

Beyond the darkening ocean burned
  The bloody sunset's embers,
While the Crimean valleys learned
  How English love remembers.

And once again a fire of hell
  Rained on the Russian quarters,
With scream of shot and burst of shell,
  And bellowing of the mortars!

And Irish Nora's eyes are dim
  For a singer, dumb and gory;
And English Mary mourns for him
  Who sang of "Annie Laurie."

Sleep, soldiers still in honored rest
  Your truth and valor wearing:
The bravest are the tenderest—
  The loving are the daring.

BAYARD TAYLOR

COLUMBUS

(January, 1487)

ST. STEPHEN'S cloistered hall was proud
  In learning's pomp that day,
For there a robed and stately crowd
  Pressed on in long array.
A mariner with simple chart
  Confronts that conclave high,
While strong ambition stirs his heart,
And burning thoughts of wonder part
  From lip and sparkling eye.

What hath he said? With frowning face,
In whispered tones they speak,
And lines upon their tablets trace,
Which flush each ashen cheek;
The Inquisition's mystic doom
Sits on their brows severe,
And bursting forth in visioned gloom,
Sad heresy from burning tomb
Groans on the startled ear.

Courage, thou Genoese! Old Time
Thy splendid dream shall crown;
Yon Western Hemisphere sublime,
Where unshorn forests frown,
The awful Andes' cloud-wrapped brow,
The Indian hunter's bow,
Bold streams untamed by helm or prow,
And rocks of gold and diamonds, thou
To thankless Spain shalt show.

Courage, World-finder! Thou hast need!
In Fate's unfolding scroll,
Dark woes and ingrate wrongs I read,
That rack the noble soul.
On! on! Creation's secrets probe,
Then drink thy cup of scorn,
And wrapped in fallen Cæsar's robe,
Sleep like that master of the globe,
All glorious,—yet forlorn.

LYDIA HUNTLY SIGOURNEY

MY COUNTRY

(A Patriotic Creed for Americans)

I AM an American.

I love my country because it stands for liberty and against all forms of slavery, tyranny, and unjust privilege.

I love my country because it is a democracy, where the

people govern themselves, and there is no hereditary class to rule them.

I love my country because the only use it has for an army and navy is to defend itself from unjust attack and to protect its citizens.

I love my country because it asks nothing for itself it would not ask for all humanity.

I love my country because it is the land of opportunity; the way to success is open to every person, no matter what his birth or circumstances.

I love my country because every child in it can get an education free in its public schools, and more money is spent on training children here than in any other country.

I love my country because women are respected and honored.

I love my country because we have free speech and a free press.

I love my country because it interferes with no person's religion.

I love my country because its people are industrious, energetic, independent, friendly and have a sense of humor.

I love my country because its heroes are such characters as George Washington and Abraham Lincoln, who loved to serve and not to rule.

I will serve my country in any way I can. I will strive to be a good citizen, and will not do anything nor take part in anything that may wrong the public. I wish to live for my country.

IF NEED BE, I WILL DIE FOR MY COUNTRY.

DR. FRANK CRANE

SONG OF SHERMAN'S MARCH TO THE SEA

(November, 1864)

OUR camp fires shone bright on the mountains
That frowned on the river below,
While we stood by our guns in the morning,
And eagerly watched for the foe;

When a rider came out from the darkness
  That hung over mountain and tree,
And shouted: "Boys, up and be ready,
  For Sherman will march to the sea."

Then cheer upon cheer for bold Sherman
  Went up from each valley and glen,
And the bugles reëchoed the music
  That came from the lips of the men:
For we knew that the stars in our banner
  More bright in their splendor would be,
And that blessings from Northland would greet us
  When Sherman marched down to the sea.

Then forward, boys, forward to battle!
  We marched on our wearisome way,
And we stormed the wild hills of Resaca;
  God bless those who fell on that day!
Then Kenesaw, dark in its glory,
  Frowned down on the flag of the free,
But the East and the West bore our standards,
  And Sherman marched on to the sea.

Still onward we pressed, till our banners
  Swept out from Atlanta's grim walls,
And the blood of the patriot dampened
  The soil where the traitor flag falls;
Yet we paused not to weep for the fallen,
  Who slept by each river and tree;
We twined them a wreath of the laurel
  As Sherman marched down to the sea.

Oh! proud was our army that morning,
  That stood where the pine darkly towers,
When Sherman said: "Boys, you are weary;
  This day fair Savannah is ours!"
Then sang we a song for our chieftain,
  That echoed o'er river and lea,
And the stars in our banner shone brighter
  When Sherman marched down to the sea.

SAMUEL HAWKINS MARSHALL BYERS

BARBARA FRIETCHIE

(September 13, 1862)

UP from the meadows rich with corn,
Clear in the cool September morn,

The clustered spires of Frederick stand
Green-walled by the hills of Maryland.

Round about them orchards sweep,
Apple and peach tree fruited deep,

Fair as the garden of the Lord
To the eyes of the famished rebel horde

On that pleasant morn of the early fall
When Lee marched over the mountain wall;

Over the mountains winding down,
Horse and foot, into Frederick town.

Forty flags with their silver stars,
Forty flags with their crimson bars,

Flapped in the morning wind: the sun
Of noon looked down, and saw not one.

Up rose old Barbara Frietchie then,
Bowed with her fourscore years and ten;

Bravest of all in Frederick town,
She took up the flag the men hauled down;

In her attic window the staff she set,
To show that one heart was loyal yet.

Up the street came the rebel tread,
Stonewall Jackson riding ahead.

Under his slouched hat left and right
He glanced; the old flag met his sight.

"Halt!"—the dust-brown ranks stood fast.
"Fire!"—out blazed the rifle-blast.

It shivered the window, pane and sash;
It rent the banner with seam and gash.

Quick, as it fell, from the broken staff
Dame Barbara snatched the silken scarf.

She leaned far out on the window sill,
And shook it forth with a royal will.

"Shoot, if you must, this old gray head,
But spare your country's flag," she said.

A shade of sadness, a blush of shame,
Over the face of the leader came;

The nobler nature within him stirred
To life at that woman's deed and word;

"Who touches a hair of yon gray head
Dies like a dog! March on!" he said.

All day long through Frederick street
Sounded the tread of marching feet:

All day long that free flag tossed
Over the heads of the rebel host.

Ever its torn folds rose and fell
On the loyal winds that loved it well;

And through the hill gaps sunset light
Shone over it with a warm good night.

Barbara Frietchie's work is o'er,
And the Rebel rides on his raids no more.

Honor to her! and let a tear
Fall, for her sake, on Stonewall's bier.

Over Barbara Frietchie's grave,
Flag of Freedom and Union, wave!

Peace and order and beauty draw
Round thy symbol of light and law;

And ever the stars above look down
On thy stars below in Frederick town!

JOHN GREENLEAF WHITTIER

OLD IRONSIDES

(September 14, 1830)

AY, tear her tattered ensign down!
Long has it waved on high,
And many an eye has danced to see
That banner in the sky;
Beneath it rung the battle shout,
And burst the cannon's roar;—
The meteor of the ocean air
Shall sweep the clouds no more.

Her deck, once red with heroes' blood,
Where knelt the vanquished foe,
When winds were hurrying o'er the flood,
And waves were white below,
No more shall feel the victor's tread,
Or know the conquered knee;—
The harpies of the shore shall pluck
The eagle of the sea!

Oh, better that her shattered hulk
Should sink beneath the wave;
Her thunders shook the mighty deep,
And there should be her grave;
Nail to the mast her holy flag,
Set every threadbare sail,
And give her to the god of storms,
The lightning and the gale!

OLIVER WENDELL HOLMES

THE LEAK IN THE DIKE

THE good dame looked from her cottage
At the close of the pleasant day,
And cheerily called to her little son
Outside the door at play:
"Come, Peter, come! I want you to go,
While there is yet light to see,
To the hut of the blind old man who lives
Across the dike, for me;
And take these cakes I made for him—
They are hot and smoking yet;
You have time enough to go and come
Before the sun is set."

Then the good wife turned to her labor,
Humming a simple song,
And thought of her husband, working hard
At the sluices all day long;
And set the turf a-blazing,
And brought the coarse, black bread,
That he might find a fire at night,
And see the table spread.

And Peter left the brother
With whom all day he had played,
And the sister who had watched their sports
In the willow's tender shade;
And told them they'd see him back before
They saw a star in sight—
Though he wouldn't be afraid to go
In the very darkest night!
For he was a brave, bright fellow,
With eye and conscience clear;
He could do whatever a boy might do,
And he had not learned to fear.
Why, he wouldn't have robbed a bird's nest,
Nor brought a stork to harm,
Though never a law in Holland
Had stood to stay his arm!

And now, with his face all glowing,
  And eyes as bright as the day
With the thoughts of his pleasant errand,
  He trudged along the way;
And soon his joyous prattle
  Made glad a lonesome place—
Alas! if only the blind old man
  Could have seen that happy face!
Yet he somehow caught the brightness
  Which his voice and presence lent;
And he felt the sunshine come and go
  As Peter came and went.

And now, as the day was sinking,
  And the winds began to rise,
The mother looked from her door again,
  Shading her anxious eyes,
And saw the shadows deepen,
  And birds to their homes come back,
But never a sign of Peter
  Along the level track.
But she said, "He will come at morning,
  So I need not fret or grieve—
Though it isn't like my boy at all
  To stay without my leave."

But where was the child delaying?
  On the homeward way was he,
And across the dike while the sun was up
  An hour above the sea.
He was stooping now to gather flowers;
  Now listening to the sound,
As the angry waters dashed themselves
  Against their narrow bound.
"Ah! well for us," said Peter,
  "That the gates are good and strong,
And my father tends them carefully,
  Or they would not hold you long!
You're a wicked sea," said Peter;
  "I know why you fret and chafe;
You would like to spoil our lands and homes;
  But our sluices keep you safe!"

But hark! through the noise of waters
  Comes a low, clear, trickling sound;
And the child's face pales with terror,
  As his blossoms drop to the ground.
He is up the bank in a moment,
  And, stealing through the sand,
He sees a stream not yet so large
  As his slender, childish hand.
'Tis a leak in the dike! He is but a boy,
  Unused to fearful scenes;
But, young as he is, he has learned to know
  The dreadful thing that means.
A leak in the dike! The stoutest heart
  Grows faint that cry to hear,
And the bravest man in all the land
  Turns white with mortal fear.
For he knows the smallest leak may grow
  To a flood in a single night;
And he knows the strength of the cruel sea
  When loosed in its angry might.

And the boy! He has seen the danger,
  And, shouting a wild alarm,
He forces back the weight of the sea
  With the strength of his single arm!
He listens for the joyful sound
  Of a footstep passing nigh;
And lays his ear to the ground, to catch
  The answer to his cry,—
And he hears the rough winds blowing,
  And the waters rise and fall,
But never an answer comes to him
  Save the echo of his call.

He sees no hope, no succor,
  His feeble voice is lost;
Yet what shall he do but watch and wait,
  Though he perish at his post!
So, faintly calling and crying
  Till the sun is under the sea;
Crying and moaning till the stars

Come out for company;
He thinks of his brother and sister,
Asleep in their safe, warm bed;
He thinks of dear father and mother;
Of himself as dying, and dead;
And of how, when the night is over,
They must come and find him at last;
But he never thinks he can leave the place
Where duty holds him fast.

The good dame in the cottage
Is up and astir with the light,
For the thought of her little Peter
Has been with her all the night.
And now she watches the pathway,
As yester-eve she had done;
But what does she see so strange and black
Against the rising sun?
Her neighbors are bearing between them
Something straight to her door;
Her child is coming home, but not
As he ever came before!

"He is dead!" she cries; "my darling!"
And the startled father hears,
And comes and looks the way she looks,
And fears the thing she fears;
Till a glad shout from the bearers
Thrills the stricken man and wife—
"Give thanks, for your son has saved our land,
And God has saved his life!"
So, there in the morning sunshine
They knelt about the boy;
And every head was bared and bent
In tearful, reverent joy.

'Tis many a year since then; but still,
When the sea roars like a flood,
Their boys are taught what a boy can do
Who is brave and true and good.
For every man in that country

Takes his son by the hand,
And tells him of little Peter,
Whose courage saved the land.

They have many a valiant hero,
Remembered through the years;
But never one whose name so oft
Is named with loving tears.
And his deed shall be sung by the cradle,
And told to the child on the knee,
So long as the dikes of Holland
Divide the land from the sea!

PHŒBE CARY

HOW THEY BROUGHT THE GOOD NEWS FROM GHENT TO AIX

I SPRANG to the stirrup, and Joris, and he;
I galloped, Dirck galloped, we galloped all three;
"Good speed!" cried the watch, as the gate-bolts undrew;
"Speed!" echoed the wall to us galloping through;
Behind shut the postern, the lights sank to rest,
And into the midnight we galloped abreast.

Not a word to each other; we kept the great pace
Neck by neck, stride by stride, never changing our place;
I turned in my saddle and made its girths tight,
Then shortened each stirrup, and set the pique right,
Rebuckled the cheek strap, chained slacker the bit,
Nor galloped less steadily Roland a whit.

'Twas moonset at starting; but while we drew near
Lokeren, the cocks crew and twilight dawned clear;
At Boom, a great yellow star came out to see;
At Düffeld, 'twas morning as plain as could be;
And from Mecheln church steeple we heard the half-chime,
So Joris broke silence with, "Yet there is time!"

At Aershot, up leaped of a sudden the sun,
And against him the cattle stood black every one,
To stare through the mist at us galloping past,
And I saw my stout galloper Roland at last,
With resolute shoulders, each butting away
The haze, as some bluff river headland its spray:

And his low head and crest, just one sharp ear bent back
For my voice, and the other pricked out on his track;
And one eye's black intelligence,—ever that glance
O'er its white edge at me, his own master, askance!
And the thick heavy spume flakes which aye and anon
His fierce lips shook upwards in galloping on.

By Hasselt, Dirck groaned; and cried Joris "Stay spur!
Your Roos galloped bravely, the fault's not in her,
We'll remember at Aix"—for one heard the quick wheeze
Of her chest, saw the stretched neck and staggering knees,
And sunk tail, and horrible heave of the flank,
As down on her haunches she shuddered and sank.

So, we were left galloping, Joris and I,
Past Looze and past Tongres, no cloud in the sky;
The broad sun above laughed a pitiless laugh,
'Neath our feet broke the brittle bright stubble like chaff;
Till over by Dalhem a dome-spire sprang white,
And "Gallop," gasped Joris, "for Aix is in sight!

"How they'll greet us!"—and all in a moment his roan
Rolled neck and croup over, lay dead as a stone;
And there was my Roland to bear the whole weight
Of the news which alone could save Aix from her fate,
With his nostrils like pits full of blood to the brim,
And with circles of red for his eye sockets' rim.

Then I cast loose my buffcoat, each holster let fall,
Shook off both my jack boots, let go belt and all,
Stood up in the stirrup, leaned, patted his ear,
Called my Roland his pet name, my horse without peer;
Clapped my hands, laughed and sang, any noise, bad or
good,
Till at length into Aix Roland galloped and stood.

And all I remember is,—friends flocking round
As I sat with his head 'twixt my knees on the ground;
And no voice but was praising this Roland of mine,
As I poured down his throat our last measure of wine,
Which (the burgesses voted by common consent)
Was no more than his due who brought good news from
Ghent.

ROBERT BROWNING

THE MINSTREL BOY

THE Minstrel boy to the war is gone,
In the ranks of death you'll find him;
His father's sword he has girded on,
And his wild harp slung behind him,
"Land of song!" said the warrior-bard,
"Though all the world betrays thee,
One sword, at least, thy rights shall guard,
One faithful harp shall praise thee!"

The Minstrel fell!—but the foeman's chain
Could not bring his proud soul under;
The harp he loved ne'er spoke again,
For he tore its chords asunder;
And said, "No chains shall sully thee,
Thou soul of love and bravery!
Thy songs were made for the pure and free,
They shall never sound in slavery!"

THOMAS MOORE

MOLLY MAGUIRE AT MONMOUTH

ON the bloody field of Monmouth
Flashed the guns of Greene and Wayne.
Fiercely roared the tide of battle,
Thick the sward was heaped with slain.

Foremost, facing death and danger,
  Hessian, horse, and grenadier,
In the vanguard, fiercely fighting,
  Stood an Irish Cannonier.

Loudly roared his iron cannon,
  Mingling ever in the strife,
And beside him, firm and daring,
  Stood his faithful Irish wife.
Of her bold contempt of danger
  Greene and Lee's Brigades could tell,
Every one knew "Captain Molly,"
  And the army loved her well.

Surged the roar of battle round them,
  Swiftly flew the iron hail,
Forward dashed a thousand bayonets,
  That lone battery to assail.
From the foeman's foremost columns
  Swept a furious fusillade,
Mowing down the massed battalions
  In the ranks of Greene's Brigade.

Fast and faster worked the gunner,
  Soiled with powder, blood, and dust,
English bayonets shone before him,
  Shot and shell around him burst;
Still he fought with reckless daring,
  Stood and manned her long and well,
Till at last the gallant fellow
  Dead—beside his cannon fell.

With a bitter cry of sorrow,
  And a dark and angry frown,
Looked that band of gallant patriots
  At their gunner stricken down.
"Fall back, comrades, it is folly
  Thus to strive against the foe."
"No! not so," cried Irish Molly;
  "We can strike another blow."

Quickly leapt she to the cannon,
In her fallen husband's place,
Sponged and rammed it fast and steady,
Fired it in the foeman's face.
Flashed another ringing volley,
Roared another from the gun;
"Boys, hurrah!" cried gallant Molly,
"For the flag of Washington!"

Greene's brigade, though shorn and shattered,
Slain and bleeding half their men,
When they heard that Irish slogan,
Turned and charged the foe again.
Knox and Wayne and Morgan rally,
To the front they forward wheel,
And before their rushing onset
Clinton's English columns reel.

Still the cannon's voice in anger
Rolled and rattled o'er the plain,
Till there lay in swarms around it
Mangled heaps of Hessian slain.
"Forward! charge them with the bayonet!"
'Twas the voice of Washington,
And there burst a fiery greeting
From the Irish woman's gun.

Monckton falls; against his columns
Leap the troops of Wayne and Lee,
And before their reeking bayonets
Clinton's red battalions flee.
Morgan's rifles, fiercely flashing,
Thin the foe's retreating ranks,
And behind them onward dashing
Ogden hovers on their flanks.

Fast they fly, these boasting Britons,
Who in all their glory came,
With their brutal Hessian hirelings
To wipe out our country's name.

Proudly floats the starry banner,
  Monmouth's glorious field is won,
And in triumph Irish Molly
  Stands beside her smoking gun.

William Collins

THE AMERICAN FLAG

When freedom, from her mountain height
  Unfurl'd her standard to the air,
She tore the azure robe of night,
  And set the stars of glory there.
She mingled with its gorgeous dyes
The milky baldric of the skies,
And striped its pure, celestial white,
With streakings of the morning light;
Then from his mansion in the sun
She call'd her eagle bearer down;
And gave into his mighty hand
The symbol of her chosen land.

* * * * * * *

Flag of the seas! on ocean wave
Thy stars shall glitter o'er the brave;
When death, careering on the gale,
Sweeps darkly round the bellied sail,
And frighted waves rush wildly back
Before the broadside's reeling rack,
Each dying wanderer of the sea
Shall look at once to heaven and thee,
And smile to see thy splendors fly
In triumph o'er his closing eye.

Flag of the free heart's hope and home!
  By angel hands to valor given;
Thy stars have lit the welkin dome,
  And all thy hues were born in heaven.

For ever float that standard sheet!
  Where breathes the foe but falls before us,
With freedom's soil beneath our feet
  And freedom's banner streaming o'er us?

JOSEPH RODMAN DRAKE

INDIAN NAMES

YE say they all have passed away,
  That noble race and brave;
That their light canoes have vanished
  From off the crested wave;
That, mid the forests where they roamed,
  There rings no hunter's shout;
But their name is on your waters,
  Ye may not wash it out.

'Tis where Ontario's billow
  Like ocean's surge is curled,
Where strong Niagara's thunders wake
  The echo of the world,
Where red Missouri bringeth
  Rich tribute from the west,
And Rappahannock sweetly sleeps
  On green Virginia's breast.

Ye say their conelike cabins,
  That clustered o'er the vale,
Have disappeared, as withered leaves
  Before the autumn's gale;
But their memory liveth on your hills,
  Their baptism on your shore,
Your everlasting rivers speak
  Their dialect of yore.

Old Massachusetts wears it
  Within her lordly crown,
And broad Ohio bears it
  Amid his young renown.

Connecticut hath wreathed it
  Where her quiet foliage waves,
And bold Kentucky breathes it hoarse
  Through all her ancient caves.

Wachusett hides its lingering voice
  Within its rocky heart,
And Alleghany graves its tone
  Throughout his lofty chart.
Monadnock, on his forehead hoar,
  Doth seal the sacred trust,
Your mountains build their monument,
  Though ye destroy their dust.

LYDIA HUNTLY SIGOURNEY

POCAHONTAS

WEARIED arm and broken sword
  Wage in vain the desperate fight:
Round him press a countless horde,
  He is but a single knight.
Hark a cry of triumph shrill
  Through the wilderness resounds,
  As with twenty bleeding wounds
Sinks the warrior fighting still.

Now they heap the fatal pyre,
  And the torch of death they light;
Ah! 'tis hard to die of fire!
  Who will shield the captive knight?
Round the stake with fiendish cry
  Wheel and dance the savage crowd,
  Cold the victim's mien and proud,
And his breast is bared to die.

Who will shield the fearless heart?
  Who avert the murderous blade?
From the throng, with sudden start,
  See! there springs an Indian maid.

Quick she stands before the knight:
  "Loose the chain, unbind the ring;
  I am daughter of the king,
And I claim the Indian right!"

Dauntlessly aside she flings
  Lifted ax and thirsty knife;
Fondly to his heart she clings,
  And her bosom guards his life!
In the woods of Powhattan,
  Still 'tis told by Indian fires,
  How a daughter of their sires
Saved the captive Englishman.

WILLIAM MAKEPEACE THACKERAY

THE LANDING OF THE PILGRIM FATHERS

(November 19, 1620)

THE breaking waves dashed high
  On a stern and rock-bound coast,
And the woods, against a stormy sky,
  Their giant branches tossed;

And the heavy night hung dark
  The hills and waters o'er,
When a band of exiles moored their bark
  On the wild New England shore.

Not as the conqueror comes,
  They, the true-hearted, came:
Not with the roll of the stirring drums,
  And the trumpet that sings of fame;

Not as the flying come,
  In silence and in fear,—
They shook the depths of the desert's gloom
  With their hymns of lofty cheer.

Amidst the storm they sang,
  And the stars heard, and the sea;
And the sounding aisles of the dim woods rang
  To the anthem of the free!

The ocean-eagle soared
  From his nest by the white wave's foam,
And the rocking pines of the forest roared;
  This was their welcome home!

There were men with hoary hair
  Amidst that pilgrim band;
Why had they come to wither there,
  Away from their childhood's land?

There was woman's fearless eye,
  Lit by her deep love's truth;
There was manhood's brow, serenely high,
  And the fiery heart of youth.

What sought they thus afar?
  Bright jewels of the mine?
The wealth of seas, the spoils of war?
  They sought a faith's pure shrine!

Aye, call it holy ground,
  The soil where first they trod!
They have left unstained what there they found—
  Freedom to worship God!

FELICIA DOROTHEA HEMANS

BANNOCKBURN

(Robert Bruce's address to his army)

SCOTS, wha hae wi' Wallace bled,
  Scots, wham Bruce has aften led;
Welcome to your gory bed,
  Or to victorie.

Now's the day, and now's the hour;
See the front o' battle lower;
See approach proud Edward's power—
Chains and slaverie!

Wha will be a traitor knave?
Wha can fill a coward's grave?
Wha sae base as be a slave?
Let him turn and flee!

Wha for Scotland's King and law
Freedom's sword will strongly draw,
Freeman stand, or freeman fa'?
Let him follow me!

By oppression's woes and pains!
By your sons in servile chains!
We will drain our dearest veins,
But they shall be free!

Lay the proud usurpers low!
Tyrants fall in every foe!
Liberty's in every blow!
Let us do, or die!

Robert Burns

THE REVENGE

(A Ballad of the Fleet, September, 1591)

At Florés in the Azores Sir Richard Grenville lay,
And a pinnace, like a fluttered bird, came flying from far away:
"Spanish ships of war at sea! we have sighted fifty-three!"
Then sware Lord Thomas Howard: "'Fore God I am no coward;
But I cannot meet them here, for my ships are out of gear,
And the half my men are sick. I must fly, but follow quick.
We are six ships of the line; can we fight with fifty-three?"

Then spake Sir Richard Grenville: "I know you are no
coward;
You fly them for a moment to fight with them again.
But I've ninety men and more that are lying sick ashore.
I should count myself the coward if I left them, my Lord
Howard,
To these Inquisition dogs and the devildoms of Spain."

So Lord Howard passed away with five ships of war that
day,
Till he melted like a cloud in the silent summer heaven;
But Sir Richard bore in hand all his sick men from the
land
Very carefully and slow,
Men of Bideford in Devon,
And we laid them on the ballast down below;
For we brought them all aboard,
And they blessed him in their pain, that they were not left
to Spain,
To the thumbscrew and the stake, for the glory of the Lord.

He had only a hundred seamen to work the ship and to fight,
And he sailed away from Florés till the Spaniard came in
sight,
With his huge sea castles heaving upon the weather bow.
"Shall we fight or shall we fly?
Good Sir Richard, tell us now,
For to fight is but to die!
There'll be little of us left by the time this sun be set."
And Sir Richard said again: "We be all good English men.
Let us bang these dogs of Seville, the children of the devil,
For I never turned my back upon Don or devil yet."

Sir Richard spoke and he laughed, and we roared a hurrah,
and so
The little *Revenge* ran on sheer into the heart of the foe,
With her hundred fighters on deck, and her ninety sick
below;

For half of their fleet to the right and half to the left were
seen,
And the little *Revenge* ran on through the long sea lane
between.

Thousands of their soldiers looked down from their decks
and laughed,
Thousands of their seamen made mock at the mad little craft
Running on and on, till delayed
By their mountainlike *San Philip* that, of fifteen hundred
tons,
And up-shadowing high above us with her yawning tiers
of guns,
Took the breath from our sails, and we stayed.

And while now the great *San Philip* hung above us like a
cloud
Whence the thunderbolt will fall
Long and loud,
Four galleons drew away
From the Spanish fleet that day,
And two upon the larboard and two upon starboard lay,
And the battle thunder broke from them all.

But anon the great *San Philip*, she bethought herself and
went,
Having that within her womb that had left her ill content;
And the rest, they came aboard us, and they fought us hand
to hand,
For a dozen times they came with their pikes and musque-
teers,
And a dozen times we shook 'em off as a dog that shakes
his ears
When he leaps from the water to the land.

And the sun went down, and the stars came out far over
the summer sea,
But never a moment ceased the fight of the one and the
fifty-three,

Ship after ship, the whole night long, their high-built galleons came,
Ship after ship, the whole night long, drew back with her dead and her shame.
For some were sunk and many were shattered, and so could fight us no more—
God of battles, was ever a battle like this in the world before?

For he said, "Fight on! fight on!"
Though his vessel was all but a wreck;
And it chanced that, when half of the short summer night was gone,
With a grisly wound to be dressed he had left the deck,
But a bullet struck him that was dressing it suddenly dead,
And himself he was wounded again in the side and the head,
And he said, "Fight on! fight on!"

And the night went down, and the sun smiled out far over the summer sea,
And the Spanish fleet with broken sides lay round us all in a ring;
But they dared not touch us again, for they feared that we still could sting,
So they watched what the end would be.
And we had not fought them in vain,
But in perilous plight were we,
Seeing forty of our poor hundred were slain,
And half of the rest of us maimed for life
In the crash of the cannonades and the desperate strife;
And the sick men down in the hold were most of them stark and cold,
And the pikes were all broken or bent, and the powder was all of it spent;
And the masts and the rigging were lying over the side;
But Sir Richard cried in his English pride,
"We have fought such a fight for a day and a night
As may never be fought again!
We have won great glory, my men!
And a day less or more
At sea or ashore,

We die—does it matter when?
Sink me the ship, Master Gunner—sink her, split her in twain!
Fall into the hands of God, not into the hands of Spain!"

And the gunner said, "Ay, ay," but the seamen made reply:
"We have children, we have wives,
And the Lord hath spared our lives.
We will make the Spaniard promise, if we yield, to let us go;
We shall live to fight again and to strike another blow."
And the lion there lay dying, and they yielded to the foe.

And the stately Spanish men to their flagship bore him then,
Where they laid him by the mast, old Sir Richard caught at last,
And they praised him to his face with their courtly foreign grace;
But he rose upon their decks, and cried:
"I have fought for Queen and Faith like a valiant man and true;
I have only done my duty as a man is bound to do.
With a joyful spirit I Sir Richard Grenville die!"
And he fell upon their decks, and he died.

And they stared at the dead that had been so valiant and true,
And had holden the power and glory of Spain so cheap
That he dared her with one little ship and his English few;
Was he devil or man? He was devil for aught they knew,
But they sank his body with honor down into the deep,
And they manned the *Revenge* with a swarthier alien crew,
And away she sailed with her loss and longed for her own;
When a wind from the lands they had ruined awoke from sleep,
And the water began to heave and the weather to moan,
And or ever that evening ended a great gale blew,
And a wave like the wave that is raised by an earthquake grew,

Till it smote on their hulls and their sails and their masts
and their flags,
And the whole sea plunged and fell on the shot-shattered
navy of Spain,
And the little *Revenge* herself went down by the island
crags
To be lost evermore in the main.

Alfred Tennyson

CASABIANCA

THE boy stood on the burning deck,
Whence all but him had fled;
The flame that lit the battle's wreck
Shone round him o'er the dead.

Yet beautiful and bright he stood,
As born to rule the storm;
A creature of heroic blood,
A proud though childlike form.

The flames rolled on—he would not go
Without his father's word;
That father, faint in death below,
His voice no longer heard.

He called aloud, "Say, father, say
If yet my task is done?"
He knew not that the chieftain lay
Unconscious of his son.

"Speak, father!" once again he cried,
"If I may yet be gone!"
And but the booming shots replied,
And fast the flames rolled on.

Upon his brow he felt their breath,
And in his waving hair;
And looked from that lone post of death,
In still, yet brave despair.

And shouted but once more aloud
  "My father! must I stay?"
While o'er him fast, through sail and shroud,
  The wreathing fires made way.

They wrapt the ship in splendor wild,
  They caught the flag on high,
And streamed above the gallant child
  Like banners in the sky.

Then came a burst of thunder sound—
  The boy—oh! where was he?
—Ask of the winds that far around
  With fragments strew the sea;

With mast, and helm, and pennon fair,
  That well had borne their part—
But the noblest thing that perished there
  Was that young, faithful heart.

Felicia Hemans

WASHINGTON

SOLDIER and statesman, rarest unison;
High poised example of great duties done
Simply as breathing, a world's honors worn
As life's indifferent gifts to all men born;
Dumb for himself, unless it were to God,
But for his barefoot soldiers eloquent,
Tramping the snow to corral where they trod,
Held by his awe in hollow-eyed content;
Modest, yet firm as Nature's self; unblamed
Save by the men his nobler temper shamed;
Never seduced through show of present good
By other than unsettling lights to steer
New-trimmed in Heaven, nor than his steadfast mood
More steadfast, far from rashness as from fear;

Rigid, but with himself first, grasping still
In swerveless poise the wave-beat helm of will;
Not honored then or now because he wooed
The popular voice, but that he still withstood;
Broad-minded, higher souled, there is but one
Who was all this and ours, and all men's—WASHINGTON.

JAMES RUSSELL LOWELL

O CAPTAIN! MY CAPTAIN!

O CAPTAIN! my Captain! our fearful trip is done,
The ship has weather'd every rock, the prize we sought is won,
The port is near, the bells I hear, the people all exulting,
While follow eyes the steady keel, the vessel grim and daring;
But O heart! heart! heart!
O the bleeding drops of red,
Where on the deck my Captain lies,
Fallen cold and dead.

O Captain! my Captain! rise up and hear the bells:
Rise up—for you the flag is flung—for you the bugle trills,
For you bouquets and ribbon'd wreaths—for you the shores a-crowding,
For you they call, the swaying mass, their eager faces turning;
Here, Captain! dear father!
This arm beneath your head!
It is some dream that on the deck
You've fallen cold and dead.

My Captain does not answer, his lips are pale and still,
My father does not feel my arm, he has no pulse nor will,
The ship is anchor'd safe and sound, its voyage closed and done,
From fearful trip the victor ship comes in with object won;

Exult O shores! and ring, O bells!
  But I with mournful tread,
Walk the deck my Captain lies,
  Fallen cold and dead.

WALT WHITMAN

WHEELER AT SANTIAGO

INTO the thick of the fight he went, pallid and sick and wan,
Borne in an ambulance to the front, a ghostly wisp of a man;
But the fighting soul of a fighting man, approved in the long ago,
Went to the front in that ambulance, and the body of Fighting Joe.

Out from the front they were coming back, smitten of Spanish shells—
Wounded boys from the Vermont hills and the Alabama dells;
"Put them into this ambulance; I'll ride to the front," he said,
And he climbed to the saddle and rode right on, that little old ex-Confed.

From end to end of the long blue ranks rose up the ringing cheers,
And many a powder-blackened face was furrowed with sudden tears,
As with flashing eyes and gleaming sword, and hair and beard of snow,
Into the hell of shot and shell rode little old Fighting Joe!

Sick with fever and racked with pain, he could not stay away,
For he heard the song of the yesteryears in the deep-mouthed cannon's bay—

He heard in the calling song of the guns there was work
for him to do,
Where his country's best blood splashed and flowed 'round
the old Red, White and Blue.

Fevered body and hero heart! This Union's heart to you
Beats out in love and reverence—and to each dear boy in
blue
Who stood or fell 'mid the shot and shell, and cheered in
the face of the foe,
As, wan and white, to the heart of the fight rode little old
Fighting Joe!

JAMES LINDSAY GORDON

THE BATTLE-HYMN OF THE REPUBLIC

MINE eyes have seen the glory of the coming of the
Lord;
He is trampling out the vintage where the grapes of wrath
are stored;
He hath loosed the fateful lightning of his terrible swift
sword:
His truth is marching on.

I have seen him in the watch fires of a hundred circling
camps;
They have builded him an altar in the evening dews and
damps;
I can read his righteous sentence by the dim and flaring
lamps:
His day is marching on.

I have read a fiery gospel, writ in burnished rows of steel:
"As ye deal with my contemners, so with you my grace shall
deal;
Let the Hero, born of woman, crush the serpent with his
heel,
Since God is marching on."

He has sounded forth the trumpet that shall never call
retreat;
He is sifting out the hearts of men before his judgment
seat;
Oh, be swift, my soul, to answer him! be jubilant, my feet!
Our God is marching on.

In the beauty of the lilies Christ was born across the sea,
With a glory in his bosom that transfigures you and me;
As he died to make men holy, let us die to make men free,
While God is marching on.

JULIA WARD HOWE

A LEGEND OF THE DECLARATION

A HUNDRED years and more have fled
Since brave Columbia burst the chains
That tyranny and avarice wed.
Then liberty was yet a dream—
A hymn still sung in whispered strains—
A first gray dawn, a herald beam
Of freedom's sun.

'Twas then oppression's ruthless hand
Was striving to regain its prey,
And spread dismay throughout the land.
Heroic souls at once convened
To crush a hatred monarch's sway,
Whose dastard rule had fully weaned
His subject's love.

Each colony her chosen sent
To Philadelphia's spacious hall,
The people's will to represent.
Success would crown them patriots brave—
One thing was needful to them all,
Or each might find a traitor's grave—
'Twas unanimity.

The Continental Congress met;
Each delegate had said his say,
Save one, who had not spoken yet.
With us the vote remained a tie:
Good Pennsylvania held the sway—
'Twas she who now must cast the die,
To wreck or save.

John Morton's called; all eyes are strained—
The federal arch is almost built—
The arch that freedom's God ordained.
He voted right, all undismayed
E'en though his true heart's blood be spilt—
And thus he nobly, safely laid
The Keystone.

And so the mighty deed was done,
That makes us what we are to-day,
By which our sovereign right was won.
John Morton gained eternal fame,
'Twill last with Independence Day,
And Pennsylvania gained a name—
The Keystone State.

George M. Vickers

IN FLANDERS FIELDS

In Flanders fields the poppies blow
Between the crosses, row on row,
That mark our place, and in the sky
The larks, still bravely singing, fly
Scarce heard amid the guns below.

We are the Dead! Short days ago
We lived, felt dawn, saw sunset glow,
Loved and were loved, and now we lie
In Flanders fields.

Take up our quarrel with the foe!
To you from failing hands we throw
The Torch. Be yours to hold it high!
If ye break faith with us who die
We shall not sleep, though poppies grow,
In Flanders fields.

LIEUT. COL. JOHN D. MCCRAE

WE'LL FLING THE STARRY BANNER OUT

WE'LL fling the Starry Banner out,
That nations from afar
May read of freedom's holy light
Grafted in stripe and star.

We'll fling the Starry Banner out,
Because it tells a story,
Of days that prompted sons and sires
To deeds of love and glory.

We'll fling the Starry Banner out,
From Maine to Golden Gate;
It breathes a love for liberty,
That kings and tyrants hate.

We'll fling the Starry Banner out,
That patriot hands unfurled;
Proudly it floats o'er land and sea,
A lamp to light the world.

We'll fling the Starry Banner out,
Nor shall a star be riven
From out its field of blue so bright,
And typical of heaven.

We'll fling the Starry Banner out,
And guard with greatest care,
Its stripes and stars, and field of blue,
In peace as well as war.

We'll fling the Starry Banner out,
  So that it may become
The pride of every patriot's heart,
  And a joy in every home.

WILLIAM F. KNOTT

AMERICA'S ANSWER

REST ye in peace, ye Flanders dead.
The fight that ye so bravely led
We've taken up. And we will keep
True faith with you who lie asleep
With each a cross to mark his bed,
And poppies blowing overhead,
Where once his own life blood ran red.
So let your rest be sweet and deep
   In Flanders fields.

Fear not that ye have died for naught.
The torch ye threw to us we caught.
Ten million hands will hold it high,
And Freedom's light shall never die!
We've learned the lesson that ye taught
   In Flanders fields.

R. W. LILLARD

RODNEY'S RIDE

(July 3, 1776)

IN that soft midland where the breezes bear
The North and the South on the genial air,
Through the county of Kent, on affairs of state,
Rode Cæsar Rodney, the delegate

Burly and big, and bold and bluff,
In his three-cornered hat and coat of snuff,
A foe to King George and the English State,
Was Cæsar Rodney, the delegate.

Into Dover village he rode apace,
And his kinsfolk knew, from his anxious face,
It was matter grave that brought him there,
To the counties three on the Delaware.

"Money and men we must have," he said,
"Or the Congress fails and our cause is dead;
Give us both and the King shall not work his will.
We are men, since the blood of Bunker Hill!"

Comes a rider swift on a panting bay:
"Ho, Rodney, ho! you must save the day,
For the Congress halts at a deed so great,
And your vote alone may decide its fate."

Answered Rodney then: "I will ride with speed;
It is Liberty's stress; it is Freedom's need.
When stands it?" "To-night. Not a moment to spare,
But ride like the wind from the Delaware."

"Ho, saddle the black! I've but half a day,
And the Congress sits eighty miles away—
And I'll be in time, if God grants me grace,
To shake my fist in King George's face."

He is up; he is off! and the black horse flies
On the northward road ere the "God speed" dies;
It is gallop and spur, as the leagues they clear,
And the clustering milestones move a-rear.

It is two of the clock; and the fleet hoofs fling
The Fieldboro's dust with a clang and a cling;
It is three; and he gallops with slack rein where
The road winds down to the Delaware.

Four; and he spurs into New Castle town,
From his panting steed he gets him down—
"A fresh one, quick! not a moment's wait!"
And off speeds Rodney, the delegate.

It is five; and the beams of the western sun
Tinge the spires of the Wilmington gold and dun;
Six; and the dust of Chester Street
Flies back in a cloud from the courser's feet.

It is seven; the horse boat broad of beam,
At the Schuylkill ferry crawls over the stream—
And at seven-fifteen by the Rittenhouse clock,
He flings his reins to the tavern jock.

The Congress is met; the debate's begun,
And Liberty lags for the vote of one—
When into the hall, not a moment late,
Walks Cæsar Rodney, the delegate.

Not a moment late! and that half day's ride
Forwards the world with a mighty stride;
For the act was passed; ere the midnight stroke
O'er the Quaker City its echoes woke.

At Tyranny's feet was the gauntlet flung;
"We are free!" all the bells through the colonies rung.
And the sons of the free may recall with pride
The day of Delegate Rodney's ride.

Elbridge Streeter Brooks

MY NATIVE LAND

Breathes there a man with soul so dead,
Who never to himself hath said,
"This is my own—my native land!"
Whose heart hath ne'er within him burned,
As home his footsteps he hath turned,
From wandering on a foreign strand?

If such there breathe, go, mark him well!
For him no minstrel's raptures swell.
High though his titles, proud his name,
Boundless his wealth as wish can claim,—
Despite those titles, power, and pelf,
The wretch, concentered all in self,
Living shall forfeit fair renown,
And, doubly dying, shall go down
To the vile dust from whence he sprung,
Unwept, unhonored, and unsung.

WALTER SCOTT

HOW SLEEP THE BRAVE

HOW sleep the brave, who sink to rest
By all their country's wishes blest!
When Spring, with dewy fingers cold,
Returns to deck their hallowed mold,
She there shall dress a sweeter sod
Than Fancy's feet have ever trod.

By fairy hands their knell is rung;
By forms unseen their dirge is sung;
There Honor comes, a pilgrim gray,
To bless the turf that wraps their clay;
And Freedom shall awhile repair
To dwell, a weeping hermit, there!

WILLIAM COLLINS

SAXON GRIT

WORN with the battle of Stamford town,
Fighting the Norman by Hastings bay,
Harold the Saxon's sun went down,
While the acorns were falling one autumn day.

Then the Norman said, "I am lord of the land:
  By tenor of conquest here I sit;
I will rule you now with the iron hand;"
  But he had not thought of the Saxon grit.

He took the land, and he took the men,
  And burnt the homesteads from Trent to Tyne,
Made the freemen serfs by a stroke of the pen,
  Eat up the corn and drank the wine,
And said to maiden, pure and fair,
  "You shall be my leman, as is most fit,
Your Saxon churl may rot in his lair;"
  But he had not measured the Saxon grit.

To the merry greenwood went bold Robin Hood,
  With his strong-hearted yeomanry ripe for the fray,
Driving the arrow into the marrow
  Of all the proud Normans who came in his way;
Scorning the fetter, fearless and free,
  Winning by valor, or foiling by wit,
Dear to our Saxon folk ever is he,
  This merry old rogue with the Saxon grit.

And Kett the tanner whipped out his knife,
  And Watt the smith his hammer brought down,
For ruth of the maid he loved better than life,
  And by breaking a head, made a hole in the Crown.
From the Saxon heart rose a mighty roar,
  "Our life shall not be by the King's permit;
We will fight for the right, we want no more;"
  Then the Norman found out the Saxon grit.

For slow and sure as the oaks had grown
  From acorns falling that autumn day,
So the Saxon manhood in thorpe and town
  To a nobler stature grew alway;
Winning by inches, holding by clinches,
  Standing by law and the human right,
Many times failing, never once quailing,
  So the new day came out of the night.

* * * * * * *

Then rising afar in the Western sea,
  A new world stood in the morn of the day,
Ready to welcome the brave and free,
  Who would wrench out the heart and march away
From the narrow, contracted, dear old land,
  Where the poor are held by a cruel bit,
To ampler spaces for heart and hand—
  And here was a chance for the Saxon grit.

Steadily steering, eagerly peering,
  Trusting in God your fathers came,
Pilgrims and strangers, fronting all dangers,
  Cool-headed Saxons, with hearts aflame.
Bound by the letter, but free from the fetter,
  And hiding their freedom in Holy Writ,
They gave Deuteronomy hints in economy,
  And made a new Moses of Saxon grit.

They whittled and waded through forest and fen,
  Fearless as ever of what might befall;
Pouring out life for the nurture of men,
  In faith that by manhood the world wins all.
Inventing baked beans and no end of machines;
  Great with the rifle and great with the ax—
Sending their notions over the oceans,
  To fill empty stomachs and straighten bent backs.

Swift to take chances that end in the dollar,
  Yet open of hand when the dollar is made,
Maintaining the meetin', exalting the scholar,
  But a little too anxious about a good trade;
This is young Jonathan, son of old John,
  Positive, peaceable, firm in the right,
Saxon men all of us, may we be one,
  Steady for freedom, and strong in her might.

Then, slow and sure, as the oaks have grown
  From the acorns that fell on that autumn day,
So this new manhood in city and town,
  To a nobler stature will grow alway;

Winning by inches, holding by clinches,
  Slow to contention, and slower to quit,
Now and then failing, never once quailing,
  Let us thank God for the Saxon grit.

ROBERT COLLYER

THE TRUSTY BOY

"WHO knows a boy, a trusty boy,
  A live lad—not a dunce—
Whom I with safety may employ?"
  Said gallant Sherman, once.

Stepped forth a brave old soldier then—
  His beard and hair were white;
"There's wide-awake and bright-eyed Ben,
  Quick, trusty, sharp of sight—

"A poor, sick widow's only joy;
  He bears his father's name."
"Send for him!" So the widow's boy
  To Sherman's quarters came.

"My little man, I've work for you,
  You're trusty, I've been told,
The pay shall be, if this you do,
  Both honor and bright gold!"

A packet in his hands was laid,
  Instructions quickly given;
"Be off," the busy general said,
  "And back here, sharp, by 'leven!"

Then forth sped lively little Ben,
  Intent, alert, and spry,
"I may not reach the post, but then
  I can most bravely TRY!"

So, on and on, with wary eye,
  Along the Rapidan,
Tho' black clouds swept across the sky,
  With lightest tread he ran.

By leaping bog and bush and rail,
  A sorry garb he wore,
When, back again, both tired and pale,
  He stood at Sherman's door.

"Well done! well done! my trusty boy!
  The mission's safely o'er;
You are indeed a noble boy—
  God bless you evermore!"

And speaking thus, the general wrote,
  A bright smile on his brow;
Then said, "You'll bear this little note
  To your good mother now."

And when she glanced that missive o'er,
  Her eyes did quickly fill;
She murmured, "God be praised once more—
  He feeds the needy still."

Now, boys, like Benny, strive to win;
  Be trusty, brave of heart!
No room give idleness or sin,
  Act well in life your part.

George B. Griffith

MY LAND

SHE is a rich and rare land;
  Oh! she's a fresh and fair land,
She is a dear and rare land—
  This native land of mine.

No men than hers are braver—
Her women's hearts ne'er waver;
I'd freely die to save her,
  And think my lot divine.

She's not a dull or cold land;
No! she's a warm and bold land;
Oh! she's a true and old land—
  This native land of mine.

Could beauty ever guard her,
And virtue still reward her,
No foe would cross her border—
  No friend within it pine.

Oh! she's a fresh and fair land,
Oh! she's a true and rare land!
Yes, she's a rare and fair land—
  This native land of mine.

THOMAS OSBORNE DAVIS

ABRAHAM LINCOLN

PRESIDENT LINCOLN stood before us as a man of the people. He was thoroughly American, had never crossed the sea, had never been spoiled by English insularity or French dissipation; a quite native, aboriginal man, as an acorn from an oak; no aping of foreigners, no frivolous accomplishments, Kentuckian born, working on a farm, a flatboatman, a captain in the Black Hawk war, a country lawyer, a representative in the rural Legislature of Illinois; on such modest foundations the broad structure of his fame was laid.

He offered no shining qualities at the first encounter; he did not offend by superiority. He had a face and manner which disarmed suspicion, which inspired confidence, which confirmed good will. He was a man without vices.

He had a strong sense of duty, which it was very easy for him to obey. Then, he had what farmers called a long head; was excellent in working out the sum for himself; in arguing his case and convincing you fairly and firmly. Then, it turned out that he was a great worker; had prodigious faculty of performance; worked easily. A good worker is so rare; everybody has some disabling quality. But this man was sound to the core, cheerful, persistent, all right for labor, and liked nothing so well.

Then, he had a vast good-nature, which made him tolerant and accessible to all; fair-minded, leaning to the claim of the petitioner; affable and not sensible to the affliction which the innumerable visits paid to him while President would have brought to any one else. And how this good-nature became a noble humanity, in many a tragic case which the events of the war brought to him, every one will remember; and with what increasing tenderness he dealt when a whole race was thrown on his compassion. The poor negro said of him, on an important occasion, "Massa Linkun am eberywhere."

Ralph Waldo Emerson

MOTHERS' DAY

I MUST NOT TEASE MY MOTHER

I MUST not tease my mother,
For she is very kind;
And everything she says to me
I must directly mind;
For when I was a baby
And could not speak or walk,
She let me in her bosom sleep,
And taught me how to talk.

I must not tease my mother;
And when she likes to read,
Or has the headache, I will step
Most silently indeed:
I will not choose a noisy play,
Nor trifling troubles tell,
But sit down quiet by her side,
And try to make her well.

I must not tease my mother;
I've heard dear father say,
When I was in my cradle sick
She nursed me night and day;
She lays me in my little bed,
She gives me clothes and food,
And I have nothing else to pay
But trying to be good.

I must not tease my mother;
She loves me all the day,
And she has patience with my faults,
And teaches me to pray.
How much I'll strive to please her,
She every hour shall see;
For should she go away or die,
What would become of me?

LYDIA HUNTLY SIGOURNEY

A BOY'S MOTHER

MY Mother, she's so good to me,
  Ef I was good as I could be
I couldn't be as good. No, sir,
Can't any boy be good as her!

She loves me when I'm glad or mad,
She loves me when I'm good or bad;
An' what's the funniest thing she says
She loves me when she punishes.

I don't like her to punish me;
That don't hurt, but it hurts to see
Her cryin'—nen I cry; an' nen
We both cry—an' be good again.

She loves me when she cuts and sews
My little coat and Sunday clothes;
An' when my pa comes home to tea
She loves him 'most as much as me.

She laughs and tells him all I said,
An' grabs me up an' pats my head;
An' I hug her an' hug my pa,
An' love him purt' nigh much as ma.

JAMES WHITCOMB RILEY

THE WATCHER

SHE always leaned to watch for us,
  Anxious if we were late,
In winter by the window,
  In summer by the gate;

And though we mocked her tenderly,
  Who had such foolish care,
The long way home would seem more safe
  Because she waited there.

Her thoughts were all so full of us,
She never could forget!
And so I think that where she is
She must be watching yet,

Waiting till we come home to her,
Anxious if we are late—
Watching from Heaven's window,
Leaning from Heaven's gate.

MARGARET WIDDEMER

OUR MOTHER

HUNDREDS of stars in the pretty sky,
Hundreds of shells on the shore together,
Hundreds of birds that go singing by,
Hundreds of birds in the sunny weather,

Hundreds of dewdrops to greet the dawn,
Hundreds of bees in the purple clover,
Hundreds of butterflies on the lawn,
But only one mother the wide world over.

UNKNOWN

WHICH LOVED HER BEST?

"I LOVE you, mother," said little John;
Then, forgetting his work, his cap went on,
And he was off to the garden swing,
Leaving his mother the wood to bring.

"I love you, mother," said rosy Nell;
"I love you better than tongue can tell";
Then she teased and pouted full half the day,
Till her mother rejoiced when she went to play.

"I love you, mother," said little Fan;
"To-day I'll help you all I can;
How glad I am that school doesn't keep!"
So she rocked the baby till it fell asleep.

Then, stepping softly, she took the broom,
And swept the floor, and dusted the room;
Busy and happy all day was she,
Helpful and cheerful as child could be.

"I love you, mother," again they said—
Three little children going to bed;
How do you think that mother guessed
Which of them really loved her best?

JOY ALLISON

A MOTHER'S LOVE

A MOTHER'S love—how sweet the name!
What is a Mother's love?
A noble, pure, and tender flame,
Enkindled from above.
To bless a heart of earthly mold;
The warmest love that can grow old—
This is Mother's love.

F. MONTGOMERY

NOBODY KNOWS—BUT MOTHER

NOBODY knows of the work it makes
To keep the home together,
Nobody knows of the steps it takes,
Nobody knows—but mother.

Nobody listens to childish woes,
Which kisses only smother;
Nobody's pained by naughty blows,
Nobody—only mother.

Nobody knows of the sleepless care
Bestowed on baby brother;
Nobody knows of the tender prayer,
Nobody—only mother.

Nobody knows of the lessons taught
Of loving one another;
Nobody knows of the patience sought,
Nobody—only mother.

Nobody knows of the anxious fears,
Lest darlings may not weather
The storm of life in after years,
Nobody knows—but mother.

Nobody kneels at the throne above
To thank the Heavenly Father
For that sweetest gift—a mother's love;
Nobody can—but mother.

ANONYMOUS

YOU MEAN MY MOTHER

IF I were asked to give a thought which in one word would speak
A unity of brotherhood, a sympathy complete,
A hundred happy, cheery ways, a mind that knows its own,
Contented 'midst a throng of folk, yet peaceful when alone,
A heart that sheds its silent glow, to brighten many another,
Without a moment of delay, I'd say, "You mean my mother."

ANONYMOUS

THE WHITE CARNATION

HERE'S to the white carnation,
Sturdy and spicy and sweet,
Wafting a breath of perfume
On the stony way of the street;
Bringing a thought of gladness
Wherever the breezes blow;
Here's to the white carnation,
Pure as the virgin snow.
This is the flower for Mother,
Wear it on Mothers' Day;
Flower for rain and sunshine,
Winsome, gallant, and gay;
Wear it in mother's honor
Pinned to the coat's lapel;
Wear it in belt and corsage,
For her who loved you well.

The mother in lowly cabin,
The mother in palace hall,
Is ever the best and dearest,
The one we love best of all.
In travail and pain she bore us,
In laughter and love she nursed,
And who that would shame a mother
Is of all mankind accursed.

Tired and wan too often,
Weary and weak at times,
But always full of the courage
That thrills when the future chimes;
Mother with hands toil hardened,
Mother in pearls and lace,
The light of heavenly beauty
Shines in your tender face.

So here's to the white carnation,
Wear it on Mothers' Day;
Flower that blooms for mother,
Winsome, gallant and gay.

Flower of perfect sweetness,
  Flower for hut and hall,
Here's to the white carnation
  And to Mother—Our Best of All.

MARGARET E. SANGSTER

THANKSGIVING DAY AND CHRISTMAS

THANKSGIVING DAY

OVER the river and through the wood,
To grandfather's house we go;
The horse knows the way
To carry the sleigh
Through the white and drifted snow.

Over the river and through the wood—
Oh, how the wind does blow!
It stings the toes
And bites the nose,
As over the ground we go.

Over the river and through the wood,
To have a first-rate play.
Hear the bells ring,
"Ting-a-ling-ding!"
Hurrah for Thanksgiving Day!

Over the river and through the wood
Trot fast, my dapple gray!
Spring over the ground,
Like a hunting hound!
For this is Thanksgiving Day.

Over the river and through the wood,
And straight through the barnyard gate.
We seem to go
Extremely slow,—
It is so hard to wait!

Over the river and through the wood—
Now grandmother's cap I spy!
Hurrah for the fun!
Is the pudding done?
Hurrah for the pumpkin pie!

LYDIA MARIA CHILD

A GOOD THANKSGIVING

SAID old Gentleman Gay, "On a Thanksgiving Day,
If you want a good time, then give something away";
So he sent a fat turkey to Shoemaker Price,
And the Shoemaker said, "What a big bird! how nice!
And, since a good dinner's before me, I ought
To give poor Widow Lee the small chicken I bought."

"This fine chicken, O see!" said the pleased Widow Lee,
"And the kindness that sent it, how precious to me!
I would like to make some one as happy as I—
I'll give Washwoman Biddy my big pumpkin pie."

"And O, sure," Biddy said, " 'tis the queen of all pies!
Just to look at its yellow face gladdens my eyes!
Now it's my turn, I think; and a sweet ginger cake
For the motherless Finigan Children I'll bake."

"A sweet cake, all our own! 'Tis too good to be true!"
Said the Finigan Children, Rose, Denny, and Hugh;
"It smells sweet of spice, and we'll carry a slice
To poor little Lame Jake—who has nothing that's nice."

"O, I thank you, and thank you!" said little Lame Jake;
"O what bootiful, bootiful, bootiful cake!
And O, such a big slice! I will save all the crumbs,
And will give 'em to each little Sparrow that comes!"

And the Sparrows they twittered, as if they would say,
Like old Gentleman Gay, "On a Thanksgiving Day,
If you want a good time, then give something away!"

MARIAN DOUGLAS

THE THANKSGIVING FEAST

ON Thanksgiving 'tis the custom
To prepare a splendid feast,
And we all look forward to it
From the greatest to the least!

Cook and mother in the kitchen
  Make the most delicious things,
Pumpkin pies and lots of doughnuts,
  Round and square and cut like rings.

In the pot the big plum pudding,
  Full of raisins and of spice,
Simmers in the boiling water
  Till it's cooked enough to slice.

Pickles, celery, and jelly—
  All of these you'll find if you
Look for them, for in the pantry
  On the shelves they're full in view.

From the heated baking oven,
  Every time the door is down,
Steals the warm, delicious odor
  Of the turkey turning brown!

Oh, I tell you we are hungry
  When at last we're called to eat,
And we all do ample justice
  To the good things sour and sweet.

SUSIE M. BEST

THANKSGIVING TURKEY

AN old turkey gobler strutted around,
  With all his black feathers plumed high;
His wings trailing proudly upon the hard ground,
  His tail toward the moon in the sky.

Perched high on a fence a rooster he spied,
  Whose crowing might waken the dead;
"Do stop that loud noise!" in a fierce rage, he cried;
  Strutting on with a toss of his head.

The rooster was dumb; but he chuckled with glee
As he thought of the grand dinner spread
On Thanksgiving Day, when that turkey would be
Served up without feathers or head.

Thanksgiving Day came—the turkey was there,
But bereft of his flaunting black gown;
He lay on his back, with his feet in the air,
And his body a delicate brown.

They carved the flesh from his every bone
And joked as they passed it around;
To the rooster, too, no mercy was shown—
For he in the soup was found.

Z. F. Riley

GIVING THANKS

FOR the hay and the corn and the wheat that is reaped,
For the labor well done, and the barns that are heaped,
For the sun and the dew and the sweet honeycomb,
For the rose and the song, and the harvest brought home—
Thanksgiving! Thanksgiving!

For the trade and the skill and the wealth in our land,
For the cunning and strength of the workingman's hand,
For the good that our artists and poets have taught,
For the friendship that hope and affection have brought—
Thanksgiving! Thanksgiving!

For the homes that with purest affection are blest,
For the season of plenty and well deserved rest,
For our country extending from sea unto sea,
The land that is known as the "Land of the Free"—
Thanksgiving! Thanksgiving!

Anonymous

WE THANK THEE

FOR flowers so beautiful and sweet,
For friends and clothes and food to eat,
For precious hours, for work and play,
We thank Thee this Thanksgiving Day.

For father's care and mother's love,
For the blue sky and clouds above,
For springtime and autumn gay
We thank Thee this Thanksgiving Day!

For all Thy gifts so good and fair,
Bestowed so freely everywhere,
Give us grateful hearts we pray,
To thank Thee this Thanksgiving Day.

MATTIE M. RENWICK

A THANKSGIVING

DEEPEST thanksgiving I do give,
Because I didn't chance to live
In what they call the "good old days"
Of homely fare and simple ways.

I like the days that we have now,
Instead of broom and churn and plow;
I like to have a bed with springs,
And telephones and vacuum things.

Those "good old times," so praised in song!
How did the women get along?
No bridge or suffrage or bead bags,
No motor cars or gladsome rags!

I'm very glad "old-fashioned cheer"
Will not be offered me this year;

No squash or pumpkin pie for me—
I much prefer patisserie.

I can't see how they lived at all
Without a cab or music hall;
Oh, earnestly I do thanks give
That our times are not primitive!

CAROLYN WELLS

THANKSGIVING NIGHT

LAST night I got to thinking, when I couldn't go to sleep,
Of the way Thanksgiving served me in the days when joy was cheap—
Of how we'd have a turkey, and of how I'd beg a taste
Whenever they would open up the oven door to "baste"
The bulging breast, and how then from the oven came a drift
Of tantalizing odor, such as only boys have sniffed.

I got to thinking of it—for I couldn't go to sleep—
Of mince pies in the pantry, where I'd sidle in and peep,
And jelly and plum butter, and the peach preserves and cake—
And then I got to thinking of how fine 'twould be to take
A trip back to the old days, when the dancing candle light
Played pranks with all the shadows on the wall, Thanksgiving night.

The boys I used to play with! I could shut my eyes and see
The whole troop of them waiting and a-waving hands to me;
All freckled, ragged trousered, with their scarfs and mittens, too,
They made a splendid picture—but the picture wasn't true;

For they've grown up, as I have, and strange paths have lured our feet—
The paths that find To-morrow, and that never, never meet.

I wondered if they also were not lying half awake
And thinking of the turkey, and the jelly, and the cake;
And if they had their fancies of the lazy little street
That leads beneath the maples where the topmost branches meet—
And suddenly I heard them—heard the murmurs low and clear,
That told me they were with me, and were very, very near.

WILBUR D. NESBIT

THANKSGIVING

FIRST PUPIL:

"Have you cut the wheat in the blowing fields,
The barley, the oats, and the nodding rye,
The golden corn and the pearly rice?
For the winter days draw nigh."

SECOND PUPIL:

"We have reaped them all from shore to shore,
And the grain is safe on the threshing floor."

THIRD PUPIL:

"Have you gathered the berries from the vine,
And the fruit from the orchard trees?
The dew and the scent from the roses and thyme,
In the hive of the honey bees?"

FOURTH PUPIL:

"The peach and the plum and the apple are ours,
And the honeycomb from the scented flowers."

FIFTH PUPIL:

"The wealth of the snowy cotton field
And the gift of the sugar cane,
The savory herb and the nourishing root—
There has been nothing given in vain."

SIXTH PUPIL:

"We have gathered the harvest from shore to shore,
And the measure is full and brimming o'er."

ALL:

Then lift up the head with a song!
And lift up the hand with a gift!
To the ancient Giver of all
The spirit in gratitude lift!
For the joy and the promise of spring,
For the hay and the clover sweet,
The barley, the rye and the oats,
The rice and the corn and the wheat,
The cotton and sugar and fruit,
The flowers and the fine honeycomb,
The country so fair and so free,
The blessings and glory of home.

AMELIA E. BARR

FOREVER ON THANKSGIVING DAY

LONG since the first fruits have been laid
In plenitude before the shrine;
Long since the purple grapes have made
The sacrifice of flame red wine—
And now across the empty field
Which gleaning hands have left all bare,
Where harvest songs one time have pealed,
The home path stretches, broad and fair.

The home path—O, the land is far
  That knows no path to lead us home!
The sky is strange that has no star
  To guide us whereso'er we roam;
The sea is sad that shows no wake
  Of ships that seek the harbor bar
Whereon glad billows leap and break
  And sing of where the home hearts are.

The eyes are blind that may not close
  To conjure visions of the hearth
Where from a laughing firelight throws
  Its glamour over heart-born mirth;
The ears are deaf that cannot hear
  The home song pulsing in the air
In measures soft and sweet and clear—
  The home song of the days back there.

For each the home path, be it street,
  Or fair, broad highway, or the sea—
The path that lures the weary feet
  To find where all the home things be.
What though one fares through lands away,
  Or drifts or beats across the foam?
Forever on Thanksgiving Day
  The heart will find the pathway home.

WILBUR D. NESBIT

CHRISTMAS HAS COME

CHRISTMAS day has come at last,
  And I am glad 'tis here;
For, don't you think, for *this one day*,
  I've waited just a year.
I'm sure it should have come before
  As sure as I'm alive;
Fifty-two Sundays make a year,
  And I've counted *seventy-five.*

There's one thing makes me very glad,
As glad as I can be;
The years grow *short* as we grow *old*,
And that will just suit me.
I wish 'twas Christmas every month—
That's long enough to wait—
For all the presents that I want,
A year is very late.
We'd have a tree, then, every month,
And presents nice and new:
(A voice in the audience says, "Where would the money come from?")
Do Christmas trees cost anything?
(A voice, "I guess they do!")
Then one a year will do.
And now I'll take my seat, dear friends,
And wait to hear my call;
For I've a present on the tree,
And I hope it is a doll.

UNKNOWN

THE NATIVITY

THE air was still o'er Bethlehem's plain,
As if the great night held its breath,
When Life Eternal came to reign
Over a world of death.

All nature felt a thrill divine
When burst that meteor on the night,
Which, pointing to the Savior's shrine,
Proclaimed the new-born Light.

Light to the shepherds! and the star
Gilded their silent midnight fold;
Light to the wise men from afar
Bearing their gifts of gold.

Light to a realm of sin and grief;
Light to a world in all its needs;
The Light of Life, a new belief
Rising o'er fallen creeds.

Light on a tangled path of thorns,
Though leading to a martyr's throne;
A light to guide till Christ returns
In glory to His own.

There still it shines, while far abroad
The Christmas choirs sing now, as then,
"Glory, glory unto our God!
Peace and good will to men!"

THOMAS BUCHANAN READ

SANTA CLAUS

LITTLE fairy snowflakes
Dancing in the flue;
Old Mr. Santa Claus,
What is keeping you?
Twilight and firelight
Shadows come and go;
Merry chime of sleigh bells
Twinkling through the snow;
Mother's knitting stockings,
Pussy's got the ball;
Don't you think that winter's
Pleasanter than all?

UNKNOWN

A VISIT FROM ST. NICHOLAS

'TWAS the night before Christmas, when all through the house,
Not a creature was stirring, not even a mouse;
The stockings were hung by the chimney with care,

In hopes that St. Nicholas soon would be there;
The children were nestled all snug in their beds,
While visions of sugar-plums danced in their heads;
And mamma in her kerchief, and I in my cap,
Had just settled our brains for a long winter's nap;—
When out on the lawn there arose such a clatter,
I sprang from my bed to see what was the matter.
Away to the window I flew like a flash,
Tore open the shutters and threw up the sash.
The moon on the breast of the new-fallen snow,
Gave the luster of midday to objects below,
When, what to my wondering eyes should appear,
But a miniature sleigh and eight tiny reindeer,
With a little old driver, so lively and quick,
I knew in a moment it must be St. Nick.
More rapid than eagles his coursers they came,
And he whistled and shouted, and called them by name:
"Now, *Dasher!* now, *Dancer!* now, *Prancer!* and *Vixen!*
On, *Comet!* on, *Cupid!* on, *Donner!* and *Blitzen!*
To the top of the porch! to the top of the wall!
Now dash away! dash away! dash away all!"
As dry leaves that before the wild hurricane fly,
When they meet with an obstacle, mount to the sky;
So up to the house-top the coursers they flew
With the sleigh full of toys and St. Nicholas too.
And then, in a twinkling, I heard on the roof
The prancing and pawing of each little hoof—
As I drew in my head, and was turning around,
Down the chimney St. Nicholas came with a bound.
He was dressed all in furs from his head to his foot,
And his clothes were all tarnished with ashes and soot;
A bundle of toys he had flung on his back,
And he looked like a peddler just opening his pack.
His eyes—how they twinkled! his dimples—how merry!
His cheeks were like roses, his nose like a cherry!
His droll little mouth was drawn up like a bow,
And the beard on his chin was as white as the snow;
The stump of a pipe he held tight in his teeth,
And the smoke it encircled his head like a wreath;
He was chubby and plump, a right jolly old elf;
And I laughed when I saw him, in spite of myself;

A wink of his eye and a twist of his head
Soon gave me to know I had nothing to dread;
He spoke not a word, but went straight to his work,
And filled all the stockings; then turned with a jerk,
And laying his finger aside of his nose,
And giving a nod, up the chimney he rose.
He sprang to his sleigh, to his team gave a whistle,
And away they all flew like the down of a thistle.
But I heard him exclaim, ere he drove out of sight,
"Happy Christmas to all, and to all a good night!"

CLEMENT C. MOORE

CHRISTMAS IN THE OLDEN TIME

HEAP on more wood!—the wind is chill;
But let it whistle as it will,
We'll keep our Christmas merry still.

Each age has deem'd the new-born year
The fittest time for festal cheer:
And well our Christian sires of old
Loved when the year its course had roll'd,
And brought blithe Christmas back again,
With all his hospitable train.
Domestic and religious rite
Gave honor to the holy night;
On Christmas Eve the bells were rung;
On Christmas Eve the mass was sung:
That only night in all the year,
Saw the stoled priest the chalice rear.
The damsel donn'd her kirtle sheen;
The hall was dress'd with holly green;
Forth to the wood did merrymen go,
To gather in the mistletoe.
Then open'd wide the Baron's hall
To vassal, tenant, serf, and all;
Power laid his rod of rule aside,
And Ceremony doff'd his pride.

The heir, with roses in his shoes,
That night might village partner choose;
The lord, underogating, share
The vulgar game of "post and pair."
All hail'd, with uncontroll'd delight
And general voice, the happy night,
That to the cottage, as the Crown,
Brought tidings of salvation down.

The fire, with well-dried logs supplied,
Went roaring up the chimney wide;
The huge hall table's oaken face,
Scrubb'd till it shone, the day to grace,
Bore then upon its massive board
No mark to part the squire and lord.
Then was brought in the lusty brawn,
By old blue-coated serving man;
Then the grim boar's head frown'd on high,
Crested with bays and rosemary.
Well can the green-garb'd ranger tell,
How, when, and where, the monster fell;
What dogs before his death he tore,
And all the baiting of the boar.
The wassail round, in good brown bowls,
Garnish'd with ribbons, blithely trowls.
There the huge sirloin reek'd; hard by
Plum porridge stood, and Christmas pie;
Nor fail'd old Scotland to produce,
At such high tide, her savory goose.
Then came the merry maskers in,
And carols roar'd with blithesome din;
If unmelodious was the song,
It was a hearty note, and strong.
Who lists may in their mumming see
Traces of ancient mystery;
White shirts supplied the masquerade,
And smutted cheeks the visors made;—
But, O! what maskers, richly dight,
Can boast of bosoms half so light!
England was merry England, when
Old Christmas brought his sports again.

'Twas Christmas broach'd the mightiest ale;
'Twas Christmas told the merriest tale;
A Christmas gambol oft could cheer
The poor man's heart through half the year.

WALTER SCOTT

HYMN FOR CHRISTMAS

OH! lovely voices of the sky
Which hymned the Savior's birth,
Are ye not singing still on high,
Ye that sang, "Peace on earth"?
To us yet speak the strains
Wherewith, in time gone by,
Ye blessed the Syrian swains,
Oh! voices of the sky!

Oh! clear and shining light, whose beams
That hour Heaven's glory shed,
Around the palms, and o'er the streams,
And on the shepherd's head.
Be near, through life and death,
As in that holiest night
Of hope, and joy, and faith—
Oh! clear and shining light!

* * * * * * *

FELICIA HEMANS

EVERYWHERE, EVERYWHERE CHRISTMAS TO-NIGHT

CHRISTMAS in lands of the fir tree and pine,
Christmas in lands of the palm tree and vine;
Christmas where snow peaks stand solemn and white,
Christmas where cornfields lie sunny and bright;
Everywhere, everywhere Christmas to-night!

Christmas where children are hopeful and gay,
Christmas where old men are patient and gray,
Christmas where peace, like a dove in its flight,
Broods o'er brave men in the thick of the fight;
Everywhere, everywhere Christmas to-night!

For the Christ child who comes is the Master of all;
No palace too great—no cottage too small.
The angels who welcome Him sing from the height,
"In the city of David a King in His might."
Everywhere, everywhere Christmas to-night!

Then let every heart keep its Christmas within
Christ's pity for sorrow, Christ's hatred of sin,
Christ's care for the weakest, Christ's courage for right,
Christ's dread of the darkness, Christ's love of the light,
Everywhere, everywhere Christmas to-night!

So the stars of the midnight which compass us round,
Shall see a strange glory and hear a sweet sound,
And cry, "Look! the earth is aflame with delight,
O sons of the morning rejoice at the sight."
Everywhere, everywhere Christmas to-night!

PHILLIPS BROOKS

O LITTLE TOWN OF BETHLEHEM

O LITTLE town of Bethlehem,
How still we see thee lie!
Above thy deep and dreamless sleep
The silent stars go by;
Yet in thy dark streets shineth
The everlasting Light;
The hopes and fears of all the years
Are met in thee to-night.

For Christ is born of Mary,
And, gathered all above,
While mortals sleep, the angels keep
Their watch of wondering love.

O morning stars, together
  Proclaim the holy birth!
And praises sing to God the King,
  And peace to men on earth.

How silently, how silently,
  The wondrous gift is given!
So God imparts to human hearts
  The blessings of His heaven.
No ear may hear His coming,
  But in this world of sin,
Where meek souls will receive Him still,
  The dear Christ enters in.

O holy Child of Bethlehem!
  Descend to us, we pray;
Cast out our sin, and enter in,
  Be born in us to-day.
We hear the Christmas angels
  The great glad tidings tell;
Oh, come to us, abide with us,
  Our Lord Emmanuel!

PHILLIPS BROOKS

GOD REST YE, MERRY GENTLEMEN

GOD rest ye, merry gentlemen; let nothing you dismay,
For Jesus Christ, our Savior, was born on Christmas day.
The dawn rose red o'er Bethlehem, the stars shone through the gray,
When Jesus Christ, our Savior, was born on Christmas day.

God rest ye, little children; let nothing you affright,
For Jesus Christ, your Savior, was born this happy night;
Along the hills of Galilee the white flocks sleeping lay,
When Christ, the child of Nazareth, was born on Christmas day.

God rest ye, all good Christians; upon this blessed morn
The Lord of all good Christians was of a woman born:
Now all your sorrows He doth heal, your sins He takes
 away;
For Jesus Christ, our Savior, was born on Christmas day.

DINAH MARIA MULOCK

AN ODE ON THE BIRTH OF OUR SAVIOR

IN numbers, and but these few,
 I sing Thy birth, O Jesu!
Thou pretty baby, born here
With sup'rabundant scorn here:
Who for Thy princely post here,
 Hadst for Thy place
 Of birth, a base
Outstable for Thy court here.

Instead of neat enclosures
Of interwoven osiers,
Instead of fragrant posies
Of daffodils and roses,
Thy cradle, Kingly Stranger,
 As gospel tells,
 Was nothing else
But here a homely manger.

But we with silks (not cruells),
With sundry precious jewels,
And lily work will dress Thee;
And, as we dispossess Thee,
Of clouts, we'll make a chamber,
 Sweet babe, for Thee
 Of ivory,
And plaster'd round with amber.

ROBERT HERRICK

A CHRISTMAS CAROL

THERE'S a song in the air!
There's a star in the sky!
There's a mother's deep prayer
And a baby's low cry!
And the star rains its fire while the Beautiful sing,
For the manger of Bethlehem cradles a king.

There's a tumult of joy
O'er the wonderful birth,
For the virgin's sweet boy
Is the Lord of the earth,
Ay! the star rains its fire and the Beautiful sing,
For the manger of Bethlehem cradles a king.

In the light of that star
Lie the ages impearled;
And that song from afar
Has swept over the world.
Every home is aflame, and the Beautiful sing
In the homes of the nations that Jesus is King.

We rejoice in the light
And we echo the song
That comes down through the night
From the heavenly throng.
Ay! we shout to the lovely evangel they bring,
And we greet in his cradle our Savior and King!

JOSIAH GILBERT HOLLAND

WHILE SHEPHERDS WATCHED THEIR FLOCKS BY NIGHT

WHILE shepherds watched their flocks by night,
All seated on the ground,
The angel of the Lord came down,
And glory shone around.

"Fear not," said he, for mighty dread
  Had seized their troubled mind;
"Glad tidings of great joy I bring
  To you and all mankind.

"To you, in David's town, this day
  Is born, of David's line,
The Savior, who is Christ the Lord,
  And this shall be the sign:

"The heavenly babe you there shall find
  To human view displayed,
All meanly wrapped in swaddling bands
  And in a manger laid."

Thus spake the seraph; and forthwith
  Appeared a shining throng
Of angels, praising God, who thus
  Addressed their joyful song:

"All glory be to God on high,
  And to the earth be peace;
Good will henceforth from Heaven to men
  Begin and never cease."

NAHUM TATE

BEFORE THE PALING OF THE STARS

BEFORE the paling of the stars,
  Before the winter morn,
Before the earliest cockcrow,
  Jesus Christ was born:
Born in a stable,
  Cradled in a manger,
In the world His hands had made
  Born a stranger.

Priest and king lay fast asleep
  In Jerusalem,
Young and old lay fast asleep
  In crowded Bethlehem;
Saint and Angel, ox and ass,
  Kept a watch together
Before the Christmas daybreak
  In the winter weather.

Jesus on His Mother's breast
  In the stable cold,
Spotless Lamb of God was He,
  Shepherd of the fold:

Let us kneel with Mary maid,
  With Joseph bent and hoary,
With Saint and Angel, ox and ass,
  To hail the King of Glory.

CHRISTINA GEORGINA ROSSETTI

ONCE IN ROYAL DAVID'S CITY

ONCE in royal David's city
  Stood a lowly cattle shed,
Where a Mother laid her baby
  In a manger for His bed;
Mary was that Mother mild,
Jesus Christ her little child.

He came down to earth from heaven,
  Who is God and Lord of all,
And His shelter was a stable,
  And His cradle was a stall,
With the poor, and mean, and lowly
Lived on earth our Savior Holy.

And through all His wondrous childhood,
He would honor and obey,
Love and watch the lowly Maiden,
In whose gentle arms He lay;
Christian children all must be
Mild, obedient, good as He.

For He is our childhood's pattern,
Day by day like us He grew,
He was little, weak, and helpless,
Tears and smiles like us He knew;
And He feeleth for our sadness,
And He shareth in our gladness.

And our eyes at last shall see Him,
Through His own redeeming love,
For that Child so dear and gentle
Is our Lord in heaven above;
And He leads His children on
To the place where He has gone.

Not in that poor lowly stable,
With the oxen standing by,
We shall see Him; but in heaven,
Set at God's right hand on high,
When like stars His children crowned
All in white shall wait around.

CECIL FRANCES ALEXANDER

JEST 'FORE CHRISTMAS

FATHER calls me William, sister calls me Will,
Mother calls me Willie, but the fellers call me Bill!
Mighty glad I ain't a girl—ruther be a boy,
Without them sashes, curls, an' things that's worn by Fauntleroy!

Love to chawnk green apples an' go swimmin' in the lake—
Hate to take the castor ile they give for belly ache!

'Most all the time, the whole year round, there ain't no flies
on me,
But jest 'fore Christmas I'm as good as I kin be!

Got a yeller dog named Sport, sick him on the cat;
First thing she knows she doesn't know where she is at;
Got a clipper sled, an' when us kids goes out to slide,
'Long comes the grocery cart, an' we all hook a ride!
But sometimes when the grocery man is worrited an' cross,
He reaches at us with his whip, an' larrups up his hoss,
An' then I laff an' holler, "Oh, ye never teched *me!*"
But jest 'fore Christmas I'm as good as I kin be!

Gran'ma says she hopes that when I git to be a man,
I'll be a missionarer like her oldest brother, Dan,
As was et up by the cannibuls that lives in Ceylon's Isle,
Where every prospeck pleases, an' only man is vile!
But gran'ma she has never been to see a Wild West show,
Nor read the Life of Daniel Boone, or else I guess she'd
know
That Buff'lo Bill and cowboys is good enough for me!
Excep' jest 'fore Christmas, when I'm good as I kin be!

And then old Sport he hangs around, so solemnlike an' still,
His eyes they keep a-sayin': "What's the matter, little Bill?"
The old cat sneaks down off her perch an' wonders what's
become
Of them two enemies of hern that used to make things hum!
But I am so perlite an' 'tend so earnestly to biz,
That mother says to father: "How improved our Willie is!"
But father, havin' been a boy hisself, suspicions me
When, jest 'fore Christmas, I'm as good as I kin be!

For Christmas, with its lots an' lots of candies, cakes, an'
toys,
Was made, they say, for proper kids an' not for naughty
boys;
So wash yer face an' bresh yer hair, an' mind yer p's an' q's,
An' don't bust out yer pantaloons, an' don't wear out yer
shoes;

Say "Yessum" to the ladies, an' "Yessur" to the men,
An' when they's company, don't pass yer plate for pie again;
But, thinkin' of the things yer'd like to see upon that tree,
Jest 'fore Christmas be as good as yer kin be!

EUGENE FIELD

THE LITTLE CHRISTMAS TREE

THE Christmas Day was coming, the Christmas Eve drew near,
The fir trees, they were talking low at midnight, cold and clear;
And this is what the fir tree said, all in the pale moonlight:
"Now, which of us shall chosen be to grace the holy night?"

The tall trees and the goodly trees raised each a lofty head,
In glad and secret confidence, though not a word they said.
But one, the baby of the band, could not restrain a sigh—
"You all will be approved," he said, "but, oh! what chance have I?

"I am so small, so very small, no one will mark or know
How thick and green my needles are, how true my branches grow.
Few toys and candles could I hold, but heart and will are free,
And in my heart of hearts I know I am a Christmas tree."

The Christmas angel hovered near; he caught the grieving word,
And, laughing low, he hurried forth, with love and pity stirred.
He sought and found St. Nicholas, the dear old Christmas saint,
And in his fatherly, kind ear rehearsed the fir tree's plaint.

Saints are all-powerful, we know, so it befell that day
That, ax on shoulder, to the grove a woodman took his way.

One baby girl he had at home, and he went forth to find
A little tree as small as she, just suited to his mind.

Oh! glad and proud the baby fir, amid its brethren tall,
To be thus chosen and singled out, the first among them all!
He stretched his fragrant branches, his little heart beat fast;
He was a real Christmas tree—he had his wish at last.

One large and shining apple, with cheeks of ruddy gold;
Six tapers, and a tiny doll were all that he could hold.
The baby laughed, the baby crowed, to see the tapers bright;
The forest baby felt the joy, and shared in the delight.

And when, at last, the tapers died, and when the baby slept,
The little fir, in silent night, a patient vigil kept.
Though scorched and brown its needles were, it had no
heart to grieve;
"I have not lived in vain," he said, "thank God for Christmas Eve!"

SUSAN COOLIDGE

THE FIRST CHRISTMAS

HANG up the baby's stocking;
Be sure you don't forget—
The dear little dimpled darling!
She ne'er saw Christmas yet;
But I've told her all about it,
And she opened her big blue eyes,
And I'm sure she understood it,
She looked so funny and wise.

Dear! what a tiny stocking!
It doesn't take much to hold
Such little pink toes as baby's
Away from the frost and cold.

But then, for the baby's Christmas
  It will never do at all;
Why, Santa wouldn't be looking
  For anything half so small.

I know what will do for the baby,
  I've thought of the very best plan—
I'll borrow a stocking of grandma,
  The longest that ever I can;
And you'll hang it by mine, dear mother,
  Right here in the corner, so!
And write a letter to Santa,
  And fasten it on to the toe.

Write, "This is the baby's stocking
  That hangs in the corner here;
You never have seen her, Santa,
  For she only came this year;
But she's just the blessedest baby—
  And now, before you go,
Just cram her stocking with goodies,
  From the top clean down to the toe."

ANONYMOUS

NEW YEAR'S EVE

IF you're waking call me early, call me early, mother dear,
For I would see the sun rise upon the glad New year.
It is the last New year that I shall ever see,
Then you may lay me low i' the mold and think no more of me.

To-night I saw the sun set: he set and left behind
The good old year, the dear old time, and all my peace of mind:
And the New year's coming up, mother, but I shall never see
The blossom on the blackthorn, the leaf upon the tree.

Last May we made a crown of flowers: we had a merry day;
Beneath the hawthorn on the green they made me Queen of May;
And we danced about the may-pole and in the hazel copse,
Till Charles's Wain came out above the tall white chimney tops.

There's not a flower on all the hills: the frost is on the pane:
I only wish to live till the snowdrops come again:
I wish the snow would melt and the sun come out on high:
I long to see a flower so before the day I die.

The building rook 'ill caw from the windy tall elm tree,
And the tufted plover pipe along the fallow lea,
And the swallow 'ill come back again with summer o'er the wave,
But I shall lie alone, mother, within the moldering grave.

Upon the chancel casement, and upon that grave of mine,
In the early, early morning the summer sun will shine,
Before the red cock crows from the farm upon the hill,
When you are warm asleep, mother, and all the world is still.

When the flowers come again, mother, beneath the waning light,
You'll never see me more in the long gray fields at night;
When from the dry dark wold the summer airs blow cool
On the oat grass and the sword grass, and the bulrush in the pool.

You'll bury me, my mother, just beneath the hawthorn shade,
And you'll come sometimes and see me where I am lowly laid.
I shall not forget you, mother, I shall hear you when you pass,
With your feet above my head in the long and pleasant grass.

I have been wild and wayward, but you'll forgive me now;
You'll kiss me, my own mother, and forgive me ere I go;
Nay, nay, you must not weep, nor let your grief be wild,
You should not fret for me, mother, you have another child.

If I can I'll come again, mother, from out my resting place;
Though you'll not see me, mother, I shall look upon your face;
Though I cannot speak a word, I shall hearken what you say,
And be often, often with you, when you think I'm far away.

Good night, good night, when I have said good night for evermore,
And you see me carried out from the threshold of the door;
Don't let Effie come to see me till my grave be growing green:
She'll be a better child to you than ever I have been.

She'll find my garden tools upon the granary floor:
Let her take 'em: they are hers: I shall never garden more:
But tell her, when I'm gone, to train the rosebush that I set,
About the parlor window and the box of mignonette.

Good night, sweet mother; call me before the day is born.
All night I lie awake, but I fall asleep at morn;
But I would see the sun rise upon the glad New year,
So, if you're waking, call me, call me early, mother dear.

ALFRED TENNYSON

THE DEATH OF THE OLD YEAR

FULL knee deep lies the winter snow,
And the winter winds are wearily sighing:
Toll ye the church bell sad and slow,
And tread softly and speak low,
For the old year lies a-dying.

Old year, you must not die;
You came to us so readily,
You lived with us so steadily,
Old year, you shall not die.

He lieth still: he doth not move:
He will not see the dawn of day.
He hath no other life above.
He gave me a friend, and a true, true love,
And the New year will take 'em away.
Old year, you must not go;
So long as you have been with us,
Such joy as you have seen with us,
Old year, you shall not go.

He froth'd his bumpers to the brim;
A jollier year we shall not see.
But tho' his eyes are waxing dim,
And tho' his foes speak ill of him,
He was a friend to me.
Old year, you shall not die;
We did so laugh and cry with you,
I've half a mind to die with you,
Old year, if you must die.

He was full of joke and jest,
But all his merry quips are o'er.
To see him die, across the waste
His son and heir doth ride post haste,
But he'll be dead before.
Every one for his own.
The night is starry and cold, my friend,
And the New year blithe and bold, my friend,
Comes up to take his own.

How hard he breathes! over the snow
I heard just now the crowing cock.
The shadows flicker to and fro:
The cricket chirps: the light burns low:
'Tis nearly twelve o'clock.

Shake hands, before you die.
Old year, we'll dearly rue for you:
What is it we can do for you?
Speak out before you die.

His face is growing sharp and thin.
Alack! our friend is gone.
Close up his eyes: tie up his chin:
Step from the corpse, and let him in
That standeth there alone,
And waiteth at the door.
There's a new foot on the floor, my friend,
And a new face at the door, my friend,
A new face at the door.

ALFRED TENNYSON

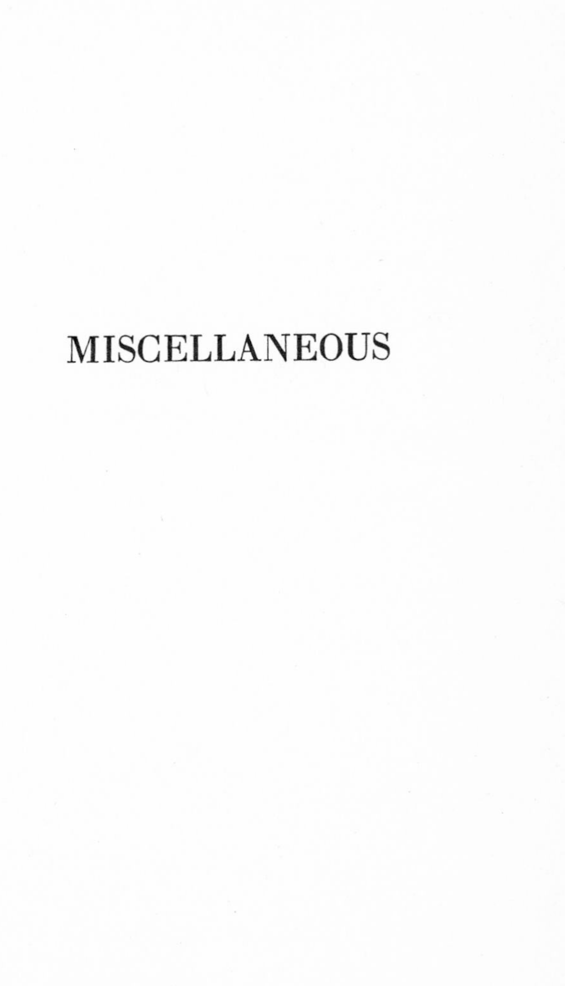

MISCELLANEOUS

UPSIDE DOWN

IF all the world were upside down,
Our lilies would be stars so gay,
Our brooks would make the milky way,
And roses of the richest dye
Would be the pretty sunset sky;
Instead of blue, the sky'd be brown—
If all the world were upside down.

If all the world were upside down,
The moon would take the ocean's place,
And stars the fields and gardens grace;
The ground, of course, would be sky blue
Another change would be quite new—
We'd wear our shoes upon our crown
If all the world were upside down.

GEORGE COOPER

PRAYER FOR THIS HOUSE

MAY nothing evil cross this door,
And may ill fortune never pry
About these windows; may the roar
And rains go by.

Strengthened by faith, the rafters will
Withstand the battering of the storm.
This hearth, though all the world grow chill
Will keep you warm.

Peace shall walk softly through these rooms,
Touching your lips with holy wine,
Till every casual corner blooms
Into a shrine.

Laughter shall drown the raucous shout
  And, though the sheltering walls are thin,
May they be strong to keep hate out
  And hold love in.

LOUIS UNTERMEYER

SONG FOR A LITTLE HOUSE *

I'M glad our house is a little house,
  Not too tall nor too wide:
I'm glad the hovering butterflies
  Feel free to come inside.

Our little house is a friendly house,
  It is not shy or vain;
It gossips with the talking trees,
  And makes friends with the rain.

And quick leaves cast a shimmer of green
  Against our whited walls,
And in the phlox, the courteous bees
  Are paying duty calls.

CHRISTOPHER MORLEY

AN ADVENTUROUS DAY †

ONE time in vacation we boys all left town
  To stay in the country for Sunday; and down
By Deacon Gray's pasture a rabbit came out
Right close to the highway and looked all about
Until it saw us, and it started to run
Right down the highroad like a shot from a gun;
So Billy Beggs threw off his coat and his hat
And chased it till both of its ears were down flat,
And, my, it just ran as if it saw a ghost,
And Bill ran so fast that he caught it—almost!

And under the bridge where it crosses the creek
We saw some fish swimming and darting as quick
As a flash in the water, and one fish would flop
Himself till he almost would come to the top;
So then we got down on the bridge and we tied
A pin on a string and dropped it down the side
With a bug on the pin, and the fishes would look
While Billy Beggs wiggled the bug on the hook;
And one fish was hungry and came up so close
That Bill gave a jerk and he caught it—almost!

And over by Skinner's a big hawk flew by
And lit on a stump that was not very high,
But didn't see us and we crawled up quite slow
Through the grass to the stump with a big stone to throw;
And Billy Beggs said that the hawk was asleep
For it never stirred once; and the grass was so deep
That we got to within a few feet from the stump,
And Billy Beggs peeked, and his heart gave a thump;
And when he got ever and ever so close
He stood up and threw and he hit it—almost!

And then it got cloudy and thundered and then
It lightened just awful and thundered again;
It rained some big drops and we started to run
To get in the barn till the shower was done;
And lightning just spattered and crackled and flashed
And we were all scared as could be, and we splashed
All through mud and water, and then a big crack
Of lightning came down and Bill Beggs hollered back
From 'way up ahead, just as pale as a ghost,
And said that last lightning had struck him—almost!

And over by Griggs's somebody came out
And hollered to us when we're all just about
So tired we could drop, and they took us right in
By the big kitchen fire 'cause we're wet to the skin;
And Mrs. Griggs gave us some blankets to wear
While all of our clothes were hung over a chair;

And she made some tea till she got us warmed through
And then the storm stopped and the sky got all blue;
And Billy Beggs told her the flash came so close
That he 'membered the whole of the Lord's Prayer—
almost!

JAMES W. FOLEY

BOATS SAIL ON THE RIVERS

BOATS sail on the rivers,
And ships sail on the seas;
But clouds that sail across the sky
Are prettier far than these.

There are bridges on the rivers,
As pretty as you please;
But the bow that bridges heaven,
And overtops the trees,
And builds a road from earth to sky,
Is prettier far than these.

CHRISTINA GEORGINA ROSSETTI

THE HAYLOFT

THROUGH all the pleasant meadow side
The grass grew shoulder high,
Till the shining scythes went far and wide
And cut it down to dry.

Those green and sweetly smelling crops
They led in wagons home;
And they piled them here in mountain tops
For mountaineers to roam.

Here is Mount Clear, Mount Rusty Nail,
Mount Eagle and Mount High;—
The mice that in these mountains dwell,
No happier are than I!

Oh, what a joy to clamber there,
Oh, what a place to play,
With the sweet, the dim, the dusty air,
The happy hills of hay!

ROBERT LOUIS STEVENSON

ROBINSON CRUSOE'S STORY

THE night was thick and hazy
When the "Piccadilly Daisy"
Carried down the crew and captain in the sea;
And I think the water drowned 'em;
For they never, never found 'em,
And I know they didn't come ashore with me.

Oh! 'twas very sad and lonely
When I found myself the only
Population on this cultivated shore;
But I've made a little tavern
In a rocky little cavern,
And I sit and watch for people at the door.

I spent no time in looking
For a girl to do my cooking,
As I'm quite a clever hand at making stews;
But I had that fellow Friday,
Just to keep the tavern tidy,
And to put a Sunday polish on my shoes.

I have a little garden
That I'm cultivating lard in,
As the things I eat are rather tough and dry;

For I live on toasted lizards,
Prickly pears, and parrot gizzards,
And I'm really very fond of beetle pie.

The clothes I had were furry,
And it made me fret and worry
When I found the moths were eating off the hair;
And I had to scrape and sand 'em,
And I boiled 'em and I tanned 'em,
Till I got the fine morocco suit I wear.

I sometimes seek diversion
In a family excursion
With the few domestic animals you see;
And we take along a carrot
As refreshment for the parrot,
And a little can of jungleberry tea.

Then we gather as we travel,
Bits of moss and dirty gravel,
And we chip off little specimens of stone;
And we carry home as prizes
Funny bugs, of handy sizes,
Just to give the day a scientific tone.

If the roads are wet and muddy
We remain at home and study,—
For the Goat is very clever at a sum,—
And the Dog, instead of fighting,
Studies ornamental writing,
While the Cat is taking lessons on the drum.

We retire at eleven,
And we rise again at seven;
And I wish to call attention, as I close,
To the fact that all the scholars
Are correct about their collars,
And particular in turning out their toes.

CHARLES E. CARRYL

TOMMY'S DREAM; OR, THE GEOGRAPHY DEMON

I HATE my geography lesson!
  It's nothing but nonsense and names;
To bother me so every morning,
  It's really the greatest of shames.

The brooks, they flow into the rivers,
  And the rivers flow into the sea;
I hope, for my part, they enjoy it,
  But what does it matter to me?

Of late, even more I've disliked it,
  And more disagreeable it seems,
Ever since the sad evening last winter,
  When I had that most frightful of dreams.

I thought that a great horrid monster
  Stood suddenly there in my room—
A frightful Geography Demon,
  Enveloped in darkness and gloom;

His body and head like a mountain,
  A volcano on top for a hat;
His arms and his legs were like rivers,
  With a brook round his neck for cravat.

He laid on my poor trembling shoulder
  His fingers, cold, clammy, and long;
And, fixing his red eyes upon me,
  He roared forth this horrible song:

"Come! come! rise and come
Away to the banks of the Muskingum!
It flows o'er the plains of Timbuctoo,
With the peaks of Teneriffe just in view.
And the cataracts leap in the pale moonshine,
And they dance o'er the cliffs of Brandywine.

"Flee! flee! rise and flee
Away to the banks of the Tombigbee!

We'll pass by Alaska's flowery strand,
Where the emerald towers of Peking stand;
We'll pass them by, and will rest a while
On Michilimackinac's tropic isle;
While the apes of Barbary frisk around,
And the parrots crow with a lovely sound.

"Hie! hie! rise and hie
Away to the banks of the Yang-tse-Ki!
There the giant mountains of Oshkosh stand,
And the icebergs gleam through the falling sand;
While the elephants sit on the palm trees high,
And the cannibals feast on bad-boy pie.

"Go, go! rise and go
Away to the banks of Hoang-ho
There the Chickasaw sachem makes his tea,
And the kettle boils and waits for thee.
We'll smite thee, ho! and we'll lay thee low,
On the beautiful banks of Hoang-ho!"

These terrible words were still sounding
  Like trumpets and drums through my head,
When the monster clutched tighter my shoulder,
  And dragged me half out of the bed.

In terror, I clung to the bed post;
  But the faithless bed post, it broke.
I screamed out loud in my anguish,
  And suddenly—well, I awoke.

He was gone. But I cannot forget him,
  The fearful Geography Sprite.
He has my first thought in the morning,
  He has my last shudder at night.

Do you blame me for hating my lesson?
  Is it strange that it frightful should seem?
Or that I more and more abhor it
  Since I had that most terrible dream?

LAURA E. RICHARDS

THE REVENGE OF RAIN-IN-THE-FACE

IN that desolate land and lone,
  Where the Big Horn and Yellowstone
  Roar down their mountain path,
By their fires the Sioux Chiefs
Muttered their woes and griefs
  And the menace of their wrath.

"Revenge!" cried Rain-in-the-Face,
"Revenge upon all the race
  Of the white Chief with yellow hair!"
And the mountains dark and high
From their crags reëchoed the cry
  Of his anger and despair.

In the meadow, spreading wide
By woodland and riverside
  The Indian village stood;
All was silent as a dream,
Save the rushing of the stream
  And the blue jay in the wood.

In his war paint and his beads,
Like a bison among the reeds,
  In ambush the Sitting Bull
Lay with three thousand braves
Crouched in the clefts and caves,
  Savage, unmerciful!

Into the fatal snare
The White Chief with yellow hair
  And his three hundred men
Dashed headlong, sword in hand;
But of that gallant band
  Not one returned again.

The sudden darkness of death
Overwhelmed them like the breath
  And smoke of a furnace fire:

By the river's bank, and between
The rocks of the ravine,
They lay in their bloody attire.

But the foemen fled in the night,
And Rain-in-the-Face, in his flight,
Uplifted high in air
As a ghastly trophy, bore
The brave heart, that beat no more,
Of the White Chief with yellow hair.

Whose was the right and the wrong?
Sing it, O funeral song,
With a voice that is full of tears,
And say that our broken faith
Wrought all this ruin and scathe,
In the Year of a Hundred Years.

HENRY WADSWORTH LONGFELLOW

UNCLE JACK'S GREAT RUN

TELL the story? You know it all.
'Twas eighty-something—in the fall.
Nothing to nothing was the score,
Till at last, we had only five minutes more.
"Steady, boys!" was the captain's cry.
And we lined up, ready to do or die.
"Fifteen-twelve!" the signal came,
And 'twas mine to win or lose the game.

Teddy, the "half-back," passed the ball
To me, and he almost let it fall;
But I gripped it, and the line gaped wide
As our rushers flung their men aside.
Then, in the twinkling of an eye,
I saw their "tackle" rushing by
To block the gap.

I made a bend,
And like a flash went round the end.
Their "end-rush" grabbed, but I wriggled free,
And away I went—two after me—
For their goal. A good half-mile it seemed.
I heard faint cheering as if I dreamed.
I dodged their "back," and I crossed the line.
I fell on the ball! The game was mine!

That's all. What? Yes, there was one thing more.
You've all heard the story told before.
You know that my chum's sister came
To see the great Thanksgiving game.
Her eyes and the ribbon she wore were blue,
And I won the game—and Aunt Nelly, too.

TUDOR JENKS

THE SPELLING MATCH

THEY'D all sat down but Bess and me,
I surely thought I'd win.
To lose on such an easy word,
It was a shame and sin!
We spelled the longest in the book,
The hardest ones—right through,
"Xylography," and "pachyderm,"
And "gneiss," and "phthisic," too.

I spelled "immalleability,"
"Pneumonia"—it was fun!
"Phlebotomy," and "zoöphyte,"
Each long and curious one.
Then teacher gave a right queer smile
When Bess spelled "aquarelle,"
And backward, quick, she turned the leaves,
And then she gave out "spell."

I'm sure I never stopped to think
  About that "double l."
It seemed like such an easy word;
  But one can never tell.
"S-p-e-l," I spelled it—
  And how they all did laugh!
And teacher said, "I think, my dear,
  Too easy 'twas, by half."

Now Bessie was not proud nor mean,
  She said, "No wonder, Jane;
For we were thinking of big words.
  You'd spell it right, again."
I'm glad that it was Bess who won,
  And not those others. Well!
If I did miss one little word,
  I showed that I could spell.

ALICE MAUDE EWELL

LINES FROM "SNOWBOUND"

UNWARMED by any sunset light
The gray day darkened into night,
A night made hoary with the swarm
And whirlwind of the blinding storm,
As zigzag, wavering to and fro,
Crossed and recrossed the wingéd snow.
And ere the early bedtime came
The white drift piled the window frame,
And through the dark the clothesline posts
Looked in like tall and sheeted ghosts.

So all night long the storm roared on;
The morning broke without a sun;
In tiny spherule traced with lines
Of Nature's geometric signs,
In starry flake, and pellicle,
All day the hoary meteor fell;
And when the second morning shone,

We looked upon a world unknown,
On nothing we could call our own.
Around the glistening wonder bent
The blue walls of the firmament,
No clouds above, no earth below,—
A universe of sky and snow!
The old familiar sights of ours
Took marvelous shapes; strange domes and towers
Rose up where sty or corncrib stood,
Or garden wall, or belt of wood;
A smooth white mound the brush pile showed,
A fenceless drift what once was road;
The bridle post an old man sat
With loose-flung coat and high cocked hat;
The well curb had a Chinese roof;
And even the long sweep, high aloof,
In its slant splendor, seemed to tell
Of Pisa's leaning miracle.

. . . .

Shut in from all the world without,
We sat the clean-winged hearth about,
Content to let the north wind roar
In baffled rage at pane and door,
While the red logs before us beat
The frost line back with tropic heat;
And ever, when a louder blast
Shook beam and rafter as it passed,
The merrier up its roaring draught
The great throat of the chimney laughed.
The house dog on his paws outspread
Laid to the fire his drowsy head,
The cat's dark silhouette on the wall
A couchant tiger's seemed to fall;
And, for the winter fireside meet,
Between the andirons' straddling feet,
The mug of cider simmered slow,
The apples spluttered in a row,
And close at hand the basket stood
With nuts from brown October's wood.

John Greenleaf Whittier

THE BUGLE SONG

THE splendor falls on castle walls
And snowy summits old in story:
The long light shakes across the lakes
And the wild cataract leaps in glory.
Blow, bugle, blow, set the wild echoes flying,
Blow, bugle; answer, echoes, dying, dying, dying.

O hark, O hear! how thin and clear,
And thinner, clearer, farther going!
O sweet and far from cliff and scar
The horns of Elfland faintly blowing!
Blow, let us hear the purple glens replying:
Blow, bugle; answer, echoes, dying, dying, dying.

O love, they die in yon rich sky,
They faint on hill or field or river:
Our echoes roll from soul to soul,
And grow forever and forever.
Blow, bugle, blow, set the wild echoes flying,
And answer, echoes, answer, dying, dying, dying.

ALFRED TENNYSON

THE SHIP OF STATE

SAIL on, sail on, O Ship of State!
Sail on, O Union, strong and great!
Humanity, with all its fears,
With all the hopes of future years,
Is hanging breathless on thy fate!
We know what Master laid thy keel,
What Workmen wrought thy ribs of steel,
Who made each mast, and sail, and rope;
What anvils rang, what hammers beat,
In what a forge and what a heat
Were forged the anchors of thy hope!
Fear not each sudden sound and shock—

'Tis of the wave, and not the rocks;
'Tis but the flapping of the sail,
And not a rent made by the gale!
In spite of rock, and tempest roar,
In spite of false lights on the shore,
Sail on, nor fear to breast the sea!
Our hearts, our hopes, are all with thee.
Our hearts, our hopes, our prayers, our tears,
Our faith, triumphant o'er our fears,
Are all with thee, are all with thee!

HENRY W. LONGFELLOW

THE HAPPY WARRIOR

CHARACTER OF THE HAPPY WARRIOR

WHO is the happy Warrior? Who is he
That every man in arms should wish to be?

It is the generous spirit, who, when brought
Among the tasks of real life, hath wrought
Upon the plan that pleased his boyish thought:
Whose high endeavors are an inward light
That makes the path before him always bright:
Who, with a natural instinct to discern
What knowledge can perform, is diligent to learn;
Abides by this resolve, and stops not there,
But makes his moral being his prime care;
Who, doomed to go in company with pain,
And fear, and bloodshed, miserable train!
Turns his necessity to glorious gain;
In face of these doth exercise a power
Which is our human natures' highest dower;
Controls them and subdues, transmutes, bereaves
Of their bad influence, and their good receives:
By objects which might force the soul to abate
Her feeling, rendered more compassionate;
Is placable—because occasions rise
So often that demand such sacrifice;

More skillful in self-knowledge, even more pure,
As tempted more; more able to endure,
As more exposed to suffering and distress;
Thence, also, more alive to tenderness.

'Tis he whose law is reason; who depends
Upon that law as on the best of friends;
To evil for a guard against worse ill,
And what in quality or act is best
Doth seldom on a right foundation rest,
He labors good on good to fix, and owes
To virtue every triumph that he knows:
Who, if he rise to station of command,
Rises by open means; and there will stand
On honorable terms, or else retire,
And in himself possess his own desire;
Who comprehends his trust, and to the same
Keeps faithful with a singleness of aim;
And therefore does not stoop, nor lie in wait
For wealth, or honors, or for worldly state;
Whom they must follow; on whose head must fall,
Like showers of manna, if they come at all:
Whose powers shed round him in the common strife,
Or mild concerns of ordinary life,
A constant influence, a peculiar grace;
But who, if he be called upon to face
Some awful moment to which Heaven has joined
Great issues, good or bad for human kind,
Is happy as a lover; and attired
With sudden brightness, like a man inspired;
And, through the heat of conflict, keeps the law
In calmness made, and sees what he foresaw;
Or if an unexpected call succeed,
Come when it will, is equal to the need:
He who, though thus endued as with a sense
And faculty for storm and turbulence,
Is yet a soul whose master bias leans
To homefelt pleasures and to gentle scenes;
Sweet images! which, whereso'er he be,
Are at his heart; and such fidelity
It is his darling passion to approve;

More brave for this, that he hath much to love.
'Tis, finally, the Man, who, lifted high,
Conspicuous object in a Nation's eye,
Or left unthought of in obscurity,—
Who, with a toward or untoward lot,
Prosperous or adverse, to his wish or not—
Plays, in the many games of life, that one
Where what he most doth value must be won:
Whom neither shape of danger can dismay,
Nor thought of tender happiness betray;
Who, not content that former worth stand fast,
Looks forward, persevering to the last,
From well to better, daily self-surpassed:
Who, whether praise of him must walk the earth
For ever, and to noble deeds give birth,
Or he must fall, to sleep without his fame,
And leave a dead unprofitable name—
Finds comfort in himself and in his cause;
And, while the mortal mist is gathering, draws
His breath in confidence of Heaven's applause.

This is the happy Warrior; this is he
That every man in arms should wish to be.

WILLIAM WORDSWORTH

AN ODE IN IMITATION OF ALCÆUS

WHAT constitutes a State?
Not high-raised battlement or labored mound,
Thick wall or moated gate;
Not cities proud with spires and turrets crowned;
Not bays and broad-armed ports,
Where, laughing at the storm, rich navies ride;
Not starred and spangled courts,
Where low-browed baseness wafts perfume to pride.
No:—men, high-minded men,
With powers as far above dull brutes endued
In forest, brake, or den,

As beasts excel cold rocks and brambles rude,—
  Men who their duties know,
But know their rights, and, knowing, dare maintain;
  Prevent the long-aimed blow,
And crush the tyrant while they rend the chain:—
  These constitute a State;
And sovereign Law, that State's collected will,
  O'er thrones and globes elate
Sits empress, crowning good, repressing ill.
  Smit by her sacred frown,
The fiend, Dissension, like a vapor sinks;
  And e'en the all-dazzling Crown
Hides his faint rays, and at her bidding shrinks.

William Jones

OH MOTHER OF A MIGHTY RACE

Oh mother of a mighty race,
  Yet lovely in thy youthful grace!
The elder dames, thy haughty peers,
Admire and hate thy blooming years.
  With words of shame
And taunts of scorn they join thy name.

For on thy cheeks the glow is spread
That tints thy morning hills with red;
Thy step—the wild deer's rustling feet
Within thy woods are not more fleet;
  Thy hopeful eye
Is bright as thine own sunny sky.

Ay, let them rail—those haughty ones,
While safe thou dwellest with thy sons.
They do not know how loved thou art,
How many a fond and fearless heart
  Would rise to throw
Its life between thee and the foe.

They know not, in their hate and pride,
What virtues with thy children bide;
How true, how good, thy graceful maids
Make bright, like flowers, the valley shades;
  What generous men
Spring, like thine oaks, by hill and glen—

What cordial welcomes greet the guest
By thy lone rivers of the West;
How faith is kept, and truth revered,
And man is loved, and God is feared,
  In woodland homes,
And where the ocean border foams.

There's freedom at thy gates and rest
For Earth's downtrodden and oppressed,
A shelter for the hunted head,
For the starved laborer toil and bread,
  Power, at thy bounds,
Stops and calls back his baffled hounds.

Oh, fair young mother! on thy brow
Shall sit a nobler grace than now.
Deep in the brightness of the skies
The thronging years in glory rise,
  And, as they fleet,
Drop strength and riches at thy feet.

William Cullen Bryant

THE SKELETON IN ARMOR

"SPEAK! speak! thou fearful guest!
Who, with thy hollow breast
Still in rude armor dressed,
  Comest to daunt me!
Wrapped not in Eastern balms,
But with thy fleshless palms
Stretched, as if asking alms,
  Why dost thou haunt me?"

Then, from those cavernous eyes
Pale flashes seemed to rise,
As when the Northern skies
Gleam in December;
And, like the water's flow
Under December's snow,
Came a dull voice of woe
From the heart's chamber.

"I was a Viking old!
My deeds, though manifold,
No Skald in song has told,
No Saga taught thee!
Take heed, that in thy verse
Thou dost the tale rehearse,
Else dread a dead man's curse;
For this I sought thee.

"Far in the Northern Land,
By the wild Baltic's strand,
I, with my childish hand,
Tamed the gerfalcon;
And, with my skates fast bound,
Skimmed the half-frozen Sound,
That the poor whimpering hound
Trembled to walk on.

"Oft to his frozen lair
Tracked I the grisly bear,
While from my path the hare
Fled like a shadow;
Oft through the forest dark
Followed the werewolf's bark,
Until the soaring lark
Sang from the meadow.

"But when I older grew,
Joining a corsair's crew,
O'er the dark sea I flew
With the marauders.

Wild was the life we led;
Many the souls that sped,
Many the hearts that bled,
    By our stern orders.

"Many a wassail bout
Wore the long Winter out;
Often our midnight shout
    Set the cocks crowing,
As we the Berserk's tale
Measured in cups of ale,
Draining the oaken pail,
    Filled to o'erflowing.

"Once as I told in glee
Tales of the stormy sea,
Soft eyes did gaze on me,
    Burning yet tender;
And as the white stars shine
On the dark Norway pine,
On that dark heart of mine
    Fell their soft splendor.

"I wooed the blue-eyed maid,
Yielding, yet half afraid,
And in the forest's shade
    Our vows were plighted.
Under its loosened vest
Fluttered her little breast,
Like birds within their nest
    By the hawk frighted.

"Bright in her father's hall
Shields gleamed upon the wall,
Loud sang the minstrels all,
    Chanting his glory;
When of old Hildebrand
I asked his daughter's hand,
Mute did the minstrels stand
    To hear my story.

"While the brown ale he quaffed,
Loud then the champion laughed,
And as the wind gusts waft
  The sea foam brightly,
So the loud laugh of scorn,
Out of those lips unshorn,
From the deep drinking horn
  Blew the foam lightly.

"She was a Prince's child,
I but a Viking wild,
And though she blushed and smiled,
  I was discarded!
Should not the dove so white
Follow the sea mew's flight,
Why did they leave that night
  Her nest unguarded?

"Scarce had I put to sea,
Bearing the maid with me,
Fairest of all was she
  Among the Norsemen!
When on the white sea strand,
Waving his armèd hand,
Saw we old Hildebrand,
  With twenty horsemen.

"Then launched they to the blast,
Bent like a reed each mast,
Yet we were gaining fast,
  When the wind failed us;
And with a sudden flaw
Came round the gusty Skaw,
So that our foe we saw
  Laugh as he hailed us.

"And as to catch the gale
Round veered the flapping sail,
'Death!' was the helmsman's hail,
  'Death without quarter!'

Midships with iron keel
Struck we her ribs of steel;
Down her black hulk did reel
    Through the black water!

"As with his wings aslant,
Sails the fierce cormorant,
Seeking some rocky haunt,
    With his prey laden,—
So toward the open main,
Beating to sea again,
Through the wild hurricane,
    Bore I the maiden.

"Three weeks we westward bore,
And when the storm was o'er,
Cloudlike we saw the shore
    Stretching to leeward;
There for my lady's bower
Built I the lofty tower,
Which, to this very hour,
    Stands looking seaward.

"There lived we many years;
Time dried the maiden's tears;
She had forgot her fears,
    She was a mother;
Death closed her mild blue eyes,
Under that tower she lies;
Ne'er shall the sun arise
    On such another!

"Still grew my bosom then,
Still as a stagnant fen!
Hateful to me were men,
    The sunlight hateful!
In the vast forest here,
Clad in my warlike gear,
Fell I upon my spear,
    Oh, death was grateful!

"Thus, seamed with many scars,
Bursting these prison bars,
Up to its native stars
My soul ascended!
There from the flowing bowl
Deep drinks the warrior's soul,
Skoal! to the Northland! *skoal!*"
Thus the tale ended.

HENRY WADSWORTH LONGFELLOW

THE BALLAD OF THE RUBBER PLANT AND THE PALM

(*The quaint humor of these verses must be appreciated by the speaker to carry it successfully to the audience*)

A RUBBER PLANT and a small Palm stood
Upon a marble floor.
From either side the fireplace
They scanned each other o'er.

"What do you rub?" the small Palm asked
His statelier neighbor tall.
"Alas!" the Rubber Plant replied,
"I cannot rub at all.

"If I had hands like yours," he said,
As wistfully he eyed
His smaller neighbor's pretty palms
With fingers opened wide,

"Then I could rub!"—"And yet," replied
The little Palm, "you see,
Though I have hands, I cannot rub,
And that's the rub with me.

"I wonder why it's always so:
That something we have got
Seems never quite complete to be
Without what we have not.

"I've often longed to rub my hands
  With glee, here in my tub;
And you, no doubt, have often wished
  You had some hands to rub.

"Now, if you were I, or I were you,—
  No, that's not right, I see,—
But if you *and* I were you *or* I,
  What a fine plant we should be!"

Still, they did as all good plants should—
  Kept green all winter long:
So no one ever knew or guessed
  That anything was wrong.

ALICE W. ROLLINS

IF YOU CAN'T GO OVER OR UNDER, GO ROUND

A BABY mole got to feeling big,
And wanted to show how he could dig;
So he plowed along in the soft, warm dirt
Till he hit something hard, and it surely hurt!
A dozen stars flew out of his snout;
He sat on his haunches, began to pout;
Then rammed the thing again with his head—
His grandpap picked him up half dead.
"Young man," he said, "though your pate is bone,
You can't butt your way through solid stone.
This bit of advice is good, I've found:
If you can't go over or under, go round."

A traveler came to a stream one day,
And because it presumed to cross his way,
And wouldn't turn round to suit his whim
And change its course to go with him,
His anger rose far more than it should,
And he vowed he'd cross right where he stood.

A man said there was a bridge below,
But not a step would he budge or go.
The current was swift and the bank was steep,
But he jumped right in with a violent leap.
A fisherman dragged him out half drowned:
"When you can't go over or under, go round."

If you come to a place that you can't get *through*,
Or *over* or *under*, the thing to do
Is to find a way *round* the impassable wall,
Not say you'll go YOUR way or not at all.
You can always get to the place you're going,
If you'll set your sails as the wind is blowing.
If the mountains are high, go round the valley;
If the streets are blocked, go up some alley;
If the parlor car's filled, don't scorn a freight;
If the front door's closed, go in the side gate.
To reach your goal this advice is sound:
If you can't go over or under, go round!

JOSEPH MORRIS

ONCE-ON-A-TIME

HEIGH-HO! What frolics we might see,
Had it only happened to you and me
To be born in some far-distant clime,
In the country of Somewhere, once-on-a-time!

Why, once-on-a-time there were mountains of gold,
And caves full of jewels, and treasures untold;
There were birds just waiting to fly before
And show you the way to the magical door.
And, under a tree, there was sure to be
A queer little woman to give you the key;
And a tiny, dancing, good-natured elf,
To say, with his scepter, "Help yourself!"
For millions of dollars grew from a dime
In the country of Somewhere, once-on-a-time.

If we lived in the country of Somewhere, you
Could do whatever you chose to do;
Instead of a boy, with the garden to weed,
You might be a knight, with a sword and a steed;
Instead of a girl, with a towel to hem,
I might be a princess, with robe and gem,
With a gay little page, and a harper old,
Who knew all the stories that ever were told—
Stories in prose, and stories in rhyme,
That happened somewhere, once-on-a-time.

In the country of Somewhere, no one looks
At maps and blackboards and grammar books;
For all your knowledge just grows and grows,
Like the song in a bird, or the sweet in a rose.
And if ever I chance, on a fortunate day,
To that wonderful region to find my way,
Why, then, if the stories all are true,
As quick as I can, I'll come for you,
And we'll row away to its happy shores,
In a silver shallop with golden oars.

EMILY HUNTINGTON MILLER

OFF THE LINE

THE boys stood up in the reading class—
A dozen or so—and each one said
That those at the foot should never pass,
Or find it easy to get to the head.

There wasn't another boy on the line
More anxious than Jimmy to keep his place:
For to be at the head was very fine,
But to go to the foot was a sad disgrace.

But Jim delighted in game of ball,
Polo, tennis, or lawn croquet;
And his mind was not on his books at all
When he took his place in the class that day.

'Twas his turn to read, and he started off
With an air attentive—a vain pretense,
For the boys around him began to cough,
And nudge and chuckle at Jim's expense.

"You've skipped a line," whispered generous Ben,
Who often had helped in this way before;
"You've skipped a line!" shouted Jim, and then
Of course the schoolroom was in a roar.

As down to the foot Jim went that day,
He learned a lesson that any dunce
Might have known, for we're sure to stray
If we try to be in two places at once.

Sport, when you sport, in an earnest way,
With a merry heart and a cheerful face;
But when at your books think not of your play,
Or else you'll certainly lose your place.

JOSEPHINE POLLARD

APPRECIATION

LIFE'S a bully good game with its kicks and cuffs—
Some smile, some laugh, some bluff;
Some carry a load too heavy to bear
While some push on with never a care,
But the load will seldom heavy be
When I appreciate you and you appreciate me.

He who lives by the side of the road
And helps to bear his brother's load
May seem to travel lone and long
While the world goes by with a merry song,
But the heart grows warm and sorrows flee
When I appreciate you and you appreciate me

When I appreciate you and you appreciate me,
  The road seems short to victory;
It buoys one up and calls "Come on,"
  And days grow brighter with the dawn;
There is no doubt or mystery
  When I appreciate you and you appreciate me.

It's the greatest thought in heaven or earth—
  It helps us know our fellow's worth;
There'd be no wars or bitterness,
  No fear, no hate, no grasping; yes,
It makes work play, and the careworn free
  When I appreciate you and you appreciate me.

WILLIAM JUDSON KIBBY

GRADATIM

HEAVEN is not reached at a single bound;
  But we build the ladder by which we rise
  From the lowly earth to the vaulted skies,
And we mount to its summit, round by round.

I count this thing to be grandly true:
  That a noble deed is a step towards God,—
  Lifting the soul from the common clod
To a purer air and a broader view.

We rise by the things that are under feet;
  By what we have mastered of good and gain;
  By the pride deposed and the passion slain,
And the vanquished ills that we hourly meet.

We hope, we aspire, we resolve, we trust,
  When the morning calls us to life and light,
  But our hearts grow weary, and, ere the night,
Our lives are trailing the sordid dust.

We hope, we resolve, we aspire, we pray,
And we think that we mount the air on wings
Beyond the recall of sensual things,
While our feet still cling to the heavy clay.

Wings for the angels, but feet for men!
We may borrow the wings to find the way—
We may hope, and resolve and aspire, and pray;
But our feet must rise, or we fall again.

Only in dreams is a ladder thrown
From the weary earth to the sapphire walls;
But the dreams depart, and the vision falls,
And the sleeper wakes on his pillow of stone.

Heaven is not reached at a single bound;
But we build the ladder by which we rise
From the lowly earth to the vaulted skies,
And we mount to its summit, round by round.

J. G. Holland

RULES FOR THE ROAD

STAND straight:
Step firmly, throw your weight:
The heaven is high above your head,
The good gray road is faithful to your tread.

Be strong:
Sing to your heart a battle song:
Though hidden foemen lie in wait,
Something is in you that can smile at Fate.

Press through:
Nothing can harm if you are true.
And when the night comes, rest:
The earth is friendly as a mother's breast.

Edwin Markham

THAT CALF

TO the yard, by the barn, came the farmer one morn,
And, calling the cattle, he said,
While they trembled with fright: "Now which of you, last night,
Shut the barn door while I was abed?"
Each one of them all shook his head.

Now the little calf Spot, she was down in the lot,
And the way the rest talked was a shame;
For no one, night before, saw her shut up the door;
But they said that she did, all the same,
For they always made her take the blame.

Said the horse (dapple gray), "I was not up that way
Last night, as I now recollect;"
And the bull, passing by, tossed his horns very high,
And said, "Let who may here object,
I say this, that calf I suspect."

Then out spoke the cow, "It is terrible now,
To accuse honest folks of such tricks."
Said the cock in the tree, "I'm sure 'twasn't me;"
And the sheep all cried, "Bah! (there were six)
Now that calf's got herself in a fix."

"Why, of course we all knew 'twas the wrong thing to do,"
Said the chickens. "Of course," said the cat.
"I suppose," cried the mule, "some folks think me a fool.
But I'm not quite so simple as that;
The poor calf never knows what she's at."

Just that moment, the calf, who was always the laugh
And the jest of the yard, came in sight.
"Did you shut my barn door?" asked the farmer once more.
"I did, sir, I closed it last night,"
Said the calf; "and I thought that was right."

Then each one shook his head. "She will catch it," they cried,
"Serves her right for her meddlesome ways."
Said the farmer, "Come here, little bossy, my dear,
You have done what I cannot repay,
And your fortune is made from to-day.

"For a wonder, last night, I forgot the door quite,
And if you had not shut it so neat,
All my colts had slipped in, and gone right to the bin,
And got what they ought not to eat,
They'd have foundered themselves upon wheat."

Then each hoof of them all began loudly to bawl,
The very mule smiled, the cock crew:
"Little Spotty, my dear, you're a favorite here,"
They cried, "we all said it was you,
We were so glad to give you your due."
And the calf answered knowingly, "Boo!"

PHŒBE CARY

THE GLAD SONG

SING a song, sing a song,
Ring the glad bells all along;
Smile at him who frowns at you,
He will smile and then they're two.

Laugh a bit, laugh a bit,
Folks will soon be catching it,
Can't resist a happy face;
World will be a merry place.

Laugh a bit and sing a song,
Where they are there's nothing wrong;
Joy will dance the whole world through,
But it must begin with you.

JOSEPH MORRIS

THE UNMUSICAL SOLOIST

MUSIC hath charms—at least it should;
Even a homely voice sounds good
That sings a cheerful, gladsome song
That shortens the way, however long.
A screechy fife, a bass drum's beat
Is wonderful music to marching feet;
A scratchy fiddle or banjo's thump
May tickle the toes till they want to jump.
But one musician fills the air
With discords that jar folks everywhere.
A pity it is he ever was born—
The discordant fellow who toots his own horn.

He gets in the front where all can see—
"Now turn the spot light right on me,"
He says, and sings in tones sonorous
His own sweet halleluiah chorus.
Refrain and verse are both the same—
The pronoun I or his own name.
He trumpets his worth with such windy tooting
That louder it sounds than cowboys shooting.
This man's a nuisance wherever he goes,
For the world soon tires of the chap who blows.
Whether mighty in station or hoer of corn,
Unwelcome's the fellow who toots his own horn.

The poorest woodchopper makes the most sound;
A poor cook clatters the most pans around;
The rattling spoke carries least of the load;
And jingling pennies pay little that's owed;
A rooster crows but lays no eggs;
A braggart blows but drives no pegs.
He works out of harmony with any team,
For others are skim milk and he is the cream.
"The world," so far as he can see,
"Consists of a few other folks and ME."
He richly deserves to be held in scorn—
The ridiculous fellow who toots his own horn.

JOSEPH MORRIS

THE PESSIMIST

NOTHING to do but work,
  Nothing to eat but food,
Nothing to wear but clothes
  To keep one from going nude.

Nothing to breathe but air
  Quick as a flash 'tis gone;
Nowhere to fall but off,
  Nowhere to stand but on.

Nothing to comb but hair,
  Nowhere to sleep but in bed,
Nothing to weep but tears,
  Nothing to bury but dead.

Nothing to sing but songs,
  Ah, well, alas! alack!
Nowhere to go but out,
  Nowhere to come but back.

Nothing to see but sights,
  Nothing to quench but thirst,
Nothing to have but what we've got;
  Thus thro' life we are cursed.

Nothing to strike but a gait;
  Everything moves that goes.
Nothing at all but common sense
  Can ever withstand these woes.

BEN KING

HERE'S HOPIN'

YEAR ain't been the very best—
  Purty hard by trouble pressed;
But the rough way leads to rest—
    Here's hopin'!

Maybe craps way short; the rills
Couldn't turn the silent mills;
But the light's behind the hills—
Here's hopin'!

Where we planted roses sweet
Thorns come up an' pricked the feet;
But this old world's hard to beat—
Here's hopin'!

P'r'aps the buildin' that we planned
'Gainst the cyclone couldn't stand;
But, thank God we've got the *land*—
Here's hopin'!

Maybe flowers we hoped to save
Have been scattered on a grave;
But the heart's still beatin' brave—
Here's hopin'!

That we'll see the mornin' light—
That the very darkest night
Can't hide heaven from our sight—
Here's hopin'!

FRANK L. STANTON

SUCCESS *

IF you want a thing bad enough
To go out and fight for it,
Work day and night for it,
Give up your time and your peace and your sleep for it,
If only desire of it
Makes you quite mad enough
Never to tire of it,
Makes you hold all other things tawdry and cheap for it,
If life seems all empty and useless without it
And all that you scheme and you dream is about it,

* From "Things as They Are," by Burton Braley, copyright, 1916, George H. Doran Company, Publishers.

If gladly you'll sweat for it,
Fret for it,
Plan for it,
Lose all your terror of God or man for it,
If you'll simply go after that thing that you want,
With all your capacity,
Strength and sagacity,
Faith, hope and confidence, stern pertinacity,
If neither cold poverty, famished and gaunt,
Nor sickness nor pain
Of body or brain
Can turn you away from the thing that you want,
If dogged and grim you besiege and beset it,
You'll get it!

BURTON BRALE

NEVER TROUBLE TROUBLE

I USED to hear a saying
That had a deal of pith;
It gave a cheerful spirit
To face existence with,
Especially when matters
Seemed doomed to go askew.
'Twas *Never trouble trouble*
Till trouble troubles you.

Not woes at hand, those coming
Are hardest to resist;
We hear them stalk like giants,
We see them through a mist.
But big things in the brewing
Are small things in the brew;
So never trouble trouble
Till trouble troubles you.

Just look at things through glasses
That show the evidence;

One lens of them is courage,
The other common sense.
They'll make it clear, misgivings
Are just a bugaboo;
No more you'll trouble trouble
Till trouble troubles you.

St. Clair Adams

SWELLITIS

SOMEBODY said he'd done it well,
And presto! his head began to swell;
Bigger and bigger the poor thing grew—
A wonder it didn't split in two.
In size a balloon could scarcely match it;
He needed a fishing pole to scratch it;—
But six and a half was the size of his hat,
And it rattled around on his head at that!

"Good work," somebody chanced to say,
And his chest swelled big as a load of hay.
About himself, like a rooster, he crowed;
Of his wonderful work he bragged and blowed.
He marched around with a peacock strut;
Gigantic to him was the figure he cut;—
But he wore a very small-sized suit,
And loosely it hung on him, to boot!

HE was the chap who made things hum!
HE was the drumstick and the drum!
HE was the shirt bosom and the starch!
HE was the keystone in the arch!
HE was the axis of the earth!
Nothing existed before his birth!
But when he was off from work a day,
Nobody knew that he was away!

This is a fact that is sad to tell:
It's the empty head that is bound to swell;

It's the lightweight fellow who soars to the skies,
And bursts like a bubble before your eyes.
A big man is humbled by honest praise,
And tries to think of all the ways
To improve his work and do it well;—
But a little man starts of himself to yell!

JOSEPH MORRIS

A SONG OF THANKSGIVING

THANK God I can rejoice
In human things—the multitude's glad voice,
The street's warm surge beneath the city light,
The rush of hurrying faces on my sight,
The million-celled emotion in the press
That would their human fellowship confess.
Thank Thee because I may my brother feed,
That Thou hast opened me unto his need,
Kept me from being callous, cold and blind,
Taught me the melody of being kind.
Thus, for my own and for my brother's sake—
Thank Thee I am awake!

Thank Thee that I can trust!
That though a thousand times I feel the thrust
Of faith betrayed, I still have faith in man,
Believe him pure and good since time began—
Thy child forever, though he may forget
The perfect mold in which his soul was set.
Thank Thee that when love dies, fresh love springs up,
New wonders pour from Heaven's cup.
Young to my soul the ancient need returns,
Immortal in my heart the ardor burns;
My altar fires replenished from above—
Thank Thee that I can love!

Thank Thee that I can hear,
Finely and keenly with the inner ear,

Below the rush and clamor of a throng
The mighty music of the under song.
And when the day has journeyed to its rest,
Lo, as I listen, from the amber west,
Where the great organ lifts its glowing spires,
There sounds the chanting of the unseen choirs.
Thank Thee for sight that shows the hidden flame
Beneath all breathing, throbbing things the same,
Thy Pulse the pattern of the thing to be . . .
    Thank Thee that I can see!

Thank Thee that I can feel!
That though life's blade be terrible as steel,
My soul is stript and naked to the fang,
I crave the stab of beauty and the pang.
To be alive,
To think, to yearn, to strive,
To suffer torture when the goal is wrong,
To be sent back and fashioned strong
Rejoicing in the lesson that was taught
By all the good the grim experience wrought;
At last, exulting, to *arrive* . . .
    Thank God I am alive!

ANGELA MORGAN

OPPORTUNITY

THEY do me wrong who say I come no more
  When once I knock and fail to find you in;
For every day I stand outside your door,
  And bid you wake, and rise to fight and win.

Wail not for precious chances passed away,
  Weep not for golden ages on the wane!
Each night I burn the records of the day,—
  At sunrise every soul is born again!

Laugh like a boy at splendors that have sped,
To vanished joys be blind and deaf and dumb;
My judgments seal the dead past with its dead,
But never bind a moment yet to come.

Though deep in mire, wring not your hands and weep;
I lend my arm to all who say "I can!"
No shame-faced outcast ever sank so deep,
But yet might rise and be again a man!

Dost thou behold thy lost youth all aghast?
Dost reel from righteous Retribution's blow?
Then turn from blotted archives of the past,
And find the future's pages white as snow.

Art thou a mourner? Rouse thee from thy spell;
Art thou a sinner? Sins may be forgiven;
Each morning gives thee wings to flee from hell,
Each night a star to guide thy feet to heaven.

WALTER MALONE

TIDE AT NIGHT

THE tide laps and steals
Up the smooth, white shore.
Slides forward—
Slips back—
With a long stride,
With a soft stride;
Trembles a moment at the full—
Steals back.
With a long stride,
With a soft stride,
The tide laps and steals
Back to the black sea.

ELIZABETH TOMPKINS

OPPORTUNITY

THERE is a tide in the affairs of men,
Which, taken at the flood, leads on to fortune;
Omitted, all the voyage of their life
Is bound in shallows and in miseries.
On such a full sea are we now afloat;
And we must take the current when it serves,
Or lose our ventures.

WILLIAM SHAKESPEARE

JUST WHISTLE

WHEN times are bad an' folks are sad
An' gloomy day by day,
Jest try your best at lookin' glad
An' whistle 'em away.

Don't mind how troubles bristle,
Jest take a rose or thistle.
Hold your own
An' change your tone
An' whistle, whistle, whistle!

A song is worth a world o' sighs.
When red the lightnings play,
Look for the rainbow in the skies
An' whistle 'em away.

Don't mind how troubles bristle,
The rose comes with the thistle.
Hold your own
An' change your tone
An' whistle, whistle, whistle!

Each day comes with a life that's new,
A strange, continued story
But still beneath a bend o' blue
The world rolls on to glory.

Don't mind how troubles bristle,
Jest take a rose or thistle.
Hold your own
An' change your tone
An' whistle, whistle, whistle!

FRANK L. STANTON

WORK

(A Song of Triumph)

WORK!
Thank God for the might of it,
The ardor, the urge, the delight of it—
Work that springs from the heart's desire,
Setting the brain and the soul on fire—
Oh, what is so good as the heat of it,
And what is so glad as the beat of it,
And what is so kind as the stern command,
Challenging brain and heart and hand?

Work!
Thank God for the pride of it,
For the beautiful, conquering tide of it,
Sweeping the life in its furious flood,
Thrilling the arteries, cleansing the blood,
Mastering stupor and dull despair,
Moving the dreamer to do and dare.
Oh, what is so good as the urge of it,
And what is so glad as the surge of it,
And what is so strong as the summons deep,
Rousing the torpid soul from sleep?

Work!
Thank God for the pace of it,
For the terrible, keen, swift race of it;
Fiery steeds in full control,
Nostrils a-quiver to greet the goal.

Work, the Power that drives behind,
Guiding the purposes, taming the mind,
Holding the runaway wishes back,
Reining the will to one steady track,
Speeding the energies faster, faster,
Triumphing over disaster.
Oh, what is so good as the pain of it,
And what is so great as the gain of it?
And what is so kind as the cruel goad,
Forcing us on through the rugged road?

Work!
Thank God for the swing of it,
For the clamoring, hammering ring of it,
Passion and labor daily hurled
On the mighty anvils of the world.
Oh, what is so fierce as the flame of it?
And what is so huge as the aim of it?
Thundering on through dearth and doubt,
Calling the plan of the Maker out.
Work, the Titan; Work, the friend,
Shaping the earth to a glorious end,
Draining the swamps and blasting the hills,
Doing whatever the Spirit wills—
Rending a continent apart,
To answer the dream of the Master heart.
Thank God for a world where none may shirk—
Thank God for the splendor of work!

ANGELA MORGAN

OPPORTUNITY *

WITH doubt and dismay you are smitten
You think there's no chance for you, son?
Why, the best books haven't been written
The best race hasn't been run,

* From "A Banjo at Armageddon," by Burton Braley, George H. Doran Company, Publishers.

The best score hasn't been made yet,
  The best song hasn't been sung,
The best tune hasn't been played yet,
  Cheer up, for the world is young!

No chance? Why the world is just eager
  For things that you ought to create
Its store of true wealth is still meager
  Its needs are incessant and great,
It yearns for more power and beauty
  More laughter and love and romance,
More loyalty, labor and duty,
  No chance—why there's nothing but chance!

For the best verse hasn't been rhymed yet,
  The best house hasn't been planned,
The highest peak hasn't been climbed yet,
  The mightiest rivers aren't spanned,
Don't worry and fret, faint hearted,
  The chances have just begun,
For the best jobs haven't been started,
  The best work hasn't been done.

BURTON BRALEY

THE WELCOME MAN

THERE'S a man in the world who is never turned down, wherever he chances to stray; he gets the glad hand in the populous town, or out where the farmers make hay; he's greeted with pleasure on deserts of sand, and deep in the aisles of the woods; wherever he goes there's the welcoming hand—he's The Man Who Delivers the Goods. The failures of life sit around and complain; the gods haven't treated them white; they've lost their umbrellas whenever there's rain, and they haven't their lanterns at night; men tire of the failures who fill with their sighs the air of their own neighborhoods; there's one who is greeted with love-lighted eyes—he's The Man Who Delivers the Goods. One fellow is lazy, and watches the clock, and waits for the whistle to blow; and one has a hammer, with which he will knock, and one tells a story of woe; and one, if requested to travel a mile, will measure the perches and roods; but one does his stunt with a whistle or smile—he's The Man Who Delivers the Goods. One man is afraid that he'll labor too hard—the world isn't yearning for such; and one man is always alert, on his guard, lest he put in a minute too much; and one has a grouch or a temper that's bad, and one is a creature of moods; so it's hey for the joyous and rollicking lad—for the One Who Delivers the Goods!

WALT MASON

IF

IF you can keep your head when all about you
  Are losing theirs and blaming it on you,
If you can trust yourself when all men doubt you,
  But make allowance for their doubting too;
If you can wait and not be tired by waiting,
  Or being lied about, don't deal in lies,
Or being hated don't give way to hating,
  And yet don't look too good, nor talk too wise:

If you can dream—and not make dreams your master;
  If you can think—and not make thoughts your aim,
If you can meet with Triumph and Disaster
  And treat those two impostors just the same;
If you can bear to hear the truth you've spoken
  Twisted by knaves to make a trap for fools,
Or watch the things you gave your life to, broken,
  And stoop and build 'em up with worn-out tools:

If you can make one heap of all your winnings
  And risk it on one turn of pitch-and-toss,
And lose, and start again at your beginnings
  And never breathe a word about your loss;

If you can force your heart and nerve and sinew
  To serve your turn long after they are gone,
And so hold on when there is nothing in you
  Except the Will which says to them: "Hold on!"

If you can talk with crowds and keep your virtue,
  Or walk with Kings—nor lose the common touch,
If neither foes nor loving friends can hurt you,
  If all men count with you, but none too much;
If you can fill the unforgiving minute
  With sixty seconds' worth of distance run,
Yours is the Earth and everything that's in it,
  And—which is more—you'll be a Man, my son!

RUDYARD KIPLING

DID NOT PASS

(For many a good boy)

"SO John, I hear you did not pass;
You were the lowest in your class,
  Got not a prize of merit,
But grumbling now is no avail;
Just tell me how you came to fail,
  With all your sense and spirit?"

"Well, sir, I missed, 'mong other things,
The list of Egypt's shepherd kings
  (I wonder who does know it.)
An error of three years I made
In dating England's first crusade;
  And, as I am no poet,

"I got Euripides all wrong,
And could not write a Latin song;
  And as for Roman history,
With Hun and Vandal, Goth and Gaul
And Gibbon's weary *Rise and Fall*,
  'Twas all a hopeless mystery.

"But, father, do not fear or sigh
If 'Cram' does proudly pass me by,
And pedagogues ignore me;
I've common sense, I've will and health,
I'll win my way to honest wealth;
The world is all before me.

"And though I'll never be a Grecian,
Know Roman laws or art Phœnician,
Or sing of love and beauty,
I'll plow, or build, or sail, or trade,
And you need never be afraid
But that I'll do my duty."

MARY E. BURNETT

CONTENTED JOHN

ONE honest John Tomkins, a hedger and ditcher,
Although he was poor, did not want to be richer;
For all such vain wishes in him were prevented
By a fortunate habit of being contented.

Though cold were the weather, or dear were the food,
John never was found in a murmuring mood;
For this he was constantly heard to declare—
What he could not prevent he would cheerfully bear.

"For why should I grumble and murmur?" he said;
"If I cannot get meat, I'll be thankful for bread;
And, though fretting may make my calamities deeper,
It can never cause bread and cheese to be cheaper."

If John was afflicted with sickness or pain,
He wished himself better, but did not complain,
Nor lie down to fret in despondence and sorrow,
But said that he hoped to be better to-morrow.

If any one wronged him or treated him ill,
Why, John was good-natured and sociable still;
For he said that revenging the injury done
Would be making two rogues where there need be but one.

And thus honest John, though his station was humble,
Passed through this sad world without even a grumble;
And I wish that some folks, who are greater and richer,
Would copy John Tomkins, the hedger and ditcher.

JANE TAYLOR

JANE AND ELIZA

THERE were two little girls, neither handsome nor plain,
One's name was Eliza, the other's was Jane;
They were both of one height, as I've heard people say,
And both of one age, I believe, to a day.

'Twas fancied by some who but slightly had seen them,
There was not a pin to be chosen between them;
But no one for long in this notion persisted,
So great a distinction there *really* existed.

Eliza knew well that she could not be pleasing,
While fretting and fuming, while sulking or teasing;
And therefore in company artfully tried,
Not to *break* her bad habits, but only to *hide*.

So, when she was out, with much labor and pain,
She contrived to look *almost* as pleasant as Jane;
But then you might see that, in forcing a smile,
Her mouth was uneasy, and ached all the while.

And in spite of her care it would sometimes befall
That some cross event happened to ruin it all;
And because it might chance that her share was the worst,
Her temper broke loose, and her dimples dispersed.

But Jane, who had nothing she wanted to hide,
And therefore these troublesome arts never tried,
Had none of the care and fatigue of concealing,
But her face always showed what her bosom was feeling.

At home or abroad there was peace in her smile,
A cheerful good-nature that needed no guile.
And Eliza worked hard, but could never obtain
The affection that freely was given to Jane.

ANN TAYLOR

THE MAN WITH THE HOE

(Written after seeing the painting by Millet)

BOWED by the weight of centuries he leans
Upon his hoe and gazes on the ground,
The emptiness of ages in his face,
And on his back the burden of the world.
Who made him dead to rapture and despair,
A thing that grieves not and that never hopes,
Stolid and stunned, a brother to the ox?
Who loosened and let down this brutal jaw?
Whose was the hand that slanted back this brow?
Whose breath blew out the light within this brain?

Is this the Thing the Lord God made and gave
To have dominion over sea and land;
To trace the stars and search the heavens for power·
To feel the passion of Eternity? *
Is this the Dream He dreamed who shaped the suns
And marked their ways upon the ancient deep?
Down all the stretch of Hell to its last gulf
There is no shape more terrible than this—
More tongued with censure of the world's blind greed—
More filled with signs and portents for the soul—
More fraught with menace to the universe.

* God made man in His own image, in the image of God made He him.—GENESIS.

What gulfs between him and the seraphim!
Slave of the wheel of labor, what to him
Are Plato and the swing of Pleiades?
What the long reaches of the peaks of song,
The rift of dawn, the reddening of the rose?
Through this dread shape the suffering ages look;
Time's tragedy is in that aching stoop;
Through this dread shape humanity betrayed,
Plundered, profaned, and disinherited,
Cries protest to the Judges of the World,
A protest that is also prophecy.

O masters, lords, and rulers in all lands,
Is this the handiwork you give to God,
This monstrous thing distorted and soul quenched?
How will you ever straighten up this shape;
Touch it again with immortality;
Give back the upward looking and the light;
Rebuild in it the music and the dream;
Make right the immemorial infamies,
Perfidious wrongs, immedicable woes?

O masters, lords, and rulers in all lands,
How will the future reckon with this Man?
How answer his brute question in that hour
When whirlwinds of rebellion shake the world?
How will it be with kingdoms and with kings—
With those who shaped him to the thing he is—
When thus dumb Terror shall reply to God,
After the silence of the centuries?

EDWIN MARKHAM

MY OWN SHALL COME TO ME

SERENE I fold my hands and wait,
Nor care for wind, nor tide, nor sea.
I rave no more 'gainst time or fate,
For lo! my own shall come to me.

I stay my haste, I make delays,
  For what avails this eager pace?
I stand amid the eternal ways,
  And what is mine shall know my face.

Asleep, awake, by night or day
  The friends I seek are seeking me;
No wind can drive my bark astray,
  Nor change the tide of destiny.

What matter if I stand alone?
  I wait with joy the coming years;
My heart shall reap when it has sown,
  And gather up its fruit of tears.

The stars come nightly to the sky;
  The tidal wave comes to the sea;
Nor time, nor space, nor deep, nor high,
  Can keep my own away from me.

The waters know their own and draw
  The brook that springs in yonder heights;
So flows the good with equal law
  Unto the soul of pure delights.

JOHN BURROUGHS

PLAYING ROBINSON CRUSOE

PUSSY can sit by the fire and sing,
  Pussy can climb a tree,
Or play with a silly old cork and string
  To 'muse herself, not me.
But I like Binkie, my dog, because
  He knows how to behave;
So, Binkie's the same as the First Friend was,
  And I am the Man in the Cave.

Pussy will play Man Friday till
  It's time to wet her paw
And make her walk on the window sill
  (For the footprint Crusoe saw);

Then she fluffles her tail and mews,
 And scratches and won't attend.
But Binkie will play whatever I choose,
 And he is my true First Friend.

Pussy will rub my knees with her head,
 Pretending she loves me hard;
But the very minute I go to my bed
 Pussy runs out in the yard,
And there she stays till the morning light;
 So I know it is only pretend;
But Binkie, he snores at my feet all night,
 And he is my Firstest Friend!

RUDYARD KIPLING

A PSALM OF LIFE

WHAT THE HEART OF THE YOUNG MAN SAID TO THE PSALMIST

TELL me not in mournful numbers,
 Life is but an empty dream!—
For the soul is dead that slumbers,
 And things are not what they seem.

Life is real! Life is earnest!
 And the grave is not its goal;
Dust thou art, to dust returnest,
 Was not spoken of the soul.

Not enjoyment, and not sorrow,
 Is our destined end or way;
But to act, that each to-morrow
 Find us farther than to-day.

Art is long, and Time is fleeting,
 And our hearts, though stout and brave,
Still, like muffled drums, are beating
 Funeral marches to the grave.

In the world's broad field of battle,
  In the bivouac of Life,
Be not like dumb, driven cattle!
  Be a hero in the strife!

Trust no Future, howe'er pleasant!
  Let the dead Past bury its dead!
Act—act in the living Present!
  Heart within, and God o'erhead!

Lives of great men all remind us
  We can make our lives sublime,
And, departing, leave behind us
  Footprints on the sands of time;

Footprints, that perhaps another,
  Sailing o'er life's solemn main,
A forlorn and shipwrecked brother,
  Seeing, shall take heart again.

Let us, then, be up and doing,
  With a heart for any fate;
Still achieving, still pursuing,
  Learn to labor and to wait.

HENRY W. LONGFELLOW

HERVÉ RIEL

ON the sea and at the Hogue, sixteen hundred ninety-two,
  Did the English fight the French,—woe to France!
And, the thirty-first of May, helter-skelter through the blue,
Like a crowd of frightened porpoises a shoal of sharks pursue,
Came crowding ship on ship to St. Malo on the Rance,
With the English fleet in view.

'Twas the squadron that escaped, with the victor in full chase;
First and foremost of the drove, in his great ship, Damfreville;
Close on him fled, great and small,
Twenty-two good ships in all;
And they signaled to the place
"Help the winners of a race!
Get us guidance, give us harbor, take us quick—or, quicker still,
Here's the English can and will!"

Then the pilots of the place put out brisk and leapt on board;
"Why, what hope or chance have ships like these to pass?" laughed they:
Rocks to starboard, rocks to port, all the passage scarred and scored,
Shall the *Formidable* here with her twelve and eighty guns
Think to make the river mouth by the single narrow way,
Trust to enter where 'tis ticklish for a craft of twenty tons,
And with flow at full beside?
Now, 'tis slackest ebb of tide.
Reach the mooring? Rather say,
While rock stands or water runs,
Not a ship will leave the bay!"

Then was called a council straight.
Brief and bitter the debate:
"Here's the English at our heels; would you have them take in tow
All that's left us of the fleet, linked together stern and bow,
For a prize to Plymouth Sound?
Better run the ships aground!"
(Ended Damfreville his speech.)
Not a minute more to wait!
"Let the Captains all and each
Shove ashore, then blow up, burn the vessels on the beach!
France must undergo her fate.

"Give the word!" But no such word
Was ever spoke or heard;
For up stood, for out stepped, for in struck amid all these
—A Captain? A Lieutenant? A Mate—first, second, third?
No such man of mark, and meet
With his betters to compete!
But a simple Breton sailor pressed by Tourville for the fleet,
A poor coasting pilot he, Hervé Riel the Croisickese.
And, "What mockery or malice have we here?" cries Hervé Riel:
"Are you mad, you Malouins? Are you cowards, fools, or rogues?
Talk to me of rocks and shoals, me who took the soundings, tell
On my fingers every bank, every shallow, every swell
'Twixt the offing here and Grève where the river disembogues?
Are you bought by English gold? Is it love the lying's for?
Morn and eve, night and day,
Have I piloted your bay,
Entered free and anchored fast at foot of Solidor.

"Burn the fleet and ruin France? That were worse than fifty Hogues!
Sirs, they know I speak the truth! Sirs, believe me there's a way!
Only let me lead the line,
Have the biggest ship to steer,
Get this *Formidable* clear,
Make the others follow mine,
And I lead them, most and least, by a passage I know well,
Right to Solidor past Grève,
And there lay them safe and sound;
And if one ship misbehave,
—Keel so much as grate the ground,
Why, I've nothing but my life,—here's my head!" cries Hervé Riel.

Not a minute more to wait.
"Steer us in, then, small and great!
Take the helm, lead the line, save the squadron!" cried his chief.
"Captains, give the sailor place!
He is Admiral, in brief."
Still the north wind, by God's grace.
See the noble fellow's face,
As the big ship with a bound,
Clears the entry like a hound,
Keeps the passage, as its inch of way were the wide seas profound!
See, safe thro' shoal and rock,
How they flow in a flock,
Not a ship that misbehaves, not a keel that grates the ground,
Not a spar that comes to grief!
The peril, see, is past,
All are harbored to the last,
And just as Hervé Riel hollas "Anchor!"—sure as fate
Up the English come, too late!

So, the storm subsides to calm:
They see the green trees wave
On the heights o'erlooking Grève.
Hearts that bled are stanched with balm.
"Just our rapture to enhance,
Let the English rake the bay,
Gnash their teeth and glare askance,
As they cannonade away!
'Neath rampired Solidor pleasant riding on the Rance!"
How hope succeeds despair on each Captain's countenance!
Out burst all with one accord,
"This is Paradise for Hell!
Let France, let France's King
Thank the man that did the thing!"
What a shout, and all one word,
"Hervé Riel!"
As he stepped in front once more,
Not a symptom of surprise

In the frank blue Breton eyes,
Just the same man as before.

Then said Damfreville, "My friend,
I must speak out at the end,
Though I find the speaking hard.
Praise is deeper than the lips:
You have saved the King his ships,
You must name your own reward.
'Faith, our sun was near eclipse!
Demand whate'er you will,
France remains your debtor still.
Ask to heart's content and have! or my name's not Damfreville."

Then a beam of fun outbroke
On the bearded mouth that spoke,
As the honest heart laughed through
Those frank eyes of Breton blue:
"Since I needs must say my say,
Since on board the duty's done,
And from Malo Roads to Crossic Point, what is it but a run?—
Since 'tis ask and have, I may—
Since the others go ashore—
Come! A good whole holiday!
Leave to go and see my wife, whom I call the Belle Aurore!"
That he asked and that he got—nothing more.

Name and deed alike are lost:
Not a pillar nor a post
In his Croisic keeps alive the feat as it befell;
Not a head in white and black
On a single fishing smack,
In memory of the man but for whom had gone to wrack
All that France saved from the fight whence England bore the bell.
Go to Paris: rank on rank
Search the heroes flung pell mell
On the Louvre, face and flank!
You shall look long enough ere you come to Hervé Riel.

So, for better and for worse,
Hervé Riel, accept my verse!
In my verse, Hervé Riel, do thou once more
Save the squadron, honor France, love thy wife, the Belle
Aurore!

Robert Browning

THE THREE BELLS OF GLASGOW

BENEATH the low-hung night cloud
That raked her splintering mast
The good ship settled slowly,
The cruel leak gained fast.

Over the awful ocean
Her signal guns pealed out.
Dear God! was that Thy answer
From the horror round about?

A voice came down the wild wind,
"Ho! ship ahoy!" its cry:
"Our stout *Three Bells* of Glasgow
Shall stand till daylight by!"

Hour after hour crept slowly,
Yet on the heaving swells
Tossed up and down the ship lights,
The lights of the *Three Bells!*

And ship to ship made signals,
Man answered back to man,
While oft, to cheer and hearten,
The *Three Bells* nearer ran:

And the captain from her taffrail
Sent down his hopeful cry.
"Take heart! Hold on!" he shouted.
"The *Three Bells* shall stand by!"

All night across the waters
  The tossing lights shone clear;
All night from reeling taffrail
  The *Three Bells* sent her cheer.

And when the dreary watches
  Of storm and darkness passed,
Just as the wreck lurched under,
  All souls were saved at last.

Sail on, *Three Bells*, forever,
  In grateful memory sail!
Ring on, *Three Bells* of rescue,
  Above the wave and gale!

Type of the Love eternal,
  Repeat the Master's cry,
As tossing through our darkness
  The lights of God draw nigh!

JOHN G. WHITTIER

HIAWATHA'S CHILDHOOD

BY the shores of Gitche Gumee,
By the shining Big-Sea-Water,
Stood the wigwam of Nokomis,
Daughter of the Moon, Nokomis.
Dark behind it rose the forest,
Rose the black and gloomy pine trees,
Rose the firs with cones upon them;
Bright before it beat the water,
Beat the clear and sunny water,
Beat the shining Big-Sea-Water.

There the wrinkled old Nokomis
Nursed the little Hiawatha,

Rocked him in his linden cradle,
Bedded soft in moss and rushes,
Safely bound with reindeer sinews;
Stilled his fretful wail by saying,
"Hush! the Naked Bear will hear thee!"
Lulled him into slumber, singing,
"Ewa-yea! my little owlet!
Who is this that lights the wigwam?
With his great eyes lights the wigwam?
Ewa-yea! my little owlet!"

Many things Nokomis taught him
Of the stars that shine in heaven;
Showed him Ishkoodah, the comet,
Ishkoodah, with fiery tresses;
Showed the Death Dance of the spirits,
Warriors with their plumes and war clubs,
Flaring far away to northward
In the frosty nights of winter;
Showed the broad, white road in heaven,
Pathway of the ghosts, the shadows,
Running straight across the heavens,
Crowded with the ghosts, the shadows.

At the door, on summer evenings,
Sat the little Hiawatha;
Heard the whispering of the pine trees,
Heard the lapping of the water,
Sounds of music, words of wonder;
"Minnie-wawa!" said the pine trees,
"Mudway-aushka!" said the water;
Saw the firefly, Wah-wah-taysee,
Flitting through the dusk of evening,
With the twinkle of its candle
Lighting up the brakes and bushes,
And he sang the song of children,
Sang the song Nokomis taught him:
"Wah-wah-taysee, little firefly,
Little, flitting, white-fire insect,
Little, dancing, white-fire creature,

Light me with your little candle,
Ere upon my bed I lay me,
Ere in sleep I close my eyelids!"

Saw the moon rise from the water
Rippling, rounding from the water,
Saw the flecks and shadows on it,
Whispered, "What is that, Nokomis?"
And the good Nokomis answered:
"Once a warrior, very angry,
Seized his grandmother, and threw her
Up into the sky at midnight;
Right against the moon he threw her;
'Tis her body that you see there."

Saw the rainbow in the heaven,
In the eastern sky, the rainbow,
Whispered, "What is that, Nokomis?"
And the good Nokomis answered:
" 'Tis the heaven of flowers you see there;
All the wild flowers of the forest,
All the lilies of the prairie,
When on earth they fade and perish,
Blossom in that heaven above us."

When he heard the owls at midnight,
Hooting, laughing in the forest,
"What is that?" he cried, in terror;
"What is that," he said, "Nokomis?"
And the good Nokomis answered:
"That is but the owl and owlet,
Talking in their native language,
Talking, scolding at each other."

Then the little Hiawatha
Learned of every bird its language,
Learned their names and all their secrets,
How they built their nests in summer,
Where they hid themselves in winter,
Talked with them whene'er he met them,
Called them "Hiawatha's Chickens."

Of all beasts he learned the language,
Learned their names and all their secrets,
How the beavers built their lodges,
Where the squirrels hid their acorns,
How the reindeer ran so swiftly,
Why the rabbit was so timid.
Talked with them whene'er he met them,
Called them "Hiawatha's Brothers."

HENRY W. LONGFELLOW

A THING OF BEAUTY

(*From "Endymion"*)

A THING of beauty is a joy forever:
Its love increases; it will never
Pass into nothingness; but still will keep
A bower quiet for us, and a sleep
Full of sweet dreams, and health, and quiet breathing.
Therefore, on every morrow, we are wreathing
A flowery band to bind us to the earth,
Spite of despondence, of the inhuman dearth
Of noble natures, of the gloomy days,
Of all the unhealthy and o'er-darken'd ways
Made for our searching: yea, in spite of all,
Some shape of beauty moves away the pall
From our dark spirits. Such the sun, the moon,
Trees old and young, sprouting a shady boon
For simple sheep; and such are daffodils
With the green world they live in; and clear rills
That for themselves a cooling covert make
'Gainst the hot season; the mid forest brake,
Rich with a sprinkling of fair muskrose blooms:
And such too is the grandeur of the dooms
We have imagined for the mighty dead;
All lovely tales that we have heard or read:
An endless fountain of immortal drink,
Pouring into us from the heaven's brink.

JOHN KEATS

FROM "IN MEMORIAM"

RING out, wild bells, to the wild sky,
The flying cloud, the frosty light:
The year is dying in the night;
Ring out, wild bells, and let him die.

Ring out the old, ring in the new,
Ring, happy bells, across the snow:
The year is going, let him go;
Ring out the false, ring in the true.

Ring out the grief that saps the mind,
For those that here we see no more;
Ring out the feud of rich and poor,
Ring in redress to all mankind.

Ring out a slowly dying cause,
And ancient forms of party strife;
Ring in the nobler modes of life,
With sweeter manners, purer laws.

Ring out the want, the care, the sin,
The faithless coldness of the times;
Ring out, ring out my mournful rhymes,
But ring the fuller minstrel in.

Ring out false pride in place and blood,
The civic slander and the spite;
Ring in the love of truth and right,
Ring in the common love of good.

Ring out old shapes of foul disease;
Ring out the narrowing lust of gold;
Ring out the thousand wars of old,
Ring in the thousand years of peace.

Ring in the valiant man and free,
The larger heart, the kindlier hand;
Ring out the darkness of the land,
Ring in the Christ that is to be.

ALFRED TENNYSON

ELEGY WRITTEN IN A COUNTRY CHURCHYARD

THE curfew tolls the knell of parting day,
  The lowing herds wind slowly o'er the lea,
The plowman homeward plods his weary way,
  And leaves the world to darkness and to me.

Now fades the glimmering landscape on the sight,
  And all the air a solemn stillness holds,
Save where the beetle wheels his droning flight,
  And drowsy tinklings lull the distant folds.

Save that from yonder ivy-mantled tower,
  The moping owl does to the moon complain
Of such as, wandering near her secret bower,
  Molest her ancient solitary reign.

Beneath those rugged elms, that yew tree's shade,
  Where heaves the turf in many a moldering heap,
Each in his narrow cell for ever laid,
  The rude forefathers of the hamlet sleep.

The breezy call of incense-breathing morn,
  The swallow twittering from the straw-built shed,
The cock's shrill clarion, or the echoing horn,
  No more shall rouse them from their lowly bed.

For them no more the blazing hearth shall burn,
  Or busy housewife ply her evening care:
No children run to lisp their sire's return,
  Or climb his knees the envied kiss to share.

Oft did the harvest to their sickle yield,
  Their furrow oft the stubborn glebe has broke;
How jocund did they drive their team a-field!
  How bowed the woods beneath their sturdy stroke!

Let not Ambition mock their useful toil,
  Their homely joys, and destiny obscure;
Nor Grandeur hear with a disdainful smile
  The short and simple annals of the poor.

The boast of heraldry, the pomp of power,
  And all that beauty, all that wealth ere gave,
Await alike the inevitable hour—
  The paths of glory lead but to the grave.

Nor you, ye proud, impute to these the fault,
  If Memory o'er their tomb no trophies raise,
Where through the long-drawn aisle and fretted vault
  The pealing anthem swells the note of praise.

Can storied urn or animated bust
  Back to its mansion call the fleeting breath?
Can Honor's voice provoke the silent dust,
  Or Flattery soothe the dull cold ear of Death?

Perhaps in this neglected spot is laid
  Some heart once pregnant with celestial fire;
Hands that the rod of empire might have swayed,
  Or waked to ecstasy the living lyre.

But knowledge to their eyes her ample page
  Rich with the spoils of time did ne'er unroll;
Chill Penury repressed their noble rage,
  And froze the genial current of the soul.

Full many a gem, of purest ray serene,
  The dark unfathomed caves of ocean bear:
Full many a flower is born to blush unseen,
  And waste its sweetness on the desert air.

Some village Hampden, that with dauntless breast
  The little tyrant of his fields withstood;
Some mute inglorious Milton here may rest,
  Some Cromwell guiltless of his country's blood.

The applause of listening senates to command,
  The threats of pain and ruin to despise,
To scatter plenty o'er a smiling land,
  And read their history in a nation's eyes.

Their lot forbade: nor circumscribed alone
Their growing virtues, but their crimes confined;
Forbade to wade through slaughter to a throne,
And shut the gates of mercy on mankind;

The struggling pangs of conscious truth to hide,
To quench the blushes of ingenuous shame,
Or heap the shrine of Luxury and Pride,
With incense kindled at the Muse's flame.

Far from the madding crowd's ignoble strife
Their sober wishes never learned to stray,
Along the cool sequestered vale of life
They kept the noiseless tenor of their way.

Yet even these bones from insult to protect,
Some frail memorial still erected nigh,
With uncouth rhymes and shapeless sculpture decked
Implores the passing tribute of a sigh.

Their name, their years, spelt by the unlettered Muse,
The place of fame and elegy supply:
And many a holy text around she strews,
That teach the rustic moralist to die.

For who, to dumb Forgetfulness a prey,
This pleasing anxious being e'er resigned,
Left the warm precincts of the cheerful day,
Nor cast one longing, lingering look behind?

On some fond breast the parting soul relies,
Some pious drops the closing eye requires;
Even from the tomb the voice of nature cries,
Even in our ashes live their wonted fires.

For thee, who, mindful of the unhonored dead,
Dost in these lines their artless tale relate;
If chance, by lonely Contemplation led,
Some kindred spirit shall inquire thy fate;

Haply some hoary-headed swain may say,
"Oft have we seen him at the peep of dawn
Brushing with hasty steps the dews away,
To meet the sun upon the upland lawn.

"There, at the foot of yonder nodding beech,
That wreathes its old fantastic root so high,
His listless length at noontide would he stretch,
And pour upon the brook that babbles by.

"Hard by yon wood, now smiling as in scorn,
Muttering his wayward fancies he would rove;
Now drooping, woeful, wan, like one forlorn,
Or crazed with care, or crossed in hopeless love.

"One morning I missed him on the 'customed hill,
Along the heath and near his favorite tree;
Another came; nor yet beside the rill,
Nor up the lawn, nor at the wood was he;

"The next, with dirges due in sad array
Slow through the church-way path we saw him borne;
Approach and read (for thou canst read) the lay
Graved on the stone beneath yon aged thorn."

THE EPITAPH

Here rests his head upon the lap of Earth,
A Youth, to Fortune and to Fame unknown;
Fair Science frowned not on his humble birth,
And Melancholy marked him for her own.

Large was his bounty, and his soul sincere,
Heaven did a recompense as largely send:
He gave to Misery all he had, a tear,
He gained from Heaven ('twas all he wished) a friend.

No farther seek his merits to disclose,
Or draw his frailties from their dread abode
(There they alike in trembling hope repose),
The bosom of his Father and his God.

THOMAS GRAY

KUBLA KHAN

In Xanadu did Kubla Khan
A stately pleasure dome decree:
Where Alph, the sacred river, ran
Through caverns measureless to man
Down to a sunless sea.
So twice five miles of fertile ground
With walls and towers were girdled round:
And there were gardens bright with sinuous rills
Where blossom'd many an incense-bearing tree;
And here were forests ancient as the hills,
Enfolding sunny spots of greenery.
But oh, that deep romantic chasm which slanted
Down the green hill athwart a cedarn cover!
A savage place! as holy and enchanted
As e'er beneath a waning moon was haunted
By woman wailing for her demon lover!
And from this chasm, with ceaseless turmoil seething,
As if this earth in fast thick pants were breathing,
A mighty fountain momently was forced;
Amid whose swift half-intermitted burst
Huge fragments vaulted like rebounding hail,
Or chaffy grain beneath the thresher's flail:
And 'mid these dancing rocks at once and ever
It flung up momently the sacred river.
Five miles meandering with a mazy motion
Through wood and dale the sacred river ran,
Then reached the caverns measureless to man,
And sank in tumult to a lifeless ocean:
And 'mid this tumult Kubla heard from far
Ancestral voices prophesying war!
The shadow of the dome of pleasure
Floated midway on the waves;
Where was heard the mingled measure
From the fountain and the caves.
It was a miracle of rare device,
A sunny pleasure dome with caves of ice!

A damsel with a dulcimer
In a vision once I saw:

It was an Abyssinian maid,
And on her dulcimer she play'd,
Singing of Mount Abora.
Could I revive within me
Her symphony and song,
To such a deep delight 'twould win me
That with music loud and long,
I would build that dome in air,
That sunny dome! those caves of ice!
And all who heard should see them there,
And all should cry, Beware! Beware!
His flashing eyes, his floating hair!
Weave a circle round him thrice,
And close your eyes with holy dread,
For he on honey dew hath fed,
And drunk the milk of Paradise.

SAMUEL TAYLOR COLERIDGE

THE CHAMBERED NAUTILUS

(*From "The Autocrat of the Breakfast Table"*)

THIS is the ship of pearl, which, poets feign,
Sails the unshadowed main,—
The venturous bark that flings
On the sweet summer wind its purpled wings
In gulfs enchanted, where the Siren sings,
And coral reefs lie bare,
Where the cold sea maids rise to sun their streaming hair.

Its webs of living gauze no more unfurl;
Wrecked is the ship of pearl!
And every chambered cell,
Where its dim dreaming life was wont to dwell,
As the frail tenant shaped his growing shell,
Before thee lies revealed,—
Its irised ceiling rent, its sunless crypt unsealed!

Year after year beheld the silent toil
  That spread his lustrous coil;
  Still, as the spiral grew,
He left the past year's dwelling for the new,
Stole with soft step its shining archway through,
  Built up its idle door,
Stretched in his last-found home, and knew the old no more.

Thanks for the heavenly message brought by thee,
  Child of the wandering sea,
  Cast from her lap, forlorn!
From thy dead lips a clearer note is born
Than ever Triton blew from wreathèd horn!
  While on mine ear it rings,
Through the deep caves of thought I hear a voice that
    sings—

Build thee more stately mansions, O my soul,
  As the swift seasons roll!
  Leave thy low-vaulted past!
Let each new temple, nobler than the last,
Shut thee from heaven with a dome more vast,
  Till thou at length art free,
Leaving thine outgrown shell by life's unresting sea!

OLIVER WENDELL HOLMES

THE BLIND MEN AND THE ELEPHANT

(A Hindoo Fable)

IT was six men of Indostan
  To learning much inclined,
Who went to see the Elephant
  (Though all of them were blind),
That each by observation
  Might satisfy his mind.

The *First* approached the Elephant,
  And happening to fall
Against his broad and sturdy side,
  At once began to bawl:
"God bless me! but the Elephant
  Is very like a wall!"

The *Second*, feeling of the tusk,
  Cried, "Ho! what have we here
So very round and smooth and sharp?
  To me 'tis mighty clear
This wonder of an Elephant
  Is very like a spear!"

The *Third* approached the animal,
  And happening to take
The squirming trunk within his hands,
  Thus boldly up and spake:
"I see," quoth he, "the Elephant
  Is very like a snake!"

The *Fourth* reached out an eager hand,
  And felt about the knee.
"What most this wondrous beast is like
  Is mighty plain," quoth he;
" 'Tis clear enough the Elephant
  Is very like a tree!"

The *Fifth* who chanced to touch the ear,
  Said: "E'en the blindest man
Can tell what this resembles most;
  Deny the fact who can,
This marvel of an Elephant
  Is very like a fan!"

The *Sixth* no sooner had begun
  About the beast to grope,
Than, seizing on the swinging tail
  That fell within his scope,
"I see," quoth he, "the Elephant
  Is very like a rope!"

And so these men of Indostan
  Disputed loud and long,
Each in his own opinion
  Exceeding stiff and strong,
Though each was partly in the right
  And all were in the wrong!

MORAL

So oft in theologic wars,
  The disputants, I ween,
Rail on in utter ignorance
  Of what each other mean,
And prate about an Elephant
  Not one of them has seen!

John Godfrey Saxe

WOODMAN, SPARE THAT TREE!

WOODMAN, spare that tree!
  Touch not a single bough!
In youth it sheltered me,
  And I'll protect it now.
'Twas my forefather's hand
  That placed it near his cot;
There, woodman, let it stand,
  Thy ax shall harm it not.

That old familiar tree,
  Whose glory and renown
Are spread o'er land and sea—
  And wouldst thou hew it down?
Woodman, forbear thy stroke!
  Cut not its earth-bound ties;
Oh, spare that agèd oak
  Now towering to the skies!

When but an idle boy,
  I sought its grateful shade;
In all their gushing joy
  Here, too, my sisters played.
My mother kissed me here;
  My father pressed my hand—
Forgive this foolish tear,
  But let that old oak stand.

My heartstrings round thee cling,
  Close as thy bark, old friend!
Here shall the wild bird sing,
  And still thy branches bend.
Old tree! the storm still brave!
  And, woodman, leave the spot;
While I've a hand to save,
  Thy ax shall harm it not.

George Pope Morris

ABOU BEN ADHEM

ABOU BEN ADHEM (may his tribe increase!)
  Awoke one night from a deep dream of peace,
And saw within the moonlight in his room,
Making it rich and like a lily in bloom,
An angel writing in a book of gold.

Exceeding peace had made Ben Adhem bold;
And to the presence in the room he said,
"What writest thou?" The vision raised its head,
And, with a look made of all sweet accord,
Answered, "The names of those who love the Lord."

"And is mine one?" said Abou. "Nay, not so,"
Replied the angel. Abou spoke more low,
But cheerily still; and said, "I pray thee, then,
Write me as one that loves his fellow men."

The angel wrote, and vanished. The next night
It came again, with a great wakening light,
And showed the names whom love of God had blessed;
And, lo! Ben Adhem's name led all the rest.

LEIGH HUNT

EXCELSIOR

THE shades of night were falling fast,
As through an Alpine village passed
A youth, who bore, 'mid snow and ice,
A banner, with the strange device,
Excelsior!

His brow was sad; his eye beneath
Flashed like a faulchion from its sheath,
And like a silver clarion rung
The accents of that unknown tongue,
Excelsior!

In happy homes he saw the light
Of household fires gleam warm and bright;
Above, the spectral glaciers shone,
And from his lips escaped a groan,
Excelsior!

"Try not the Pass!" the old man said,
"Dark lowers the tempest overhead,
The roaring torrent is deep and wide!"
And loud that clarion voice replied,
Excelsior!

"O stay!" the maiden said, "and rest
Thy weary head upon this breast!"
A tear stood in his bright blue eye,
But still he answered, with a sigh,
Excelsior!

"Beware the pine tree's withered branch!
Beware the awful avalanche!"
This was the peasant's last good night!
A voice replied, far up the height,
Excelsior!

At break of day, as heavenward
The pious monks of Saint Bernard
Uttered the oft-repeated prayer,
A voice cried through the startled air,
Excelsior!

A traveler, by the faithful hound,
Half-buried in the snow, was found,
Still grasping in his hand of ice
That banner, with the strange device
Excelsior!

There, in the twilight cold and gray,
Lifeless, but beautiful, he lay,
And from the sky, serene and far,
A voice fell, like a falling star,
Excelsior!

Henry Wadsworth Longfellow

THE PIPER

PIPING down the valleys wild,
Piping songs of pleasant glee,
On a cloud I saw a child,
And he laughing said to me:

"Pipe a song about a lamb."
So I piped with merry cheer.
"Piper, pipe that song again";
So I piped; he wept to hear.

"Drop thy pipe, thy happy pipe,
  Sing thy songs of happy cheer":
So I sang the same again,
  While he wept with joy to hear.

"Piper, sit thee down and write
  In a book that all may read—"
So he vanished from my sight;
  And I plucked a hollow reed,

And I made a rural pen,
  And I stain'd the water clear,
And I wrote my happy songs,
  Every child may joy to hear.

William Blake

ON ANOTHER'S SORROW

CAN I see another's woe,
  And not be in sorrow too?
Can I see another's grief,
And not seek for kind relief?

Can I see a falling tear,
And not feel my sorrow's share?
Can a father see his child,
Weep, nor be with sorrow filled?

Can a mother sit and hear
An infant groan, an infant fear?
No, no! never can it be!
Never, never can it be!

And can He who smiles on all,
Hear the wren with sorrows small,
Hear the small bird's grief and care;
Hear the woes that infants bear—

And not sit beside the nest,
Pouring pity in their breast,
And not sit the cradle near,
Weeping tear on infant's tear?

And not sit both night and day,
Wiping all our tears away;
Oh no! never can it be:
Never, never can it be!

He doth give His joy to all:
He becomes an infant small,
He becomes a man of woe,
He doth feel the sorrow too.

Think not thou canst sigh a sigh,
And thy Maker is not by:
Think not thou canst weep a tear,
And thy Maker is not near.

Oh, He who gives to us His joy,
That our grief He may destroy:
Till our grief is fled and gone
He doth sit by us and moan.

WILLIAM BLAKE

THE LOTOS EATERS

"COURAGE!" he said, and pointed toward the land,
"This mounting wave will roll us shoreward soon."
In the afternoon they came unto a land
In which it seemèd always afternoon.
All round the coast the languid air did swoon,
Breathing like one that hath a weary dream.
Full-faced above the valley stood the moon;
And like a downward smoke, the slender stream
Along the cliff to fall and pause and fall did seem.

A land of streams! some, like a downward smoke,
Slow-dropping veils of thinnest lawn, did go;
And some thro' wavering lights and shadows broke,
Rolling a slumbrous sheet of foam below.
They saw the gleaming river seaward flow
From the inner land: far off, three mountain-tops,
Three silent pinnacles of agèd snow,
Stood sunset flush'd: and, dew'd with showery drops,
Up clomb the shadowy pine above the woven copse.

The charmèd sunset linger'd low adown
In the red west: thro' mountain clefts the dale
Was seen far inland, and the yellow down
Border'd with palm, and many a winding vale
And meadow, set with slender galingale;
A land where all things always seem'd the same!
And round about the keel with faces pale,
Dark faces pale against that rosy flame,
The mild-eyed melancholy Lotos eaters came.

Branches they bore of that enchanted stem,
Laden with flower and fruit, whereof they gave
To each, but whoso did receive of them,
And taste, to him the gushing of the wave
Far, far away did seem to mourn and rave
On alien shores; and if his fellow spake,
His voice was thin, as voices from the grave;
And deep asleep he seem'd, yet all awake,
And music in his ears his beating heart did make.

They sat them down upon the yellow sand,
Between the sun and moon upon the shore;
And sweet it was to dream of Fatherland,
Of child, and wife, and slave; but evermore
Most weary seem'd the sea, weary the oar,
Weary the wandering fields of barren foam.
Then some one said, "We will return no more;"
And all at once they sang, "Our island home
Is far beyond the wave: we will no longer roam."

ALFRED TENNYSON

THE ARROW AND THE SONG

I SHOT an arrow into the air,
It fell to earth, I knew not where;
For, so swiftly it flew, the sight
Could not follow it in its flight.

I breathed a song into the air,
It fell to earth, I knew not where;
For who has sight so keen and strong,
That it can follow the flight of song?

Long, long afterward, in an oak
I found the arrow, still unbroke;
And the song, from beginning to end,
I found again in the heart of a friend.

HENRY WADSWORTH LONGFELLOW

THE RAVEN

ONCE upon a midnight dreary, while I pondered, weak and weary,
Over many a quaint and curious volume of forgotten lore—
While I nodded, nearly napping, suddenly there came a tapping,
As of some one gently rapping, rapping at my chamber door—
" 'Tis some visitor," I muttered, "tapping at my chamber door—
Only this, and nothing more."

Ah! distinctly I remember, it was in the bleak December,
And each separate dying ember wrought its ghost upon the floor;
Eagerly I wished the morrow; vainly I had sought to borrow
From my books surcease of sorrow—sorrow for the lost Lenore—

For the rare and radiant maiden whom the angels name
Lenore—
Nameless here for evermore.

And the silken, sad, uncertain rustling of each purple curtain
Thrilled me—filled me with fantastic terrors never felt before;
So that now, to still the beating of my heart, I stood repeating,
" 'Tis some visitor entreating entrance at my chamber door—
Some late visitor entreating entrance at my chamber door:
This it is, and nothing more."

Presently my soul grew stronger; hesitating then no longer,
"Sir," said I, "or madam, truly your forgiveness I implore;
But the fact is, I was napping, and so gently you came rapping,
And so faintly you came tapping, tapping at my chamber door,
That I scarce was sure I heard you." Here I opened wide the door:
Darkness there, and nothing more.

Deep into that darkness peering, long I stood there, wondering, fearing,
Doubting, dreaming dreams no mortal ever dared to dream before;
But the silence was unbroken, and the stillness gave no token,
And the only word there spoken was the whispered word, "Lenore!"
This I whispered, and an echo murmured back the word, "Lenore!"
Merely this, and nothing more.

Back into my chamber turning, all my soul within me burning,
Soon again I heard a rapping, somewhat louder than before:

"Surely," said I, "surely that is something at my window
lattice;
Let me see then, what thereat is, and this mystery explore—
Let my heart be still a moment, and this mystery explore.
'Tis the wind, and nothing more."

Open here I flung the shutter, when, with many a flirt and
flutter,
In there stepped a stately Raven, of the saintly days of yore;
Not the least obeisance made he, not a minute stopped or
stayed he;
But with mien of lord or lady, perched above my chamber
door—
Perched upon a bust of Pallas, just above my chamber
door—
Perched, and sat, and nothing more.

Then this ebony bird beguiling my sad fancy into smiling,
By the grave and stern decorum of the countenance it wore:
"Though thy crest be shorn and shaven, thou," I said, "art
sure, no craven;
Ghastly, grim, and ancient Raven, wandering from the
nightly shore,
Tell me what thy lordly name is on the night's Plutonian
shore?"
Quoth the Raven, "Nevermore."

Much I marveled this ungainly fowl to hear discourse so
plainly,
Though its answer little meaning, little relevancy bore;
For we cannot help agreeing that no living human being
Ever yet was blessed with seeing bird above his chamber
door—
Bird or beast upon the sculptured bust above his chamber
door
With such name as "Nevermore."

But the Raven, sitting lonely on that placid bust, spoke only
That one word, as if his soul in that one word he did out-
pour:

Nothing further then he uttered, not a feather then he fluttered,
Till I scarcely more than muttered—"Other friends have flown before,
On the morrow *he* will leave me, as my hopes have flown before."
Then the bird said, "Nevermore."

Startled by the stillness broken by reply so aptly spoken,
"Doubtless," said I, "what it utters is its only stock and store,
Caught from some unhappy master, whom unmerciful disaster
Followed fast and followed faster, till his songs one burden bore—
Till the dirges of his hope this melancholy burden bore—
Of 'Never, nevermore.' "

But the Raven still beguiling all my sad soul into smiling,
Straight I wheeled a cushioned seat in front of bird, and bust, and door;
Then upon the velvet sinking, I betook myself to linking
Fancy into fancy, thinking what this ominous bird of yore—
What this grim, ungainly, ghastly, gaunt, and ominous bird of yore—
Meant in croaking "Nevermore."

Thus I sat engaged in guessing, but no syllable expressing
To the fowl whose fiery eyes now burned into my bosom's core;
This and more I sat divining, with my head at ease reclining
On the cushion's velvet lining, that the lamplight gloated o'er,
But whose velvet violet lining, with the lamplight gloating o'er,
She shall press, ah, nevermore!

Then methought the air grew denser, perfumed from an unseen censer

Swung by seraphim, whose footfalls tinkled on the tufted floor.
"Wretch," I cried, "thy God hath lent thee—by these angels he hath sent thee
Respite—respite and nepenthe from my memories of Lenore!
Quaff, oh quaff this kind nepenthe, and forget this lost Lenore!"
Quoth the Raven, "Nevermore."

"Prophet," said I, "thing of evil—prophet still, if bird or devil!
Whether tempter sent, or whether tempest tossed thee here ashore
Desolate, yet all undaunted, on this desert land enchanted,
On this home by horror haunted—tell me truly, I implore,
Is there—*is* there balm in Gilead?—tell me, tell me, I implore!"
Quoth the Raven, "Nevermore."

"Prophet," said I, "thing of evil!—prophet still, if bird or devil!
By that heaven that bends above us—by that God we both adore—
Tell this soul, with sorrow laden, if, within the distant Aiden,
It shall clasp a sainted maiden, whom the angels name Lenore:
Clasp a rare and radiant maiden, whom the angels name Lenore!"
Quoth the Raven, "Nevermore."

"Be that word our sign of parting, bird or fiend," I shrieked upstarting—
"Get thee back into the tempest and the night's Plutonian shore;
Leave no black plume as a token of that lie thy soul hath spoken,
Leave my loneliness unbroken—quit the bust above my door,

Take thy beak from out my heart, and take thy form from
off my door!"
Quoth the Raven, "Nevermore."

And the Raven, never flitting, still is sitting, still is sitting,
On the pallid bust of Pallas, just above my chamber door;
And his eyes have all the seeming of a demon's that is
dreaming,
And the lamplight o'er him streaming, throws his shadow
on the floor;
And my soul from out that shadow, that lies floating on
the floor,
Shall be lifted—nevermore!

EDGAR ALLAN POE

SIR LAUNFAL AND THE LEPER

(*From "The Vision of Sir Launfal"*)

As Sir Launfal made morn through the darksome gate,
He was aware of a leper, crouched by the same,
Who begged with his hand and moaned as he sate;
And a loathing over Sir Launfal came;
The sunshine went out of his soul with a thrill,
The flesh 'neath his armor did shrink and crawl,
And midway its leap his heart stood still
Like a frozen waterfall;
For this man, so foul and bent of stature,
Rasped harshly against his dainty nature,
And seemed the one blot on the summer morn,—
So he tossed him a piece of gold in scorn.

The leper raised not the gold from the dust:
"Better to me the poor man's crust,
Better the blessing of the poor,
Though I turn me empty from his door;
That is no true alms which the hand can hold:
He gives nothing but worthless gold
Who gives from a sense of duty;

But he who gives a slender mite,
And gives to that which is out of sight,
  That thread of the all-sustaining Beauty
Which runs through all and doth all unite,—
The hand cannot clasp the whole of his alms,
The heart outstretches its eager palms,
For a god goes with it and makes it store
To the soul that was starving in darkness before."

JAMES RUSSELL LOWELL

I REMEMBER

I REMEMBER, I remember,
  The house where I was born,
The little window, where the sun
  Came peeping in at morn:
He never came a wink too soon,
  Nor brought too long a day,
But now I often wish the night
  Had borne my breath away!

I remember, I remember,
  The roses, red and white,
The violets, and the lily cups,
  Those flowers made of light!
The lilacs, where the robin built,
  And where my brother set
The laburnum on his birthday:
  The tree is living yet!

I remember, I remember,
  Where I was used to swing,
And thought the air must rush as fresh,
  To swallows on the wing.
My spirit flew in feathers then,
  That is so heavy now;
And summer pools could hardly cool
  The fever on my brow!

I remember, I remember,
The fir trees, dark and high;
I used to think their slender tops
Were close against the sky:
It was a childish ignorance:
But now, 'tis little joy
To know I'm further off from heaven
Than when I was a boy.

THOMAS HOOD

THE SON OF GOD GOES FORTH TO WAR

THE Son of God goes forth to war,
A kingly crown to gain;
His blood-red banner streams afar!
Who follows in His train?
Who best can drink his cup of woe,
Triumphant over pain,
Who patient bears his cross below,
He follows in His train!

Thy martyr first, whose eagle eye
Could pierce beyond the grave;
Who saw his Master in the sky,
And called on Him to save:
Like Him, with pardon on his tongue,
In midst of mortal pain,
He prayed for them that did the wrong!
Who follows in His train?

A glorious band, the chosen few,
On whom the Spirit came;
Twelve valiant saints, their hope they knew,
And mocked the cross and flame!
They met the tyrant's brandished steel,
The lion's gory mane:
They bowed their necks, the death to feel!
Who follows in their train?

A noble army—men and boys,
The matron and the maid,—
Around the Savior's throne rejoice
In robes of light arrayed.
They climbed the steep ascent of Heaven,
Through peril, toil, and pain!
O God! to us may grace be given
To follow in their train!

REGINALD HEBER

KING JOHN AND THE ABBOT OF CANTERBURY

AN ancient story I'll tell you anon
Of a notable prince, that was called King John;
And he ruled England with main and with might,
For he did great wrong and maintained little right.

And I'll tell you a story, a story so merry,
Concerning the Abbot of Canterbury;
How for his housekeeping and high renown,
They rode post for him to fair London town.

An hundred men, the King did hear say,
The Abbot kept in his house every day;
And fifty gold chains, without any doubt,
In velvet coats waited the Abbot about.

"How now, Father Abbot, I hear it of thee,
Thou keepest a far better house than me;
And for thy housekeeping and high renown,
I fear thou work'st treason against my crown."

"My liege," quo' the Abbot, "I would it were knowne,
I never spend nothing but what is my owne;
And I trust your Grace will not put me in fear,
For spending of my owne true-gotten gear."

"Yes, yes, Father Abbot, thy fault is highe,
And now for the same thou needst must dye;

For except thou canst answer me questions three,
Thy head shall be smitten from thy bodie.

"And first," quo' the King, "when I'm in this stead,
With my crowns of gold so faire on my head,
Among all my liege men, so noble of birthe,
Thou must tell to one penny what I am worthe.

"Secondlye, tell me, without any doubt,
How soon I may ride the whole world about,
And at the third question thou must not shrinke,
But tell me here truly what I do thinke."

"Oh, these are hard questions for my shallow witt,
Nor can I answer your Grace as yet;
But if you will give me but three weeks' space,
I'll do my endeavor to answer your Grace."

"Now three weeks' space to thee will I give,
And that is the longest time thou hast to live;
For if thou dost not answer my questions three,
Thy land and thy livings are forfeit to me."

Away rode the Abbot all sad at that word,
And he rode to Cambridge and Oxenford;
But never a doctor there was so wise,
That could with his learning an answer devise.

Then home rode the Abbot of comfort so cold,
And he met his Shepherd a-going to fold:
"How now, my Lord Abbot, you are welcome home;
What news do you bring us from good King John?"

"Sad news, sad news, Shepherd, I must give,
That I have but three days more to live;
I must answer the King his questions three,
Or my head will be smitten from my bodie.

"The first is to tell him, there in that stead,
With his crown of gold so fair on his head,
Among all his liege men so noble of birthe,
To within one penny of what he is worthe.

"The seconde, to tell him, without any doubt,
How soone he may ride this whole world about:
And at the third question I must not shrinke,
But tell him truly what he does thinke."

"Now cheare up, Sire Abbot, did you never hear yet,
That a fool he may learne a wise man witt?
Lend me a horse, and serving men, and your apparel,
And I'll ride to London to answere your quarrel.

"Nay, frowne not, if it hath bin told unto mee,
I am like your Lordship, as ever may bee:
And if you will but lend me your gowne,
There is none shall know us in fair London towne."

"Now horses and serving men thou shalt have,
With sumptuous array most gallant and brave;
With crozier, and mitre, and rochet, and cope,
Fit to appear 'fore our Father the Pope."

"Now welcome, Sire Abbot," the King he did say,
" 'Tis well thou'rt come back to keepe thy day;
For and if thou canst answer my questions three,
Thy living and thy life both saved shall bee.

"And first, when thou seest me, here in this stead,
With my crown of golde so fair on my head,
Among all my liege men so noble of birthe,
Tell me to one penny what I am worthe."

"For thirty pence our Savior was sold
Among the false Jews, as I have bin told:
And twenty-nine is the worth of thee,
For I thinke, thou art one penny worse than he."

The King he laughed, and swore by St. Bittel,
"I did not think I had been worth so little!
Now, secondly, tell me, without any doubt,
How soon I may ride this whole world about."

"You must rise with the sun, and ride with the same,
Until the next morning he riseth again;
And then your Grace need not make any doubt,
But in twenty-four hours you'll ride it about."

The King he laughed, and swore by St. Jone,
"I did not think it could be done so soon.
Now from the third question thou must not shrink,
But tell me here truly what I do think."

"Yea, that I shall do and make your Grace merry;
You think I'm the Abbot of Canterbury;
But I'm his poor shepherd, as plain you may see,
That am come to beg pardon for him and for me."

The King he laughed, and swore by the mass,
"I'll make thee Lord Abbot this day in his place!"
"Nay, nay, my Liege, be not in such speed,
For alack, I can neither write nor read."

"Four nobles a week, then, I will give thee,
For this merry jest thou hast shown unto me;
And tell the old Abbot, when thou gettest home,
Thou hast brought him a pardon from good King John."

UNKNOWN

ANNABELLE LEE

IT was many and many a year ago,
In a kingdom by the sea,
That a maiden there lived whom you may know
By the name of Annabelle Lee;
And this maiden she lived with no other thought,
Than to love and be loved by me.

I was a child, and she was a child,
In this kingdom by the sea;

But we loved with a love that was more than love,
  I and my Annabelle Lee:
With a love that the winged seraphs of heaven
  Coveted her and me.

And this was the reason that long ago,
  In this kingdom by the sea,
A wind blew out of a cloud, chilling
  My beautiful Annabelle Lee,
So that her high-born kinsman came,
  And bore her away from me,
To shut her up in a sepulcher,
  In this kingdom by the sea.

* * * * * * *

But the moon never beams without bringing me dreams
  Of the beautiful Annabelle Lee;
And the stars never rise but I feel the bright eyes
  Of the beautiful Annabelle Lee;
And so, all the night tide, I lie down by the side
Of my darling—my darling—my life and my bride,
  In the sepulcher there by the sea,
  In the tomb by the sounding sea.

Edgar Allan Poe

LADY CLARE

IT was the time when lilies blow
  And clouds are highest up in air;
Lord Ronald brought a lily-white doe
  To give his cousin, Lady Clare.

I trow they did not part in scorn:
  Lovers long betroth'd were they:
They too will wed the morrow morn:
  God's blessing on the day!

"He does not love me for my birth,
Nor for my lands so broad and fair;
He loves me for my own true worth,
And that is well," said Lady Clare.

In there came old Alice the nurse;
Said: "Who was this that went from thee?"
"It was my cousin," said Lady Clare;
"To-morrow he weds with me."

"O God be thank'd!" said Alice the nurse,
"That all comes round so just and fair:
Lord Ronald is heir of all your lands,
And you are not the Lady Clare."

"Are ye out of your mind, my nurse, my nurse,"
Said Lady Clare, "that ye speak so wild?"
"As God's above," said Alice the nurse,
"I speak the truth: you are my child.

"The old Earl's daughter died at my breast;
I speak the truth, as I live by bread!
I buried her like my own sweet child,
And put my child in her stead."

"Falsely, falsely have ye done,
O mother," she said, "if this be true,
To keep the best man under the sun
So many years from his due."

"Nay now, my child," said Alice the nurse,
"But keep the secret for your life,
And all you have will be Lord Ronald's
When you are man and wife."

"If I'm a beggar born," she said,
"I will speak out, for I dare not lie.
Pull off, pull off the brooch of gold,
And fling the diamond necklace by."

"Nay now, my child," said Alice the nurse,
"But keep the secret all ye can."
She said: "Not so: but I will know
If there be any faith in man."

"Nay now, what faith?" said Alice the nurse,
"The man will cleave unto his right."
"And he shall have it," the lady replied,
"Tho' I should die to-night."

"Yet give one kiss to your mother dear!
Alas! my child, I sinn'd for thee."
"O mother, mother, mother," she said,
"So strange it seems to me.

"Yet here's a kiss for my mother dear,
My mother dear, if this be so,
And lay your hand upon my head,
And bless me, mother, ere I go."

She clad herself in a russet gown,
She was no longer Lady Clare:
She went by dale, and she went by down,
With a single rose in her hair.

The lily-white doe Lord Ronald had brought
Leapt up from where she lay,
Dropt her head in the maiden's hand,
And follow'd her all the way.

Down stept Lord Ronald from his tower:
"O Lady Clare, you shame your worth!
Why come you drest like a village maid,
That are the flower of the earth?"

"If I come drest like a village maid,
I am but as my fortunes are:
I am a beggar born," she said,
"And not the Lady Clare."

"Play me no tricks," said Lord Ronald,
"For I am yours in word and in deed.
Play me no tricks," said Lord Ronald,
"Your riddle is hard to read."

O and proudly stood she up!
Her heart within her did not fail:
She look'd into Lord Ronald's eyes,
And told him all her nurse's tale.

He laugh'd a laugh of merry scorn:
He turn'd and kiss'd her where she stood.
"If you are not the heiress born,
And I," said he, "the next in blood—

"If you are not the heiress born,
And I," said he, "the lawful heir,
We two will wed to-morrow morn,
And you shall still be Lady Clare."

Alfred Tennyson

A PORTRAIT

I WILL paint her as I see her:
Ten times have the lilies blown,
Since she looked upon the sun.

And her face is lily clear—
Lily shaped, and drooped in duty
To the law of its own beauty.

Oral cheeks encolored faintly,
Which a trail of golden hair
Keeps from fading off to air:

And a forehead fair and saintly,
Which two blue eyes undershine,
Like meek prayers before a shrine.

Face and figure of a child—
Though too calm, you think, and tender,
For the childhood you would lend her.

Yet child—simple, undefiled,
Frank, obedient—waiting still
On the turnings of your will.

Moving light, as all young things—
As young birds, or early wheat
When the wind blows over it.

Only free from flutterings
Of loud mirth that scorneth measure—
Taking love for her chief pleasure.

Choosing pleasures (for the rest)
Which come softly—just as she,
When she nestles at your knee.

Quiet talk she likest best,
In a bower of gentle looks—
Watering flowers, or reading books.

And her voice, it murmurs lowly,
As a silver stream may run,
Which yet feels, you feel, the sun.

And her smile, it seems half holy,
As if drawn from thoughts more fair
Than our common jestings are.

And if any poet knew her,
He would sing of her with falls
Used in lovely madrigals.

And if any painter drew her,
He would paint her unaware
With a halo round her hair.

And if reader read the poem,
He would whisper, "You have done a
Consecrated little Una!"

And a dreamer (did you show him
That same picture) would exclaim,
" 'Tis my angel, with a name!"

And a stranger—when he sees her
In the street even—smileth stilly,
Just as you would at a lily.

And all voices that address her,
Soften, sleeken every word,
As if speaking to a bird.

And all fancies yearn to cover
The hard earth whereon she passes
With the thymy scented grasses.

And all hearts do pray, "God love her!"
Ay, and always, in good sooth,
We may all be sure He doth.

ELIZABETH BARRETT BROWNING

THE MAY QUEEN

YOU must wake and call me early, call me early, mother dear;
To-morrow 'ill be the happiest time of all the glad New Year;
Of all the glad New Year, mother, the maddest, merriest day;
For I'm to be Queen o' the May, mother, I'm to be Queen o' the May.

There's many a black black eye, they say, but none so bright
as mine;
There's Margaret and Mary, there's Kate and Caroline:
But none so fair as little Alice in all the land they say,
So I'm to be Queen o' the May, mother, I'm to be Queen
o' the May.

I sleep so sound all night, mother, that I shall never wake,
If you do not call me loud when the day begins to break:
But I must gather knots of flowers, and buds and garlands
gay,
For I'm to be Queen o' the May, mother, I'm to be Queen
o' the May.

As I came up the valley whom think ye should I see,
But Robin leaning on the bridge beneath the hazel tree?
He thought of that sharp look, mother, I gave him yester-
day—
But I'm to be Queen o' the May, mother, I'm to be Queen
o' the May.

He thought I was a ghost, mother, for I was all in white,
And I ran by him without speaking, like a flash of light.
They call me cruel hearted, but I care not what they say,
For I'm to be Queen o' the May, mother, I'm to be Queen
o' the May.

They say he's dying all for love, but that can never be:
They say his heart is breaking, mother—what is that to me?
There's many a bolder lad 'ill woo me any summer day,
And I'm to be Queen o' the May, mother, I'm to be Queen
o' the May.

Little Effie shall go with me to-morrow to the green,
And you will be there, too, mother, to see me made the
Queen;
For the shepherd lads on every side will come from far
away,
And I'm to be Queen o' the May, mother, I'm to be Queen
o' the May.

The honeysuckle round the porch has wov'n its wavy bowers,
And by the meadow trenches blow the faint sweet cuckoo flowers;
And the wild marsh marigold shines like fire in swamps and hollows gray,
And I'm to be Queen o' the May, mother, I'm to be Queen o' the May.

The night winds come and go, mother, upon the meadow grass,
And the happy stars above them seem to brighten as they pass;
There will not be a drop of rain the whole of the live-long day,
And I'm to be Queen o' the May, mother, I'm to be Queen o' the May.

All the valley, mother, will be fresh and green and still,
And the cowslip and the crowfoot are over all the hill,
And the rivulet in the flowery dale will merrily glance and play,
For I'm to be Queen o' the May, mother, I'm to be Queen o' the May.

So you must wake and call me early, call me early, mother dear,
To-morrow 'ill be the happiest time of all the glad New Year;
To-morrow 'ill be of all the year the maddest, merriest day,
For I'm to be Queen o' the May, mother, I'm to be Queen o' the May.

ALFRED TENNYSON

CONCLUSION TO THE MAY QUEEN AND NEW YEAR'S EVE

I THOUGHT to pass away before, and yet alive I am;
And in the fields all round I hear the bleating of the lamb.

How sadly, I remember, rose the morning of the year!
To die before the snowdrop came, and now the violet's here.

O sweet is the new violet, that comes beneath the skies,
And sweeter is the young lamb's voice to me that cannot rise,
And sweet is all the land about, and all the flowers that
blow,
And sweeter far is death than life to me that long to go.

It seemed so hard at first, mother, to leave the blessèd sun,
And now it seems as hard to stay, and yet His will be done!
But still I think it can't be long before I find release:
And that good man, the clergyman, has told me words of
peace.

O blessings on his kindly voice, and on his silver hair!
And blessings on his whole life long, until he meet me
there!
O blessings on his kindly heart, and on his silver head!
A thousand times I blest him, as he knelt beside my bed.

He taught me all the mercy, for he showed me all the sin.
Now, though my lamp was lighted late, there's One will let
me in:
Nor would I now be well, mother, again if that could be,
For my desire is but to pass to Him that died for me.

I did not hear the dog howl, mother, or the dead-watch beat,
There came a sweeter token when the night and morning
meet:
But sit beside my bed, mother, and put your hand in mine,
And Effie on the other side, and I will tell the sign.

All in the wild March morning I heard the angels call;
It was when the moon was setting, and the dark was over
all;
The trees began to whisper, and the wind began to roll,
And in the wild March morning I heard them call my soul.

For, lying broad awake, I thought of you and Effie dear;
I saw you sitting in the house, and I no longer here;

With all my strength I prayed for both, and so I felt
resigned,
And up the valley came a swell of music on the wind.

I thought that it was fancy, and I listened in my bed,
And then did something speak to me—I know not what was
said;
For great delight and shuddering took hold of all my mind,
And up the valley came again the music on the wind.

But you were sleeping; and I said, "It's not for them, it's
mine";
And if it comes three times, I thought, I take it for a sign.
And once again it came, and close beside the window bars,
Then seemed to go right up to Heaven and die among the
stars.

So now I think my time is near. I trust it is, I know
The blessed music went that way my soul will have to go.
And for myself, indeed, I care not if I go to-day.
But, Effie, you must comfort *her* when I am past away.

And say to Robin a kind word, and tell him not to fret;
There's many worthier than I, would make him happy yet.
If I had lived—I cannot tell—I might have been his wife;
But all these things have ceased to be, with my desire of life.

O look! the sun begins to rise, the heavens are in a glow;
He shines upon a hundred fields, and all of them I know;
And there I move no longer now, and there his light may
shine—
Wild flowers in the valley for other hands than mine.

O sweet and strange it seems to me, that ere this day is done
The voice, that now is speaking, may be beyond the sun—
For ever and for ever with those just souls and true—
And what is life, that we should moan? why make we such
ado?

For ever and for ever, all in a blessed home—
And there to wait a little while till you and Effie come—

To be within the light of God, as I lie upon your breast—
And the wicked cease from troubling, and the weary are
at rest.

ALFRED TENNYSON

THE NAMES

IN Christian world MARY the garland wears!
REBECCA sweetens on a Hebrew's ear;
Quakers for pure PRISCILLA are more clear;
And the light Gaul by amorous NINON swears.
Among the lesser lights how LUCY shines!
What air of fragrance ROSAMOND throws around!
How like a hymn doth sweet CECILIA sound!
Of MARTHAS, and of ABIGAILS, few lines
Have bragg'd in verse. Of coarsest household stuff
Should homely JOAN be fashioned. But can
You BARBARA resist, or MARIAN?
And is not CLARE for love excuse enough?
Yet, by my faith in numbers, I profess,
These all, than Saxon EDITH, please me less.

CHARLES LAMB

LA BELLE DAME SANS MERCI

"O WHAT can ail thee, knight-at-arms,
Alone and palely loitering?
The sedge has wither'd from the Lake,
And no birds sing.

"O what can ail thee, knight-at-arms,
So haggard and so woebegone?
The squirrel's granary is full,
And the harvest's done.

"I see a lily on thy brow
With anguish moist and fever dew,
And on thy cheeks a fading rose
Fast withereth too."

"I met a Lady in the Meads,
Full beautiful—a fairy's child,
Her hair was long, her foot was light,
And her eyes were wild.

"I made a garland for her head,
And bracelets too, and fragrant zone;
She look'd at me as she did love,
And made sweet moan.

"I set her on my pacing steed
And nothing else saw all day long,
For sidelong would she bend, and sing
A fairy's song.

"She found me roots of relish sweet,
And honey wild and manna dew,
And sure in language strange she said
'I love thee true.'

"She took me to her elfin grot,
And there she wept, and sigh'd full sore,
And there I shut her wild, wild eyes
With kisses four.

"And there she lullèd me asleep,
And there I dream'd—Ah! woe betide!
The latest dream I ever dreamt
On the cold hillside.

"I saw pale Kings and Princes too,
Pale warriors, death pale were they all;
They cried—'La belle Dame sans Merci
Hath thee in thrall!'

"I saw their starved lips in the gloam
With horrid warning gapèd wide,
And I awoke and found me here
On the cold hill's side.

"And this is why I sojourn here
Alone and palely loitering,
Though the sedge is wither'd from the Lake
And no birds sing."

JOHN KEATS

THE GLOVE AND THE LIONS

KING FRANCIS was a hearty king, and loved a royal sport,
And one day, as his lions fought, sat looking on the court;
The nobles fill'd the benches, and the ladies in their pride,
And 'mongst them sat the Count de Lorge, with one for whom he sigh'd;
And truly 'twas a gallant thing to see that crowning show—
Valor and love, and a king above, and the royal beasts below.
Ramped and roared the lions, with horrid, laughing jaws;
They bit, they glared, gave blows like beams, a wind went with their paws;
With wallowing might and stifled roar they rolled one on another,
Till all the pit, with sand and mane, was in a thundrous smother;
The bloody foam above the bars came whisking through the air;
Said Francis, then, "Faith, gentlemen, w'ere better here than there!"

De Lorge's love o'erheard the King, a beauteous, lively dame,
With smiling lips, and sharp, bright eyes, which always seemed the same:

She thought, "The Count my lover, is as brave as brave can be,
He surely would do wondrous things to show his love for me!
King, ladies, lovers, all look on, the occasion is divine;
I'll drop my glove to prove his love, great glory will be mine!"

She dropped her glove to prove his love, then looked at him and smiled;
He bowed, and in a moment leaped among the lions wild;
The leap was quick; return was quick; he has regained his place,
Then threw the glove, but not with love, right in the lady's face!
"In truth!" cried Francis, "rightly done!" and he rose from where he sat;
"No love," quoth he, "but vanity, sets love a task like that."

LEIGH HUNT

SKIPPER IRESON'S RIDE

OF all the rides since the birth of time,
Told in story or sung in rhyme,—
On Apuleius's Golden Ass,
Or one-eyed Calender's horse of brass,
Witch astride of a human back,
Islam's prophet on Al-Borák,—
The strangest ride that ever was sped
Was Ireson's out from Marblehead!

Body of turkey, head of fowl,
Wings a-droop like a rained-on fowl,
Feathered and ruffled in every part,
Skipper Ireson stood in the cart,
Scores of women, old and young,
Strong of muscle, and glib of tongue,

Pushed and pulled up the rocky lane,
Shouting and singing the shrill refrain:
"Here's Flud Oirson, fur his horrd horrt,
Torr'd an' furtherr'd an' corr'd in a corrt
By the women o' Morble'ead!"

Wrinkled scolds with hands on hips,
Girls in bloom of cheek and lips,
Wild eyed, free limbed, such as chase
Bacchus round some antique vase,
Brief of skirt, with ankles bare,
Loose of kerchief and loose of hair,
With conch shells blowing and fish horns' twang,
Over and over the Mænads sang:
"Here's Flud Oirson, fur his horrd horrt,
Torr'd an' furtherr'd an' corr'd in a corrt
By the women o' Morble'ead!"

Small pity for him!—He sailed away
From a leaking ship in Chaleur Bay,—
Sailed away from a sinking wreck,
With his own townspeople on her deck!
"Lay by! lay by!" they called to him.
Back he answered, "Sink or swim!
Brag of your catch of fish again!"
And off he sailed through the fog and rain
Old Floyd Ireson, for his hard heart,
Tarred and feathered and carried in a cart
By the women of Marblehead!

Fathoms deep in dark Chaleur
That wreck shall lie forevermore.
Mother and sister, wife and maid,
Looked from the rocks of Marblehead
Over the moaning and rainy sea,—
Looked for the coming that might not be!
What did the winds and the sea birds say
Of the cruel captain who sailed away?—
Old Floyd Ireson, for his hard heart,
Tarred and feathered and carried in a cart
By the women of Marblehead!

Through the street, on either side,
Up flew windows, doors swung wide;
Sharp-tongued spinsters, old wives gray,
Treble lent the fish horn's bray.
Sea-worn grandsires, cripple bound,
Hulks of old sailors run aground,
Shook head, and fist, and hat, and cane,
And cracked with curses the hoarse refrain:
"Here's Flud Oirson, fur his horrd horrt,
Torr'd an' furtherr'd an' corr'd in a corrt
By the women o' Morble'ead!"

Sweetly along the Salem road
Bloom of orchard and lilac showed.
Little the wicked skipper knew
Of the fields so green and the sky so blue.
Riding there in his sorry trim,
Like an Indian idol glum and grim,
Scarcely he seemed the sound to hear
Of voices shouting, far and near:
"Here's Flud Oirson, fur his horrd horrt,
Torr'd an' furtherr'd an' corr'd in a corrt
By the women o' Marble'ead!"

"Hear me, neighbors!" at last he cried,—
"What to me is this noisy ride?
What is the shame that clothes the skin
To the nameless horror that lives within?
Waking or sleeping, I see a wreck,
And hear a cry from a reeling deck!
Hate me and curse me,—I only dread
The hand of God and the face of the dead!"
Said old Floyd Ireson, for his hard heart,
Tarred and feathered and carried in a cart
By the women of Marblehead!

Then the wife of the skipper lost at sea
Said, "God has touched him! why should we!"
Said an old wife mourning her only son,
"Cut the rogue's tether and let him run!"

So with soft relentings and rude excuse,
Half scorn, half pity, they cut him loose,
And gave him a cloak to hide him in,
And left him alone with his shame and sin,
  Poor Floyd Ireson, for his hard heart,
  Tarred and feathered and carried in a cart
    By the women of Marblehead!

JOHN GREENLEAF WHITTIER

THE INCHCAPE ROCK

NO stir in the air, no stir in the sea,
  The ship was as still as she could be;
Her sails from heaven received no motion,
Her keel was steady in the ocean.

Without either sign or sound of their shock,
The waves flow'd over the Inchcape Rock;
So little they rose, so little they fell,
They did not move the Inchcape bell.

The good Abbot of Aberbrothok
Had placed that bell on the Inchcape Rock;
On a buoy in the storm it floated and swung,
And over the waves its warning rung.

When the rock was hid by the surge's swell,
The mariners heard the warning bell:
And then they knew the perilous rock,
And blest the Abbot of Aberbrothok.

The sun in heaven was shining gay,
All things were joyful on that day;
The sea birds scream'd as they wheel'd around,
And there was pleasure in their sound.

The buoy of the Inchcape bell was seen,
A darker speck on the ocean green;
Sir Ralph the Rover walk'd his deck,
And he fixed his eye on the darker speck

He felt the cheering power of spring,
It made him whistle, it made him sing;
His heart was mirthful to excess—
But the Rover's mirth was wickedness.

His eyes were on the Inchcape float:
Quoth he, "My men, put out the boat,
And row me to the Inchcape Rock,
And I'll plague the Abbot of Aberbrothok."

The boat is lower'd, the boatmen row,
And to the Inchcape Rock they go;
Sir Ralph bent over from the boat,
And he cut the bell from the Inchcape float.

Down sunk the bell with a gurgling sound—
The bubbles rose and burst around;
Quoth Sir Ralph, "The next who comes to the Rock
Won't bless the Abbot of Aberbrothok."

Sir Ralph the Rover sail'd away;
He scoured the seas for many a day;
And, now grown rich with plunder'd store,
He steers his course for Scotland's shore.

So thick a haze o'erspreads the sky,
They cannot see the sun on high;
The wind hath blown a gale all day,
At evening it hath died away.

On the deck the Rover takes his stand,
So dark it is they see no land.
Quoth Sir Ralph, "It will be lighter soon,
For there is the dawn of the rising moon."

"Canst hear," said one, "the breakers roar?
For methinks we should be near the shore.
Now where we are I cannot tell,
But I wish I could hear the Inchcape bell."

They hear no sound—the swell is strong;
Though the wind hath fallen they drift along
Till the vessel strikes with a shivering shock—
"Mercy! it is the Inchcape Rock!"

Sir Ralph the Rover tore his hair,
And beat his breast in his despair:
The waves rush in on every side,
And the ship sinks down beneath the tide.

ROBERT SOUTHEY

LOCHINVAR

O, YOUNG Lochinvar is come out of the west,
Through all the wide Border his steed was the best,
And save his good broadsword he weapons had none;
He rode all unarmed, and he rode all alone,
So faithful in love, and so dauntless in war,
There never was knight like the young Lochinvar.

He stayed not for brake, and he stopped not for stone,
He swam the Eske river where ford there was none;
But, ere he alighted at Netherby gate,
The bride had consented, the gallant came late:
For a laggard in love, and a dastard in war,
Was to wed the fair Ellen of brave Lochinvar.

So boldly he entered the Netherby hall,
Among bridesmen and kinsmen, and brothers and all;
Then spoke the bride's father, his hand on his sword
(For the poor craven bridegroom said never a word),

"O come ye in peace here, or come ye in war,
Or to dance at our bridal, young Lord Lochinvar?"

"I long wooed your daughter, my suit you denied;—
Love swells like the Solway, but ebbs like its tide—
And now I am come, with this lost love of mine,
To lead but one measure, drink one cup of wine.
There are maidens in Scotland more lovely by far,
That would gladly be bride to the young Lochinvar."

The bride kissed the goblet; the knight took it up,
He quaffed off the wine, and he threw down the cup,
She looked down to blush, and she looked up to sigh,
With a smile on her lips and a tear in her eye.
He took her soft hand, ere her mother could bar,—
"Now tread we a measure!" said young Lochinvar.

So stately his form, and so lovely her face,
That never a hall such a galliard did grace;
While her mother did fret, and her father did fume,
And the bridegroom stood dangling his bonnet and plume;
And the bridemaidens whispered, " 'Twere better by far
To have matched our fair cousin with young Lochinvar."

One touch to her hand, and one word in her ear,
When they reached the hall door, and the charger stood
near;
So light to the croupe the fair lady he swung,
So light to the saddle before her he sprung!
"She is won! we are gone, over bank, bush, and scaur;
They'll have fleet steeds that follow," quoth young Loch-
invar.

There was mounting 'mong Græmes of the Netherby clan;
Forsters, Fenwicks, and Musgraves, they rode and they ran;
There was racing, and chasing, on Cannobie Lee,
But the lost bride of Netherby ne'er did they see.
So daring in love, and so dauntless in war,
Have ye e'er heard of gallant like young Lochinvar?

WALTER SCOTT

THE LAY OF THE LAST MINSTREL

THE way was long, the wind was cold,
The Minstrel was infirm and old;
His withered cheek and tresses gray
Seemed to have known a better day:
The harp, his sole remaining joy,
Was carried by an orphan boy:
The last of all the Bards was he,
Who sung of Border chivalry.
For, well-a-day! their date was fled,
His tuneful brethren all were dead;
And he, neglected and oppressed,
Wished to be with them, and at rest.
No more, on prancing palfrey borne,
He carolled, light as lark at morn;
No longer courted and caressed,
High placed in hall, a welcome guest,
He poured, to lord and lady gay,
The unpremeditated lay;
Old times were changed—old manners gone—
A stranger filled the Stuarts' throne.
The bigots of the iron time
Had called his harmless art—a crime.
A wandering harper, scorned and poor,
He begged his bread from door to door;
And tuned, to please a peasant's ear,
The harp, a king had loved to hear.
He passed, where Newark's stately tower
Looks out from Yarrow's birchen bower:
The Minstrel gazed with wishful eye—
No humbler resting place was nigh.
With hesitating step, at last,
The embattled portal arch he passed;
Whose ponderous grate and massy bar
Had oft rolled back the tide of war,
But never closed the iron door
Against the desolate and poor.
The Duchess marked his weary pace,
His timid mien and reverend face;
And bade her page the menials tell

That they should tend the old man well—
For she had known adversity,
Though born in such a high degree;
In pride of power, in beauty's bloom,
Had wept o'er Monmouth's bloody tomb.
When kindness had his wants supplied,
And the old man was gratified,
Began to rise his minstrel pride;
And he began to talk, anon,
Of good Earl Francis, dead and gone;
And of Earl Walter—rest him God!—
A braver ne'er to battle rode:
And how full many a tale he knew
Of the old warriors of Buccleugh;
And, would the noble Duchess deign
To listen to an old man's strain,
Though stiff his hand, his voice though weak,
He thought, even yet,—the sooth to speak,—
That if she loved the harp to hear,
He could make music to her ear.
The humble boon was soon obtained;
The aged Minstrel audience gained;
But when he reached the room of state,
Where she, with all her ladies, sat,
Perchance he wished his boon denied;
For, when to tune his harp he tried,
His trembling hand had lost the ease
Which marks security to please;
And scenes, long past, of joy and pain,
Came wildering o'er his aged brain;—
He tried to tune his harp, in vain.
Amid the strings his fingers strayed,
And an uncertain warbling made;
And, oft, he shook his hoary head.
But when he caught the measure wild,
The old man raised his face, and smiled;
And lighted up his faded eye,
With all a poet's ecstasy!
In varying cadence, soft or strong,
He swept the sounding chords along;
The present scene, the future lot,

His toils, his wants, were all forgot;
Cold diffidence, and age's frost,
In the full tide of soul were lost;
Each blank in faithless memory's void,
The poet's glowing thought supplied;
And, while his harp responsive rung,
'Twas thus the latest minstrel sung:
"Breathes there the man, with soul so dead—
Who never to himself hath said,
This is my own, my native land!—
Whose heart hath ne'er within him burned,
As home his footsteps he hath turned
From wandering on a foreign strand?
If such there breathe, go—mark him well;
For him, no minstrel raptures swell:
High though his titles, proud his name,
Boundless his wealth, as wish can claim;
Despite those titles, power and pelf,
The wretch, concentered all in self,
Living, shall forfeit fair renown,
And, doubly dying, shall go down
To the vile dust from whence he sprung,
Unwept, unhonored, and unsung!"

WALTER SCOTT

THE VILLAGE BLACKSMITH *

UNDER a spreading chestnut tree
The village smithy stands;
The smith, a mighty man is he,
With large and sinewy hands,
And the muscles of his brawny arms
Are strong as iron bands.

* "The 'village smithy' stood in Brattle Street, Cambridge. There came a time when the chestnut tree that shaded it was cut down, and then the children of the place put their pence together and had a chair made for the poet from its wood."

His hair is crisp, and black, and long;
  His face is like the tan;
His brow is wet with honest sweat,
  He earns whate'er he can,
And looks the whole world in the face,
  For he owes not any man.

Week in, week out, from morn till night,
  You can hear his bellows blow;
You can hear him swing his heavy sledge,
  With measured beat and slow,
Like a sexton ringing the village bell,
  When the evening sun is low.

And children coming home from school
  Look in at the open door;
They love to see the flaming forge,
  And hear the bellows roar,
And catch the burning sparks that fly
  Like chaff from a threshing floor.

He goes on Sunday to the church,
  And sits among his boys;
He hears the parson pray and preach,
  He hears his daughter's voice
Singing in the village choir,
  And it makes his heart rejoice.

It sounds to him like her mother's voice
  Singing in Paradise!
He needs must think of her once more,
  How in the grave she lies;
And with his hard, rough hand he wipes
  A tear out of his eyes.

Toiling—rejoicing—sorrowing,
  Onward through life he goes;
Each morning sees some task begin,
  Each evening sees it close;
Something attempted, something done,
  Has earned a night's repose.

Thanks, thanks to thee, my worthy friend,
  For the lesson thou hast taught!
Thus at the flaming forge of life
  Our fortunes must be wrought;
Thus on its sounding anvil shaped
  Each burning deed and thought.

HENRY W. LONGFELLOW

THE INVITATION

BEST and brightest, come away,—
  Fairer far than this fair Day,
Which, like thee, to those in sorrow
Comes to bid a sweet good morrow
To the rough year just awake
In its cradle on the brake.
The brightest hour of unborn Spring
Through the winter wandering,
Found, it seems, the halcyon morn
To hoar February born;
Bending from Heaven, in azure mirth,
It kiss'd the forehead of the earth,
And smiled upon the silent sea,
And bade the frozen streams be free,
And waked to music all their fountains,
And breathed upon the frozen mountains,
And like the prophetess of May
Strew'd flowers upon the barren way,
Making the wintry world appear
Like one on whom thou smilest, dear.

  Away, away, from men and towns,
To the wild wood and the downs—
To the silent wilderness
Where the soul need not repress
Its music, lest it should not find
An echo in another's mind,
While the touch of Nature's art
Harmonizes heart to heart.

Radiant Sister of the Day,
Awake! arise! and come away!
To the wild woods and the plains,
To the pools where winter rains
Image all their roofs of leaves,
Where the pine its garland weaves
Of sapless green, and ivy dun,
Round stems that never kiss the sun;
Where the lawns and pastures be
And the sandhills of the sea;
Where the melting hoarfrost wets
The daisy star that never sets,
And windflowers and violets
Which yet join not scent to hue
Crown the pale year weak and new;
When the night is left behind
In the deep east, dim and blind,
And the blue moon is over us,
And the multitudinous
Billows murmur at our feet,
Where the earth and ocean meet,
And all things seem only one
In the universal Sun.

PERCY BYSSHE SHELLEY

THE CANE-BOTTOMED CHAIR

IN tattered old slippers that toast at the bars,
And a ragged old jacket perfumed with cigars,
Away from the world and its toils and its cares,
I've a snug little kingdom up four pairs of stairs.

To mount to this realm is a toil, to be sure,
But the fire there is bright and the air rather pure;
And the view I behold on a sunshiny day
Is grand, through the chimney pots over the way.

This snug little chamber is crammed in all nooks
With worthless old knickknacks and silly old books,
And foolish old odds and foolish old ends,
Cracked bargains from brokers, cheap keepsakes from
friends.

Old armor, prints, pictures, pipes, china (all cracked),
Old rickety tables, and chairs broken-backed;
A twopenny treasury, wondrous to see;
What matter! 'tis pleasant to you, friend, and me.

No better divan need the Sultan require,
Than the creaking old sofa that basks by the fire,
And 'tis wonderful, surely, what music you get
From the rickety, ramshackle, wheezy spinet.

That praying rug came from a Turcoman's camp;
By Tiber once twinkled that brazen old lamp;
A Mameluke fierce yonder dagger has drawn:
'Tis a murderous knife to toast muffins upon.

Long, long through the hours, and the night, and the chimes,
Here we talk of old books, and old friends, and old times:
As we sit in a fog made of rich Latakie,
This chamber is pleasant to you, friend, and me.

But of all the cheap treasures that garnish my nest,
There's one that I love and I cherish the best;
For the finest of couches that's padded with hair
I never would change thee, my cane-bottomed chair.

'Tis a bandy-legged, high-shouldered, worm-eaten seat,
With a creaking old back, and twisted old feet;
But since the fair morning when Fanny sat there,
I bless thee and love thee, old cane-bottomed chair.

If chairs have but feeling, in holding such charms,
A thrill must have passed through your withered old arms!
I looked, and I longed, and I wished in despair;
I wished myself turned to a cane-bottomed chair.

It was but a moment she sat in this place,
She'd a scarf on her neck, and a smile on her face!
A smile on her face, and a rose in her hair,
And she sat there, and bloomed in my cane-bottomed chair.

And so I have valued my chair ever since,
Like the shrine of a saint, or the throne of a prince;
Saint Fanny, my patroness sweet I declare,
The queen of my heart and my cane-bottomed chair.

When the candles burn low, and the company's gone,
In the silence of night as I sit here alone—
I sit here alone, but we yet are a pair—
My Fanny I see in my cane-bottomed chair.

She comes from the past, and revisits my room;
She looks as she then did, all beauty and bloom;
So smiling and tender, so fresh and so fair,
And yonder she sits in my cane-bottomed chair.

William Makepeace Thackeray

THE DESERTED VILLAGE

Sweet Auburn! loveliest village of the plain,
Where health and plenty cheered the laboring swain;
Where smiling spring its earliest visits paid,
And parting summer's lingering bloom delayed;
Dear lovely bowers of innocence and ease,
Seats of my youth, when every sport could please!
How often have I loitered o'er thy green,
Where humble happiness endeared each scene;
How often have I paused on every charm—
The sheltered cot, the cultivated farm,
The never-failing brook, the busy mill,
The decent church that topp'd the neighboring hill,
The hawthorn bush, with seats beneath the shade,
For talking age and whispering lovers made!

How often have I blessed the coming day,
When toil remitting lent its turn to play,
And all the village train, from labor free,
Led up their sports beneath the spreading tree:
While many a pastime, circled in the shade,
The young contended as the old surveyed;
And many a gambol frolicked o'er the ground,
And sleights of art and feats of strength went round;
And still, as each repeated pleasure tired,
Succeeding sports the mirthful band inspired;
The dancing pair that simply sought renown,
By holding out to tire each other down;
The swain, mistrustless of his smutted face,
While secret laughter titter'd round the place;
The bashful virgin's side-long looks of love,
The matron's glance that would those looks reprove.
These were thy charms, sweet village! sports like these,
With sweet succession, taught e'en toil to please;
These round thy bowers their cheerful influence shed,
These *were* thy charms—but all these charms are fled.

OLIVER GOLDSMITH

THE OLD ARMCHAIR

I LOVE it—I love it, and who shall dare
To chide me for loving that old armchair!
I've treasured it long as a sainted prize—
I've bedewed it with tears, I've embalmed it with sighs;
'Tis bound by a thousand bands to my heart,
Not a tie will break, not a link will start;
Would you learn the spell?—A mother sat there,
And a sacred thing is that old armchair.

In childhood's hour I lingered near,
The hallowed seat with listening ear;
And gentle words that mother would give,
To fit me to die, and teach me to live.
She told me shame would never betide
With truth for my creed, and God for my Guide;

She taught me to lisp my earliest prayer,
As I knelt beside that old armchair.
I sat and watched her many a day,
When her eyes were dim and her locks were gray,
And I almost worshiped her when she smiled
And turned from her Bible to bless her child.
Years rolled on, but the last one sped,
My idol was shattered—my earth star fled;
I learnt how much the heart can bear,
When I saw her die in that old armchair.

'Tis past! 'tis past! but I gaze on it now
With quivering breath and throbbing brow;
'Twas there she nursed me—'twas there she died,
And memory flows with lava tide!
Say it is folly, and deem me weak,
While the scalding tears run down my cheek;
But I love it—I love it, and cannot tear
My soul from my mother's old armchair.

Eliza Cook

THE OLD CLOCK ON THE STAIRS

SOMEWHAT back from the village street
Stands the old-fashioned country seat.
Across its antique portico
Tall poplar trees their shadows throw;
And from its station in the hall
An ancient timepiece says to all—
"For ever—never!
Never—for ever!"

* * * * * * *

By day its voice is low and light;
But in the silent dead of night,
Distinct as a passing footstep's fall
It echoes along the vacant hall,

Along the ceiling, along the floor,
And seems to say, at each chamber door—
"For ever—never!
Never—for ever!"

Through days of sorrow and of mirth,
Through days of death and days of birth
Through every swift vicissitude
Of changeful time, unchanged it has stood,
And as if, like God, it all things saw,
It calmly repeats those words of awe—
"For ever—never!
Never—for ever!"

In that mansion used to be
Free-hearted Hospitality;
His great fires up the chimney roared;
The stranger feasted at his board;
But, like the skeletons at the feast,
That warning timepiece never ceased—
"For ever—never!
Never—for ever!"

There groups of merry children played,
There youths and maidens dreaming strayed;
Oh, precious hours! Oh, golden prime,
And affluence of love and time!
Even as a miser counts his gold,
Those hours the ancient timepiece told—
"For ever—never!
Never—for ever!"

From that chamber, clothed in white,
The bride came forth on her wedding night;
There, in that silent room below,
The dead lay in his shroud of snow;
And in the hush that followed the prayer,
Was heard the old clock on the stair—
"For ever—never!
Never—for ever!"

All are scattered now and fled,
Some are married, some are dead;
And when I ask, with throbs of pain,
"Ah! when shall they all meet again!"
As in the days long since gone by,
The ancient timepiece makes reply—
"For ever—never!
Never—for ever!"

Never here—for ever there,
Where all parting, pain, and care,
And death, and time shall disappear,—
For ever there, but never here!
The horologe of Eternity
Sayeth this incessantly—
"For ever—never!
Never—for ever!"

HENRY WADSWORTH LONGFELLOW

LINES FROM "THE LADY OF THE LAKE"

THE western waves of ebbing day
Roll'd o'er the glen their level way;
Each purple peak, each flinty spire,
Was bathed in floods of living fire.
But not a setting beam could glow
Within the dark ravines below,
Where twined the path, in shadow hid,
Round many a rocky pyramid.

* * * * * * *

Boon nature scatter'd, free and wild,
Each plant or flower, the mountain's child.
Here eglantine embalm'd the air,
Hawthorn and hazel mingled there;
The primrose pale and violet flower
Found in each cliff a narrow bower;

Foxglove and nightshade, side by side,
Emblems of punishment and pride,
Group'd their dark hues with every stain
The weather-beaten crags retain.
With boughs that quaked at every breath,
Gray birch and aspen wept beneath;
Aloft, the ash and warrior oak
Cast anchor in the rifted rock;
And, higher yet, the pine tree hung
His shatter'd trunk, and frequent flung,
Where seem'd the cliffs to meet on high,
His boughs athwart the narrow'd sky.
Highest of all, where white peaks glanced,
Where glist'ning streamers waved and danced,
The wanderer's eye could barely view
The summer heaven's delicious blue;
So wondrous wild, the whole might seem
The scenery of a fairy dream.

WALTER SCOTT

DISPUTE BETWEEN NOSE AND EYES

BETWEEN Nose and Eyes a strange contest arose,
The spectacles set them unhappily wrong;
The point in dispute was, as all the world knows,
To which the said spectacles ought to belong.

So Tongue was the lawyer, and argued the cause
With a great deal of skill, and a wig full of learning,
While chief Baron Ear, sat to balance the laws,
So famed for his talent, in nicely discerning.

"In behalf of the Nose, it will quickly appear,
And your lordship," he said, "will undoubtedly find
That the Nose has had spectacles always in wear,
Which amounts to possession—time out of mind."

Then holding the Spectacles up to the court—
"Your lordship observes they are made with a straddle,
As wide as the ridge of the Nose is—in short,
Designed to sit close to it, just like a saddle.

"Again, would your lordship a moment suppose
('Tis a case that has happened, and may be again);
That the visage or countenance had not a nose,
Pray who would, or who could, wear spectacles then?

"On the whole it appears, and my argument shows
With a reasoning the court will never condemn,
That the spectacles plainly were made for the nose,
And the nose was as plainly intended for them."

Then shifting his side (as a lawyer knows how)
He pleaded again in behalf of the Eyes;
But what were his arguments few people know,
For the court did not think they were equally wise.

So his lordship decreed with a grave solemn tone,
Decisive and clear, without one "if" or "but,"
That, whenever the Nose put his spectacles on,
By daylight or candlelight, Eyes should be shut.

William Cowper

HOW-D'-Y'-DO AND GOOD-BY

ONE day, Good-by met How-d'-y'-do,
Too close to shun saluting,
But soon the rival sisters flew,
From kissing to disputing.

"Away!" says How-d'-y'-do, "your mien
Appals my cheerful nature;
No name so sad as yours is seen
In Sorrow's nomenclature.

"Where'er I give one sunshine hour,
 Your cloud comes o'er to shade it;
Whene'er I plant one bosom flower,
 Your mildew drops to fade it.

"Ere How-d'-y'-do has tun'd each tongue
 To Hope's delightful measure;
Good-by in Friendship's ear is sung,
 The knell of parting pleasure!

"From sorrow's past, my chemic skill
 Draws smiles of consolation,
While you from present joys distil
 The tears of separation."—

Good-by replied, "Your statement's true,
 And well your cause you've pleaded;
But pray who'd think of How-d'-y'-do,
 Unless Good-by preceded?

"Without my prior influence,
 Could yours have ever flourished;
And can your hand one flower dispense
 But those my tears have nourish'd?

"How oft, if at the court of Love,
 Concealment be the fashion,
Wher How-d'-y'-do has failed to move,
 Good-by reveals the passion.

"How oft, when Cupid's fires decline,
 As every heart remembers,
One sigh of mine, and only mine,
 Revives the dying embers.

"Go bid the timid lover choose,
 And I'll resign my charter;
If he, for ten kind How-d'-y'-do's,
 One kind Good-by would barter.

"From Love and Friendship's kindred source
We both derive existence,
And they would both lose half their force,
Without our joint assistance.

" 'Tis well the world our merit knows,
Since time there's no denying,
One half in How-d'-y'-doing goes,
And t'other in Good-bying."

William Robert Spencer

THE LETTERS AT SCHOOL

ONE day the letters went to school,
And tried to teach each other,
They got so mixed, 'twas really hard
To pick one from the other.

A went in first, and Z went last;
The rest were all between them,—
K L and M and N O P—
I wish you could have seen them!

B C D E and J K L,
Soon jostled well their betters;
Q R S T—I grieve to say—
Were very naughty letters.

Of course, ere long they came to words—
What else could be expected!
Till E made D J C and T
Decidedly dejected.

Now through it all the consonants
Were rudest and uncouthest,
While all the pretty vowel girls
Were certainly the smoothest.

And nimble U kept far from Q,
With face demure and moral,
"Because," she said, "we are, we two,
So apt to start a quarrel!"

But spiteful P said, "Pooh for U!"
(Which made her feel quite bitter),
And, calling O L E to help,
He really tried to hit her.

Cried A, "Now, E and C come here!
If both will aid a minute,
Good P will join in making peace!
Or else the mischief's in it."

And smiling E the ready sprite,
Said, "Yes, and count me double."
This done, sweet peace shone o'er the scene,
And gone was all the trouble!

Meanwhile, when U and P made up,
The cons'nants looked about them,
And kissed the vowels, for, you see,
They couldn't do without them.

UNKNOWN

THE MILKMAID

A MILKMAID, who poised a full pail on her head,
Thus mused on her prospects in life, it is said:
"Let me see—I should think that this milk will procure
One hundred good eggs, or fourscore, to be sure.

"Well then—stop a bit—it must not be forgotten,
Some of these may be broken, and some may be rotten;
But if twenty for accident should be detached,
It will leave me just sixty sound eggs to be hatched.

"Well, sixty sound eggs—no, sound chickens, I mean;
Of these some may die—we'll suppose seventeen.
Seventeen! not so many—say ten at the most,
Which will leave fifty chickens to boil or to roast.

"But then, there's their barley, how much will they need?
Why they take but one grain at a time when they feed—
So that's a mere trifle; now then, let us see,
At a fair market price, how much money there'll be.

"Six shillings a pair—five—four—three-and-six.
To prevent all mistakes, that low price I will fix:
Now what will that make? fifty chickens, I said—
Fifty times three-and-sixpence—*I'll ask brother Ned.*

"O! but stop—three-and-sixpence a *pair* I must sell 'em;
Well, a pair is a couple—now then let us tell 'em;
A couple in fifty will go—(my poor brain!)
Why just a score times, and five pair will remain.

"Twenty-five pair of fowls—now how tiresome it is
That I can't reckon up such money as this!
Well there's no use in trying, so let's give a guess—
I'll say twenty pounds, *and it can't be no less.*

"Twenty pounds, I am certain, will buy me a cow,
Thirty geese and two turkeys—eight pigs and a sow;
Now if these turn out well, at the end of the year,
I shall fill both my pockets with guineas, 'tis clear."

Forgetting her burden, when this she had said,
The maid superciliously tossed up her head;
When, alas! for her prospects—her milk pail descended,
And so all her schemes for the future were ended.

This moral, I think, may be safely attached,—
"Reckon not on your chickens before they are hatched."

JEFFREYS TAYLOR

APPLE-SEED JOHN

POOR Johnny was bended well nigh double
With years of toil, and care, and trouble;
But his large old heart still felt the need
Of doing for others some kindly deed.

"But what can I do," old Johnny said:
"I who work so hard for daily bread?
It takes heaps of money to do much good;
I am far too poor to do as I would."

The old man sat thinking deeply a while,
Then over his features gleamed a smile,
And he clapped his hands with a boyish glee,
And said to himself: "There's a way for me!"

He worked, and he worked with might and main,
But no one knew the plan in his brain.
He took ripe apples in pay for chores,
And carefully cut from them all the cores.

He filled a bag full, then wandered away,
And no man saw him for many a day.
With knapsack over his shoulder slung,
He marched along, and whistled or sung.

He seemed to roam with no object in view,
Like one who had nothing on earth to do;
But, journeying thus o'er the prairies wide,
He paused now and then, and his bag untied.

With pointed cane deep holes he would bore,
And in every hole he placed a core;
Then covered them well, and left them there
In keeping of sunshine, rain, and air.

Sometimes for days he waded through grass,
And saw not a living creature pass,
But often, when sinking to sleep in the dark,
He heard the owls hoot and the prairie dogs bark.

Sometimes an Indian of sturdy limb
Came striding along and walked with him;
And he who had food shared with the other,
As if he had met a hungry brother.

When the Indian saw how the bag was filled,
And looked at the holes that the white man drilled,
He thought to himself 'twas a silly plan
To be planting seed for some future man.

Sometimes a log cabin came in view,
Where Johnny was sure to find jobs to do,
By which he gained stores of bread and meat,
And welcome rest for his weary feet.

He had full many a story to tell,
And goodly hymns that he sung right well;
He tossed up the babes, and joined the boys
In many a game full of fun and noise.

And he seemed so hearty, in work or play,
Men, women, and boys all urged him to stay;
But he always said: "I have something to do,
And I must go on to carry it through."

The boys who were sure to follow him round,
Soon found what it was he put in the ground;
And so, as time passed and he traveled on,
Ev'ry one called him "Old Apple-Seed John."

Whenever he'd used the whole of his store,
He went into cities and worked for more;
Then he marched back to the wilds again,
And planted seed on hillside and plain.

In cities, some said the old man was crazy;
While others said he was only lazy;
But he took no notice of gibes and jeers,
He knew he was working for future years.

He knew that trees would soon abound
Where once a tree could not have been found;
That a flick'ring play of light and shade
Would dance and glimmer along the glade;

That blossoming sprays would form fair bowers,
And sprinkle the grass with rosy showers;
And the little seeds his hands had spread,
Would become ripe apples when he was dead.

So he kept on traveling far and wide,
Till his old limbs failed him, and he died.
He said at the last: " 'Tis a comfort to feel
I've done good in the world, though not a great deal."

Weary travelers, journeying west,
In the shade of his trees find pleasant rest;
And they often start, with glad surprise,
At the rosy fruit that round them lies.

And if they inquire whence came such trees,
Where not a bough once swayed in the breeze,
The answer still comes, as they travel on:
"These trees were planted by Apple-Seed John."

Lydia Maria Child

THE WATERFALL AND THE EGLANTINE

"BEGONE, thou fond presumptuous Elf,"
  Exclaimed an angry voice,
"Nor dare to thrust thy foolish self
  Between me and my choice!"
A small Cascade fresh swoln with snows
Thus threatened a poor Briar Rose,
That, all bespattered with his foam,
And dancing high and dancing low,
Was living, as a child might know,
  In an unhappy home.

"Dost thou presume my course to block?
  Off, off! or, puny Thing!
I'll hurl thee headlong with the rock
  To which thy fibers cling."
The Flood was tyrannous and strong,
The patient Briar suffered long,
Nor did he utter groan or sigh,
Hoping the danger would be past;
But, seeing no relief, at last,
  He ventured to reply.

"Ah!" said the Briar, "blame me not:
  Why should we dwell in strife?
We who in this sequestered spot
  Once lived a happy life!
You stirred me on my rocky bed—
What pleasure through my veins you spread!
The summer long, from day to day,
My leaves you freshened and bedewed:
Nor was it common gratitude
  That did your cares repay.

"When spring came on with bud and bell,
  Among the rocks did I,
Before you hang my wreaths to tell
  That gentle days were nigh!
And in the sultry summer hours,
I sheltered you with leaves and flowers;
And in my leaves—now shed and gone—
The linnet lodged, and for us two
Chanted his pretty songs, when you
  Had little voice or none.

"But now proud thoughts are in your breast—
  What grief is mine you see,
Ah! would you think, even yet how blest
  Together we might be!
Though of both leaf and flower bereft,
Some ornaments to me are left—

Rich store of scarlet hips is mine,
With which I, in my humble way,
Would deck you many a winter day;
A happy Eglantine!"

What more he said I cannot tell,
The stream came thundering down the dell,
With aggravated haste:
I listened, nor aught else could hear;
The Briar quaked—and much I fear
Those accents were his last.

WILLIAM WORDSWORTH

JOHNNY'S OPINION OF GRANDMOTHERS

(Speech for a droll boy, should be spoken in a deliberate and thoughtful tone as if reflecting)

GRANDMOTHERS are very nice folks;
They beat all the aunts in creation;
They let a chap do as he likes
And don't worry about education.

I'm sure I can't see it at all,
What a poor fellow ever could do
For apples and pennies and cakes,
Without a grandmother or two.

Grandmothers speak softly to ma's,
To let a boy have a good time;
Sometimes they will whisper, 'tis true,
T'other way when a boy wants to climb.

Grandmothers have muffins for tea,
And pies, a whole row, in the cellar,
And they're apt (if they know it in time)
To make chicken pies for a feller.

And if he is bad now and then,
  And makes a great racketing noise,
They only look over their specs
  And say, "Ah, these boys will be boys—

"Life is only so short at the best;
  Let the children be happy to-day."
Then they look for a while at the sky,
  And the hills that are far; far away.

Quite often, as twilight comes on,
  Grandmothers sing hymns very low
To themselves, as they rock by the fire,
  About heaven, and when they shall go.

And then a boy, stopping to think,
  Will find a hot tear in his eye,
To know what must come at the last,
  For grandmothers all have to die.

I wish they could stay here and pray,
  For a boy needs their prayers every night.
Some boys more than others, I s'pose;
  Such fellers as me need a sight.

UNKNOWN

THE BAREFOOT BOY

BLESSINGS on thee, little man,
  Barefoot boy, with cheek of tan!
With thy turned-up pantaloons,
And thy merry whistled tunes;
With thy red lip, redder still
Kissed by strawberries on the hill;
With the sunshine on thy face,
Through thy torn brim's jaunty grace;
From my heart I give thee joy,—
I was once a barefoot boy!

Prince thou art,—the grown-up man
Only is a republican.
Let the million dollared ride!
Barefoot, trudging at his side,
Thou hast more than he can buy
In the reach of ear and eye,—
Outward sunshine, inward joy:
Blessings on thee, barefoot boy!

Oh for boyhood's painless play,
Sleep that wakes in laughing day,
Health that mocks the doctor's rules,
Knowledge never learned of schools,
Of the wild bee's morning chase,
Of the wild flower's time and place,
Flight of fowl and habitude
Of the tenants of the wood;
How the tortoise bears his shell,
How the woodchuck digs his cell,
And the ground mole sinks his well;
How the robin feeds her young,
How the oriole's nest is hung;
Where the whitest lilies blow,
Where the freshest berries grow,
Where the ground nut trails its vine,
Where the wood grape's clusters shine;
Of the black wasp's cunning way,
Mason of his walls of clay,
And the architectural plans
Of gray hornet artisans!
For, eschewing books and tasks,
Nature answers all he asks;
Hand in hand with her he walks,
Face to face with her he talks,
Part and parcel of her joy—
Blessings on the barefoot boy!

Oh for boyhood's time of June,
Crowding years in one brief moon,
When all things I heard or saw,
Me, their master, waited for.

I was rich in flowers and trees,
Humming-birds and honey-bees;
For my sport the squirrel played,
Plied the snouted mole his spade;
For my taste the blackberry cone
Purpled over hedge and stone;
Laughed the brook for my delight
Through the day and through the night–
Whispering at the garden wall,
Talked with me from fall to fall;
Mine the sand-rimmed pickerel pond,
Mine the walnut slopes beyond,
Mine, on bending orchard trees,
Apples of Hesperides!
Still as my horizon grew,
Larger grew my riches too;
All the world I saw or knew
Seemed a complex Chinese toy,
Fashioned for a barefoot boy!

Oh for festal dainties spread,
Like my bowl of milk and bread;
Pewter spoon and bowl of wood,
On the door stone, gray and rude!
O'er me, like a regal tent,
Cloudy ribbed, the sunset bent,
Purple curtained, fringed with gold,
Looped in many a wind-swung fold;
While for music came the play
Of the pied frogs' orchestra;
And, to light the noisy choir,
Lit the fly his lamp of fire.
I was monarch: pomp and joy
Waited on the barefoot boy!

Cheerily, then, my little man,
Live and laugh, as boyhood can!
Though the flinty slopes be hard,
Stubble-speared the new-mown sward,
Every morn shall lead thee through
Fresh baptisms of the dew;

Every evening from thy feet
Shall the cool wind kiss the heat:
All too soon these feet must hide
In the prison cells of pride,
Lose the freedom of the sod,
Like a colt's for work be shod,
Made to tread the mills of toil,
Up and down in ceaseless moil:
Happy if their track be found
Never on forbidden ground;
Happy if they sink not in
Quick and treacherous sands of sin.
Ah! that thou couldst know thy joy,
Ere it passes, barefoot boy!

John Greenleaf Whittier

THE REFORMATION OF GODFREY GORE

GODFREY GORDON GUSTAVUS GORE—
No doubt you have heard the name before—
Was a boy who never would shut a door!

The wind might whistle, the wind might roar,
And teeth be aching and throats be sore,
But still he never would shut the door.

His father would beg, his mother implore,
"Godfrey Gordon Gustavus Gore,
We really *do* wish you would shut the door!"

Their hands they wrung, their hair they tore;
But Godfrey Gordon Gustavus Gore
Was deaf as the buoy out at the Nore.

When he walked forth the folks would roar,
"Godfrey Gordon Gustavus Gore,
Why don't you think to shut the door?"

They rigged out a Shutter with sail and oar,
And threatened to pack off Gustavus Gore
On a voyage of penance to Singapore.
But he begged for mercy, and said, "No more!
Pray do not send me to Singapore
On a Shutter, and then I will shut the door!"

"You will?" said his parents; "then keep on shore!
But mind you do! For the plague is sore
Of a fellow that never will shut the door,
Godfrey Gordon Gustavus Gore!"

WILLIAM BRIGHTLY RANDS

MY RECOLLECTEST THOUGHTS

MY recollectest thoughts are those
Which I remember yet;
And bearing on, as you'd suppose,
The things I don't forget.

But my resemblest thoughts are less
Alike than they should be;
A state of things, as you'll confess,
You very seldom see.

And yet the mostest thought I love
Is what no one believes—
That I'm the sole survivor of
The famous Forty Thieves!

CHARLES EDWARD CARRYL

INDEX OF AUTHORS

INDEX OF TITLES

INDEX OF FIRST LINES

A

B

Y